Young Students
LEARNING
LIBRARY®

YOUNG STUDENTS LEARNING LIBRARY®
SCIENCE YEARBOOK

Margaret DiCanio, Ph.D., Editor

Teddi DiCanio, Photo Editor

Newfield Publications

NEWFIELD
PUBLICATIONS

Middletown, Connecticut

YOUNG STUDENTS LEARNING LIBRARY
SCIENCE YEARBOOK 1993

Copyright ©1993 by New England Publishing Associates, Inc. and Margaret DiCanio.

Copy Editor: Larry Hand
Designer: Don Brunelle
Administrator: Susan Brainard

Young Students Learning Library is a federally registered trademark of Newfield Publications.

Special edition prepared for Newfield Publications by New England Publishing Associates, Inc.

ISBN 0-8374-9803-1

Printed in the United States of America

Table of Contents

PART ONE: Life Science

EVENTS AND TRENDS IN LIFE SCIENCE 2

Chapter 1 Archeology and Anthropology
Solving the Riddle of the Mayan Language Reveals a Violent Society 7
The Galilee Boat 13

Chapter 2 Plants and Animals
Change is Brewing in Systematics 19
Sharks, Hunters of the Deep Threatened with Extinction 26

Chapter 3 Biology and Social Science
Brain Injuries, Major or Minor, Can Have Severe Consequences 33
Parapsychology: Scientists Disagree Whether It Is a Science 43

Chapter 4 Changing Environment
From Rio, Principles for Sustainable Development 57
War Leftovers 69

Chapter 5 Health and Medicine
Emergency Trauma Centers: an Overwhelming Dilemma 77
The Life and Death Impact of Global Discrimination Against Women 85

Part Two: Earth and Space Science

EVENTS AND TRENDS IN EARTH SCIENCE 97

Chapter 6 The Stars and the Universe
Cosmic-Ray Shower Detection Has Once Again Become a Frontier of Science 101
The U.S. Cerro Tololo Telescope's Long Record of Success Faces Challenges from New Competitors 107

Chapter 7 Earth in the Past
Hydrothermal and Other Kind of Vents, Riches From Inner Earth 113
Battle Lines in the War for the West are Being Redrawn 119

Chapter 8 Earth and Its Oceans
Balance of Nature, A Theory Under Fire 127
Scientists who are Women are Gaining Recognition for Their Work 132

Chapter 9 Weather and Climate
Solar Architecture and Technology Are Rediscovered Periodically 139
Underground, a Place to Live and Work and Discover Past Climates 148

Part Three: Physical Science and Mathematics

EVENTS AND TRENDS IN PHYSICAL SCIENCE AND MATHEMATICS 155

Chapter 10 Computer Science
Supercomputing in Pittsburgh and Around the Country 159
Illinois Institute of Technology's Institute of Design 164

Chapter 11 Physics
Buildings are Higher, But Principles Have Not Changed Much 171
Traffic Crashes, a Major Source of Death and Injury 179

Chapter 12 Chemistry
The Rapidly Changing World of Smart Structures and Smart Materials 185
Elias James Corey, Nobel Prize Winner Who Worked Backwards 190

Chapter 13 Mathematics
The Close Bond Between Music and Science 193
Factoring Very Large Numbers and Spot-Checking Long Proofs 198

Appendix
.... 201

Glossary
.... 203

Index
.... 213

Photo Credits

p.1 (In order, around the circle, starting at upper right) George Harrison/ U.S. Fish and Wildlife Service (USFWS); Dan Rosenburg/ USFWS; Courtesy of Boston Public Library (BPL)/ Print Department; Richard E. Durst/ Still Media Records Center (SMRC); USFWS; International Rice Research Institute (IRRI); p.3 Teddi DiCanio; pp.6-12 Peabody Museum of Archaeology and Ethnology, Harvard University; pp.13-18 D. Syon/ Courtesy Israel Antiquities Authority and Shelley Wachsmann, Dept. of Anthropology/ Texas A&M University; p.20 Courtesy of the BPL/ Rare Book Dept.; p.21 (top) Chris Serrheen/ USFWS; (bottom) USFWS; p.22 U.S. Dept. of Agriculture (USDA); p.23 Courtesy of the BPL/ Print Dept.; p.24 Jon R. Nickles/ USFWS; p.25 (top left) USFWS; (top right) Lawrence Gamble/ USFWS; (bottom) Teddi DiCanio; p.26 Earthwatch; p.27 USFWS; pp.28-30 Courtesy of Gregory B. Skomal/ Division of Marine Fisheries/ Commonwealth of Massachusetts; p.31 National Oceanic and Atmospheric Administration (NOAA); p.32 Courtesy of GregorB. Skomal/ Division of Marine Fisheries/ Commonwealth of Massachusetts; p.34 Cecil Stoughton/ National Park Service; p.37 Teddi DiCanio; p.38 & 39 Dr. Martin Reivich/ Cerebrovascular Research Center, School of Medicine, University of Pennsylvania; p.40 Brookhaven National Laboratory, Upton, New York; p.41 Dr. Robert Grossman/ Dept. of Radiology, Hospital of the University of Pennsylvania; p.42 U.S Dept. of Transportation/ National Highway and Safety Administration; p.43 Courtesy of Richard S. Broughton/ Foundation for Research on the Nature of Man, Institute for Parapsychology; p.44 Teddi DiCanio; p.47 Courtesy of the BPL/ Print Dept.; p.49 (top and bottom right) Courtesy of the BPL/ Print Dept.; (bottom left) Courtesy of the BPL/ Fine Arts Dept.; p.50 Dr. Helmut Schmidt/ Mind Science Foundation; p.51 Margaret DiCanio; p.54 ©1987 by R.G. Jahn and B.J. Dunne, Margins of Reality, (HBJ, 1987), Princeton Engineering Anomalies Research Lab; p.56 Courtesy of Richard S. Broughton/ Foundation for Research on the Nature of Man, Institute for Parapsychology; p.58 Eros Data Center/ U.S. Geological Survey (USGS); p.59 Herman Lankford/ North Carolina State University (NCSU), Visual Communication; p.61 NASA; p.62 & 63 Teddi DiCanio; p.64 (top and middle) International Center for Tropical Agriculture (CIAT): (bottom) International Laboratory for Research on Animal Diseases (ILRAD); p.65 USDA; pp.66 & 67 Institute of Design/ Illinois Institute of Technology (IIT); p.68 Library of Congress; p.69 SMRC; P.70 (top) Greg Snaza/ SMRC; p.70 (bottom) Library of Congress; p.71 IRRI; p.72 (top) Alan Wycheck/ SMRC; (bottom) Don Sallee/ SMRC; p.73 (top) Jose Lopez, Jr./ SMRC; p.73 SMRC; p.74 (top) Harry Gerwein/ SMRC; (bottom) Ken Hackman/ SMRC; p.78 (top) Pete Hatzakos/ SMRC; (bottom) Bert Mau/ SMRC; pp.79 & 81 Maryland Institute for Emergency Medical Services; p.82 Arden Lynn/ USDA; p.84 AP/ Wide World Photos; pp.86 & 87 Don Brunelle; 8 National Cancer Institute/ National Institutes of Health; p.90 Margaret DiCanio; p.92 Courtesy of the BPL/ Print Dept.; p.93 IRRI; p.95 (In order around the circle, starting at upper right) National Optical Astronomy Observatories (NOAO); USDA; USDA, Forest Service; Courtesy of the BPL/ Print Dept.; NOAO; The Massachusetts Institute of Technology (MIT) Museum; p.96 Teddi DiCanio; p.100 NOAO; p.103 NASA; pp.104-112 NOAO; pp.114 & 115 USGS; p.116 NOAA; p.117 USGS; p.119 Eros Data Center/ USGS; p.120 USDA, Forest Service; pp.121-123 Courtesy of the BPL/ Print Dept.; p.124 (left) Roland de Gouvenain/ Bureau of Land Management (BLM), Palm Springs-South Coast Resource Area; (right) Luther Goldman/ USFWS; p.125 James Pickering/ BLM, California State Office; p.126 (top) Courtesy of the BPL/ Print Dept.; (bottom) Library of Congress; p.128 June Davidek/ USDA; p.129 USDA, Forest Service; p.130 USDA; p.131 (top) Eros Data Center/ USGS; (bottom) Gary L. Johnson/ USDA; p.133 Courtesy of the BPL/ Print Dept.; p.134 News Service, University of Massachusetts at Amherst; p.135 University of California (UC) at Berkeley; 36 (top) NOAA; p.136 (bottom) Joe Wrinn/ Harvard University News Office; p.137 June Scherr/ Photo Information/ UC Berkeley; 38 NOAA; pp. 140 & 141 (bottom) Courtesy of the BPL/ Print Dept.; p.141 (top) USDA; p.143 Dept. of Special Collections, Library, UC, Santa Barbara; p.143 Mesa Verde National Park/ National Park Service; p.144 Courtesy of the BPL/ Fine Arts Dept.; p.147 The MIT Museum; p.149 (top) Davis Caves Construction, Inc., Armington, IL;(bottom) & 150 Wood C. Campbell/Wilhoit & Campbell, Architects, Watkinsville, Georgia; p.151 Teddi DiCanio; p.152 Mesa Verde National Park/ National Park Service; p.153 (In order around the circle, starting at upper right) Institute of Design/ IIT; U.S. Dept. of Transportation/ Federal Highway Dept.; Institute of Design/ IIT; NOAA; U.S. Dept. of Transportation/ Federal Highway Dept.; Institute of Design/ IIT; p.154 Gary Meek/ Georgia Institute of Technology; p.158 (top) Georgia Institute of Technology; (bottom) Luedtke Landman/ Georgia Institute of Technology; p.160 Pittsburgh Supercomputing Center; p.161 Uzi Landman and Charles Cleveland/ Georgia Institute of Technology; p.162 The image was produced at the Pittsburgh Supercomputing Center by Joel Welling of the Pittsburgh Supercomputing Center computer graphics staff in collaboration with architect Alaa Eldin Ibrahim of the University of Texas at Austin; pp.164-169 Institute of Design/ IIT; pp.172 & 173 Courtesy of BPL/ Print Dept.; p.174 Teddi DiCanio; pp.175-178 Courtesy of BPL/ Print Dept.; p.179 Courtesy of Joseph R. Sheram, Jr. of Guardian Interlock Systems; pp.180-182 U.S. Dept. of Transportation/ Federal Highway Administration; p.183 Library of Congress; p.184 Courtesy of BPL/ Print Dept.; p.186 Georgia Institute of Technology; p.188 Herman Lankford NCSU, Visual Communications; 91 Jane Reed/ Harvard University News Office; p.194 (top) Teddi DiCanio; (bottom) Eros Data Center/ USGS; p.195 Teddi DiCanio; 01 Rick O'Quinn/ University of Georgia.

PART ONE

LIFE SCIENCE

Events and Trends in Life Science

The absence of women as researchers and as the subjects of health care research received some long overdue media attention in 1992 as women gained in political power in the United States and around the world. The status of the environment also came in for a large share of attention. Much of the press coverage was stimulated by the second Earth Summit held in Rio de Janeiro, Brazil in June 1992, which brought together leaders from around the world. Here are some of the other topics that received press attention in 1992.

Archeology and Anthropology

To understand the archeological news of the 1990s, it is necessary to go back to the 1960s. For it was during 1960–1968 that the world's archeologists joined forces in a race to rescue the monuments of ancient Nubia, a black African culture that is today very much in the news. The monuments were threatened by the rising Nile River waters being impounded—that is, enclosed for irrigation—by the building of the Aswan High Dam, which was completed in 1971. The best-known achievement of the international rescue operation was the dismantling and reconstruction above the water line of the temple at Abu Simbel, erected in the 13th century by Ramses II.

Less celebrated was the salvage of thousands of Nubian artifacts, which are objects made by humans, that reflect a culture dating back almost 6,000 years. On February 11, 1992 *The New York Times* published an article entitled "Nubian Treasures Reflect Black Influence on Egypt," based on an interview with Dr. Emily Teeter, curator of an exhibit that opened in February 1992 at the University of Chicago's Oriental Institute. Evaluating the tools, weapons, and vessels found, she said, "It's clear Nubia was an important civilization in its own right and not just a stepsister of Egypt."

Nubian studies is a new field of archeology—having stopped being an adjunct of Egyptology—according to Dr. Bruce Williams of the University of Chicago, the author of five volumes in a series on Nubian excavations. Growing interest in Nubia comes at a time of sometimes heated debate on the relationship of ancient Egypt to other African civilizations.

Many African scholars and African-American scholars insist that Egypt was a black society and that Cleopatra herself was black. Moreover, they contend since Greece borrowed some of its culture from Egypt, Western civilization was in large part an invention of Africa.

Dr. Marin Bernal, a Cornell University government professor and the author of a projected four-volume work entitled *Black Athena*, does not agree that ancient Egyptians were mostly black. Instead, he thinks they were a cultural mixture of peoples from Africa, the Mediterranean, and Asia Minor.

Still another viewpoint is that of Dr. Mary Lefkowitz, a professor of humanities at Wellesley College, who believes that no one should claim the Greeks stole their most significant ideas from the Egyptians or anyone else. Finally, Dr. Timothy Kendall, an associate curator of the Boston Museum of Fine Arts and a specialist on Nubia, feels that an "Afrocentrist" focus on ancient Egypt has contributed to the neglect of ancient Nubia, which itself was a black African culture of enormous influence and power.

Such disagreement is perhaps understandable. Up until the salvage excavations of the 1960s, archeologists had mostly a second-hand view of Nubian culture, from Egyptian art and documents. This is because the Nubians did not develop a writing system until late in the first millennium B.C., and their texts remain mostly undeciphered.

Plants and Animals

News in animal behavior concerns food hoarding. Many animal species—bears, honeybees, chipmunks, and acorn woodpeckers to name a few—hoard a food supply to survive winter. Other creatures, such as desert rodents, who face year-round food shortages, hoard brief harvests that follow occasional rains.

However, the hoarded stockpile may not be there when the animal returns to claim it. A November 19,

1991 *New York Times* article entitled "A Hoarder's Life: Filling the Cache—and Finding It," described strategies animals use to protect stores.

Each protection strategy carries risks, according to Dr. Stephen Vander Wall, a University of Utah ecologist. In his 1990 book *Food Hoarding in Animals,* Dr. Vander Wall pointed out that Eastern chipmunks keep their larders in easily defended burrows, but they risk losing the whole collection in one well-executed raid. On the other hand, the reserves of white mice are buried among hundreds of sites with no protection, so even if some sites are lost, the mice have something left.

Keeping food stores unspoiled is a common problem. For instance, desert rodents make huge underground sites containing hundreds of thousands of seeds, but those seeds are vulnerable to attack by more than 30 species of fungi. Some of the fungi—plants such as molds, mildew, and yeast—are beneficial, but others are poisonous. Beneficial fungi often make the stored food easier to digest. The animals seem able to "manage" fungal growth so that benefits outweigh risks.

For example, some animals harvest green vegetables and transport them to hay piles near their burrows, where the vegetables are slowly cured, or preserved. The small rabbitlike pika and the stout-bodied, short-tailed vole both manage their food in this way.

Another problem in keeping food stores unspoiled is freezing. Carcasses of rodents stored by owls during winter often freeze. So to thaw a frozen meal, the owl sits on it as if it were an egg. Many species keep stored prey alive until meal time by paralyzing or rendering it unconscious.

Protecting a cache against the many possible hazards is not easy. A University of Maryland study found that a two- to three-year supply of beechnuts stored by chipmunks in underground burrows was attacked by beetles, infected by blue mold, and stolen by other chipmunks. Despite an enormous expenditure of energy spent on food storage, the rodent was left with only a small supply.

Despite the risks, scientists such as Dr. Vander Wall believe that the intake of calories from stored reserves exceeds the output in energy expended in gathering and hoarding; otherwise, genes that promote hoarding would have disappeared long ago from animals that hoard.

Biology and Social Science

In the field of social science, childhood friendships and loneliness have come under intense scrutiny recently. Researchers have begun to recognize that early friendship has been underrated as a lifelong source of emotional strength and are developing ways to prevent social difficulties and remedy them when they occur.

An April 28, 1991 *New York Times Magazine* article entitled "Sidelined by Loneliness" reported a joint project among four universities—-Duke, Vanderbilt, Pennsylvania State, and the University of Washington—-to work with first- and second-grad-

Squirrels are perhaps the world's best-known, most prolific, persistent, single-minded food hoarders. Gray squirrels store each separate nut in a separate hole. Yet, according to Dr. Lucia Jacobs of the University of Utah, gray squirrels are extremely adept at remembering where they buried their nuts.

ers from diverse backgrounds who lack the social skills to make friends, a situation that can influence them later in life. Harvard University professor Robert Selman, who with Lynn Hickey Schultz wrote *Making Friends in Youth* (1990), believes that childhood friendships prepare young people with the skills needed in marriage and other long-term relationships.

Friends guide each other to fit easily within the boundaries of social norms. The penalties of social incompetence are far-reaching. Some children on the margins, those who are not actively despised, become successful adults. But for many, life tends to be marred by depression and chronic anxiety, that is, worry and apprehension. The consequences for those who are actively rejected range from poor school performance to drug use—sometimes even suicide.

Neglect of childhood friendship as a legitimate area of study is due to a focus throughout most of the century on Freudian psychology, which emphasizes family relationships. Psychoanalyst Harry Stack Sullivan in the 1940s ignored the focus of Sigmund Freud and placed paramount importance on finding a "chum" in preadolescence. In "chumship," two youngsters try to understand life, protect each other from pain, swap secrets, discuss sex, and learn about the needs of others. A maverick in his time, Sullivan has become increasingly respected.

There are a number of reasons for rejection—or at the very least, a lack of acceptance. A youngster may: look different; lack skills other children admire; lag in social development so that he or she responds in immature ways; or be so mature the other youngsters cannot understand him or her.

Whatever the underlying cause of friendlessness, much of the current research is directed toward measures to correct it. Selman at Harvard uses "pair therapy," in which he obliges two youngsters to relate to each other with little direction. Myrna Shure, a psychologist at Hahnemann University in Philadelphia, Pennsylvania trains teachers to help children learn there are many ways to solve conflicts short of aggression. A tried-and-true method for marginal youngsters is to join an organization like Little League or Girl Scouts.

Kenneth Dodge, a psychologist at Vanderbilt University, believes that it is a parent's job to teach a child

the value of cooperation and sharing in early childhood. However, Dodge and others warn that parents should not become so overinvolved that they appear to empathize with the youngsters who do not like their child.

A friendless child who has the love and support of the family will at least have that as a buffer. After all, it is better to be rejected for six hours a day than to be rejected full time.

Health and Medicine

In the field of health, cures for stuttering have made news. The daily lives of some stutterers have been greatly enhanced by the Vocal Feedback Device (VFD) invented by Dr. George Shames of the University of Pittsburgh. A June 19, 1989 *Newsweek* article entitled "High-Tech Aid for Stutterers" described the device, which operates by using vibrations to create a feedback loop between the mind and the body.

The patient wears a neck band containing a vibrator. When the patient speaks, the movements of his or her vocal cords are amplified and transmitted back through the neck band in the form of vibrations. The vibrations heighten the patient's awareness of his or her speech patterns and foster concentration. The device has no mechanical effect on the voice. The voice makes it work.

There have been two different treatment philosophies that direct treatment of stutterers. One school called "desensitization" focuses on learning to live with the disability. The other, called "precision fluency shaping," emphasizes slow, careful speaking. The VFD fits within the latter perspective. The technology encourages the patient to slow down and concentrate.

Treatment begins with 10 hours of therapy, during which the patient listens to his own voice through a large stationary amplifier equipped with flashing lights and audio feedback keyed to vocal patterns. Following the 10 hours, the patient moves out into the world with the 7-ounce VFD.

The goal of treatment is for the stutterer to eventually wean himself or herself from the device. However, lifelong problems do not disappear overnight. The VFD's portability makes it possible for the patient to take quick treatments when the need arises.

Even if patients can never wean themselves from the device, most probably will view themselves as better off than they had been. A 23-year-old college student, who had been through every other kind of therapy available, after 10 hours of clinic therapy was able to carry on a 25-minute interview without stumbling. He told *Newsweek* that he hoped to be able to do without the device in a year, but he would not be upset if he could not. He said, "I came here expecting nothing, and ended up getting the world."

Changing Environment

In their fight to save the forests of the Pacific Northwest, environmentalists have focused attention recently on the northern spotted owl and the ancient trees. Meanwhile, other astonishing inhabitants of the old-growth forests have gone unnoticed.

For example, scientists have conducted extensive analyses of diversity among arthropods, organisms that have a horny, segmented, external covering and jointed limbs. At the same time they have made studies of the soil beneath the region's forest floor. They found that the biological variety of arthropods, including insects—spiders, mites, and centipedes—found underfoot is comparable to the diversity found in tropical rain forests.

In a single study site in an Oregon old-growth forest, researchers found an estimated 8,000 separate species. During an interview for a July 2, 1991 *New York Times* article entitled "A Wealth of Forest Species Is Found Underfoot," Dr. Andrew Moldenke, an entomologist (scientist who studies insects) at Oregon State University in Corvallis, said: "We have come to suspect that these invertebrates [animals without a backbone or spinal column] of the forest soil are probably the most critical factor in determining the long-term productivity of the forest."

For dead organisms to become nutrients that can be taken up by the roots of plants, they must be made soluble (capable of being dissolved). The twigs, fallen leaves, and dead organisms in tropical forests' warm, wet ecosystems—communities of interacting animals, plants, and bacteria—are decomposed rapidly by bacteria and fungi. In the temperate Northwest forests, arthropods seem to be the key to decomposition.

The digestive tracts of arthropods contain bacteria and fungi that process the once-living tissue into basic nutrient chemicals. Billions of tiny insects, mites, "microspiders," and other invertebrates function as recycling factories to reduce tons of organic litter and debris into smaller and smaller bits.

Not long after vegetation falls to the ground, millipedes descend on it and grind it up. In minutes, the ground-up vegetation is passed through the insects' digestive tracts and redeposited as fecal pellets in virtually the same place. These small bits of chopped-up tissue are in turn eaten by other arthropods.

As each successive arthropod takes its sliver of nutrition from the once-living cell matter, the matter is more exposed to bacteria, which decomposes it, making it more nutritious for the next arthropod. Eventually insoluble cell material becomes soluble. Precisely how all the interactions occur and which are most important is not clear.

To study soil and arthropod ecosystems, Dr. Moldenke and his students use a technique called thin-section microscopy, developed by oil-exploration geologists. The technique begins with a soil sample that has been carefully removed and placed in a pressure chamber. Epoxy, an adhesive, is introduced gradually. Once the epoxy hardens, the sample is rocklike and can be sliced into exceedingly thin samples for viewing under a microscope.

The technique preserves the soil, keeping in place its larger bits of partly decayed plant matter as well as its microscopic soil particles. By analyzing the thousands of arthropods in a tin can full of soil, Dr. Moldenke has determined that a researcher can predict with accuracy the condition of an entire site.

Because trees are so old, they don't tell much about current changes in the environment. The state of the arthropod community permits a researcher to examine events over as short a time as a few months.

Detail from a Mayan sculptured stone lintel located in Piedras Negras, Guatemala.

1

ARCHEOLOGY AND ANTHROPOLOGY

Solving the Riddle of the Mayan Language Reveals a Violent Society

Today a common Mayan heritage is shared by five nations in the Yucatan Peninsula. Mayan ruins and descendants of Mayan people exist in southern Mexico, Guatemala, Belize, and in small areas of El Salvador and Honduras. The Maya were founders of the greatest civilization to flourish in pre-Columbian America. They studied astronomy, devised precise calendars, created a true writing system, developed an extensive seafaring commerce, and built complex cities. There are thousands of Mayan sites, only a few of which have been thoroughly excavated.

Thanks to recent discoveries, two widely accepted theories held by prominent Mayan scholars about the Maya's culture have been overturned. One theory was that Mayan glyphs, carved figures or carved pictographs, are unsolvable, an idea advanced by Paul Schellhas in 1945. Another is that the Maya were a peaceful people governed by astronomer-priests, a theory put forth in the 1970s by J. Eric Thompson. Both notions are wrong.

Before exploring the reasons for this turnaround, it's important to take a brief look at Mayan history. The Maya appeared about 4000 B.C., and their civilization began to build about the time of Christ. The Maya, highly skilled in general, were superb architects. From 200 B.C. to A.D. 900, the so-called Classic Period, they built some 200 cities. Their civilization peaked about A.D. 850–900, when they built some of their most magnificent structures. Long before the Spanish arrived, the civilization had begun a slow decline.

The reason for the decline is not known. Why they developed such a rich culture also is not known.

One reason proposed is that the area where they lived provided a plentiful food supply. The tropical forest offered wild animals, and a wide range of fruits and crops could be grown easily. At the peak of the Mayan civilization, the population was 20 times as dense as it is today, an indication that the rain forest, when managed properly, can support a large number. The availability of sufficient food that did not require a full-time effort to obtain may have left time available for the Maya to develop their complex culture.

By 1502, when the Spanish encountered the first Maya during Columbus' fourth voyage, large cities were no longer being built. The Spanish brought guns and diseases. More than anything, the diseases struck the final blow to the culture.

At its peak, the Mayan world was organized into 50 or more independent states encompassing more than 100,000 square miles of forest and plain. Living gods, who called themselves *ahau*, ruled over millions of farmers, craftsmen, merchants, warriors, and nobility. Mayan capitals, graced by pyramids, temples, palaces, and vast open plazas, functioned through the labor of urban populations numbering in the tens of thousands.

The Maya's written history began 2,000 years ago. They wrote on paper, recording their history in thousands of books. Over time, the books crumpled to dust or were burned by the Spanish, who viewed the Maya as heathen. Only four books survived. In their struggle to decipher the Mayan language, scholars relied mostly on epigraphs (inscriptions on buildings, monuments, and tombs) and carvings on stone, jade, bone, or other materials impervious to decay in the

An aerial view of Chichen Itza, Mexico.

tropics. The early decipherments done by epigraphers were based on knowledge of Mayan numbers and calendars and on 17th-century documents that gave clues to certain sounds. Researchers also could make reasonable assumptions; for example, a person in full regalia was a nobleman, and one who was naked was a captive.

The Crucial Scholars

The arduous work of a handful of scholars finally broke the Mayan code. The pivotal work most responsible for penetrating the mystery of the Mayan language was done by Yuri Valentinovich Knorosov of the Ethnographic Institute in Leningrad, which is now St. Petersburg, Russia. A critical juncture in Knorosov's career came in 1947, two years after Schellhas had declared the decipherment of Mayan glyphs to be impossible. Knorosov's teacher—archeologist and orientalist Sergei Tokarev—goaded him with the challenge: "If you believe that any writing system produced by humans can be read by humans, why don't you try to read the Maya hieroglyphs?"

Knorosov began with the work of Fray Diego de Landa, a fanatical and cruel Franciscan missionary famed for his mastery of the Mayan tongue, who recorded Mayan customs and history. Landa persecuted the Maya because he perceived that idolatry (worship of idols) was widespread among them.

Landa conducted an *auto-da-fe*, a public ceremony in which the Inquisition (a trial by a Catholic tribunal for heresy) imposed a sentence, usually public burning, to be carried out by secular authorities.

During the ceremony, Landa burned a large number of Mayan texts and codices (classic manuscripts) "because they contained nothing but superstitions and the Devil's falsehoods."

In 1564, Landa was recalled to Spain for overstepping his authority in the investigation and torture of native lords and commoners. During his exile, he wrote an "Account of the Affairs of Yucatan," which has come to be the single most important Colonial-period document on the lowland Maya. The original was lost, but a 17th-century abridgment was found in 1862.

In his document, Landa included details of Mayan life on the eve of the conquest. He outlined the Mayan calendar and gave the glyphs for the days and the months. Although he made a crucial error that stymied scholars for a century, Landa's description of the Mayan writing system was decisive for Knorosov's breakthrough.

Knorosov published an article in 1952 in which he rejected several basic conclusions accepted by scholars. He refuted the concept of an evolutionary

Arch from the Governor's Palace at Uxmal, Yucatan Peninsula.

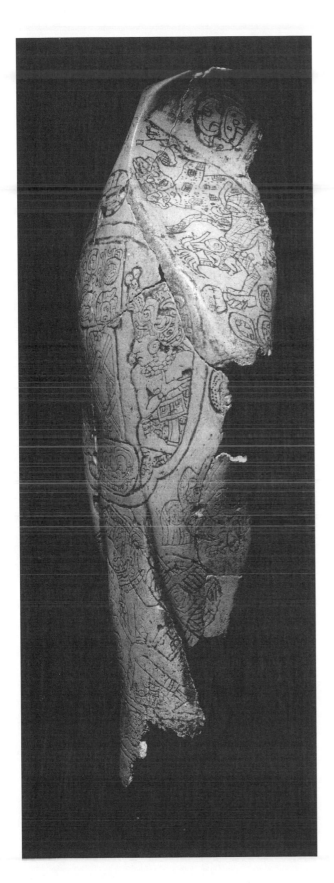

approach to the development of languages. This theory holds that writing evolves, beginning with the pictographic stage, where a picture represents an idea, proceeding to the ideographic stage, where an idea or object is conveyed by a sign with little or no pictorial reference, then moving on to the phonetic stage, in which a sign stands only for a sound.

Knorosov insisted that all three stages coexist in all early scripts, including Egyptian, Mesopotamian, and Chinese, which like the Mayan system are hieroglyphic, meaning pictures represent words, syllables, or sounds rather than alphabetical letters. Such societies maintain a monopoly on writing by confining it to a class of priestly scribes.

According to Knorosov, Landa's alphabet was a syllabary, a list of signs standing for consonant-vowel combinations and not individual letters. Despite attacks on his discoveries, Knorosov's logic proved compelling. In a flurry of papers that followed, he applied his system to the few surviving Mayan codices.

American epigrapher David Kelley published a paper in 1962 accepting many of Knorosov's readings. He took the Russian's approach one step further by using it to read an inscription at Chichen Itza, a principal Mayan center in the Mexican state of Yucatan near Valladolid. The inscription was the name of a great leader, which Kelley translated as Ka-ku-pa-cal, "Fiery Shield." As a result, the direction of Mayan studies underwent a profound change.

The next key step in making the Mayan language accessible was taken by Linda Schele, an instructor of painting and drawing at the University of South Alabama at Mobile. Schele was drawn into the Maya's world in 1970, while touring Mayan sites with her architect husband and some of her students.

A Mexican friend suggested the group visit the ruins of the ancient Mayan city of Palenque, located in the northern part of the state of Chiapas in southern Mexico, near the Guatemalan border. At the site, the group was guided into the jungle

Detail of a carved Peccary (a type of pig) Skull from the Copan Valley in Honduras.

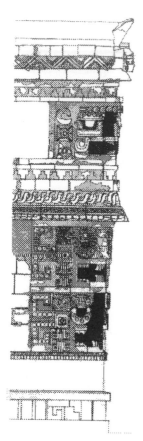

Line drawings of the east wing corners of Monjas, a structure at Chichen Itza.

by Moises Morales, who shared with them his vision of Palenque.

About her first visit, Schele wrote in *A Forest of Kings: The Untold Story of the Ancient Maya* (1990): "As I walked through the lichen-painted ruins of that magic palace, I felt my imagination stirred by the pathos of the lost world. The enchantment of the forest with its emerald green light and towering trees shrouded in the rich world of orchids, bromeliads, and liana vines produced a kind of exotic beauty I had never imagined." In time, the Scheles bought a house in a town close to Palenque and Linda Schele devoted all her free time to study of the site.

An incident critical to being able to read the ancient Mayan language came in 1973, when Mayan scholar Gillett Griffin visited Palenque with David Joralemon, a Yale University graduate student. Griffin described the events in a September/October 1991 *Archaeology* article entitled "A Most Happy Mayanist."

In 1972 Joralemon had conducted a seminar on Late Classic Mayan gods depicted on carvings, wall panels, architecture, and stelae, upright stones or slabs with an inscribed or sculptured surface used as monuments or commemorative tablets. By the time Joralemon arrived in Palenque, Schele intimately knew every carved stone in the city.

Standing before an epigraph, Joralemon pointed to a depiction of a god with a smoking cigar sticking out of his head and said, "That's God K." Schele pointed to a similar god and said, "We call this one the Jester God, because of the jester's cap he's wear-

ing." After hours of sharing information, Schele was buoyed up by Joralemon's interpretations of Mayan iconography. She speculated that a conference of experts brought together on the site could settle many scholarly differences.

The conference Schele instigated, the Primera Mesa Redonda de Palenque (the first roundtable of Palenque), was held in December 1973. Forty people came, among them Peter Mathews, an Australian who was a junior at the University of Calgary in Alberta, Canada. It became apparent to the group that Mathews knew more about Mayan glyphs than anyone present. He had brought with him four notebooks in which he had copied every glyph ever recorded from Palenque since the late 18th century.

Several days into the conference, participant Michael Coe said to the other participants, "Linda knows every stone in Palenque and Peter knows every glyph," and turned to Schele and Mathews and said, "Why don't the two of you see if you can put together a dynastic [succession of rulers in the same family] history of Palenque? No one has ever attempted that."

That evening Mathews and Schele stood before the group and Schele announced, "We have six rulers and the man in the tomb is Shield." At which point Moises Morales angrily asked, "Why is it that when a name is given a king it is put into *English* or *Spanish?* . . . These people were *Maya* and what's more the people who built Palenque were *Chol*. The Chols still live and speak Chol in the mountains behind Palenque. We have a Chol in our audience and we have a Chol dictionary."

Chastened by Morales' criticism, the scholars turned their attention to Chol, but there turned out to be no modern word for shield in Chol. However, two other Mayan languages contained words for shield. The more likely one was chosen. The man in the tomb was named Pacal. The title that accompanied Pacal's name was translated by one of the epigraphers present as "great lord."

After 1,300 years, the name of the man who had created the great city of Palenque was spoken aloud. Quickly followed the names of his mother, his wife, and their oldest son. For the first time in the modern era, scholars had a glimpse of history as Pacal's dynasty had recorded it.

The next important step toward unraveling the Mayan language was made possible by one of the Mesa Redonda participants, Elizabeth Benson, a scholar from Dumbarton Oaks, an important center for Mayan studies in Washington, D.C. She convened a mini-conference of all the most important glyphicists in the world.

Most of the experts came, but the conference got off to a rocky start. Differences in temperament, working methods, ages, and backgrounds resulted in an impasse, and many people left. Those who remained, a hard core of enthusiasts, including Linda Schele, continued to struggle with their differences. Despite them, they worked together successfully using Mayan dictionaries and codices. They also used natural histories, which are the studies of the origins, evolution, interrelationships, and descriptions of natural objects and organisms.

The mini-conference was the first of seven held by the group. They adopted a set of working rules. Unless everyone present accepted a decipherment of a glyph, it was set aside until they reached consensus. Before the first Mesa Redonda, about 30% of the glyphs at Palenque could be guessed, mostly glyphs for dates. A decade later, 95% of them could be read.

Of the 28 Mayan languages spoken today, Chol and Yucatec are most similar to the language spoken by ancient Maya. The grammars of the two languages have helped immensely.

Schele's New Vision of the Maya

A decoder of Mayan glyphs must be an exacting linguist, and be comfortable with mathematics, astronomy, anthropology, and natural history. Linda Schele, a self-taught epigrapher, possesses such abilities. Her collaborative approach has brought together many scholars. Schele's book *The Blood of Kings: Dynasty and Ritual in Maya Art,* co-authored with Mary Ellen Miller, constituted a milestone in Mayan studies. She is credited with shaping a whole new vision of the ancient culture.

The accepted view of the Maya as a gentle people living in a benign theocracy was supported by the absence of fortifications found among the sites archeologists unearthed. The decipherment of Mayan texts revealed a different picture, according to Dr. Arthur Damarest, a Vanderbilt University archeologist inter-

viewed for a November 19, 1991 *New York Times* article entitled "What Doomed the Maya? Maybe Warfare Run Amok." Evidence, the article says, points to the conclusion that "the Maya were one of the most violent state-level societies in the New World, especially after A.D. 600."

Even the ruins of Mayan cities reflect a violent past. Stones provide pictures of severed heads, and rulers are seen together with bound captives. In ruins uncovered by earlier generations of archeologists, evidence of violence was found beneath the ruins of public buildings in the form of dismembered or decapitated remains of sacrificed victims.

Writings and artifacts indicate constant raiding and warfare between the elites of adjacent city-states. They also imply that the prestige of ruling dynasties seemed to depend on their success in battle and on the sacrifice of prisoners of war. In addition to human sacrifice, ritual bloodletting was common.

Archeologists believe that for centuries wars were

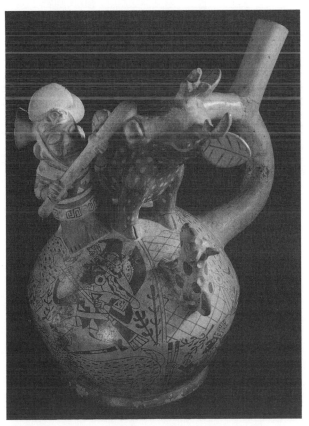

From the Chicamac Valley in Peru, a styrrup spout bottle.

confined to ritualized conflict between the elite troops of rulers, with the losing ruler sometimes being decapitated in an elaborate ceremony commemorated in Mayan art. In the opinion of Dr. David Freidel, an archeologist at Southern Methodist University, such conflicts maintained a balance of roughly equal power among the city-states.

But excavations by Damarest and his Vanderbilt team at the ancient city of Dos Pilas, in northern Guatemala, revealed the remnants of extensive, hastily erected fortifications. Along with other evidence, the fortifications suggest that in the seventh or eighth century, militarism escalated to a level that involved the entire population in a fight for survival. Damarest speculates that escalating warfare upset the fragile ecological balance that Mayan farmers had maintained for centuries in the tropical forest.

Violence was not absent in earlier Mayan culture. Research at Nakbe in northern Guatemala done by Dr. Richard Hansen, a University of California at Los Angeles archeologist, and his colleagues uncovered the ruins of pyramids and stone buildings dating back some 2,600–2,300 years. They found that over the next two centuries symbolism on public architecture that depicted political power came to include decapitation, a ritual that gained such prominence in later Mayan culture.

Sculpted head from the Museo Arqueogico e Histori de Yucatan.

In a November 1991 *Natural History* article entitled "The Owl, Shield, and Flint Blade," Linda Schele wrote about other early battles. El Mirador, in northern Guatemala, is filled with architectural evidence of royal power. One of the largest Mayan cities ever excavated, El Mirador was settled and rose to prominence some 2,500 years ago.

Farther south, the towns of Uaxactun and Tikal, settled about the same time as El Mirador, also grew in population and size and built large public structures depicting the same imagery of royal power. Early rulers of these two kingdoms are shown with bound captives and other indicators that suggest they never were peaceful neighbors.

The Rationale for Violence Remains Unclear

The public history commissioned by Mayan nobility suggests that battle and sacrifice were highly ritualized, timed by astronomical events, and fought between high-ranking, well-trained warriors. The wars were designed to secure sacrificial victims for Mayan pageants. But they were fought also to establish political and economic power over rivals, secure plunder, and control labor by moving populations from the land between kingdoms.

The constant danger of attack led to the formation of large coalitions of kingdoms and alliances with lesser lords. Some of the alliances were solidified by selective marriages, but they were neither permanent nor secure. Toward the end of the Classic period, in the eighth and ninth centuries, warfare became so chronic that the agricultural and social networks of the southern lowlands could no longer survive.

As consensus has grown about the translation of the ancient Mayan language, scholars have separated into three camps about the meaning of the deciphered glyphs. One group accepts the glyphs as accurate accounts of the past. A second group views them as distorted propaganda of the kings and secondary lords. A third contends that while the glyphs may describe actual events, they leave out the daily lives of peasant farmers.

Arguments over the nature of Classic Mayan societies are not likely to abate in the near future. Epigraphers possess literal translations for less than half of the ancient epigraphs, making any broad interpretations tentative.

The Galilee Boat

Israel's winter rains were sparse during 1985 and 1986. To irrigate drought-stricken fields throughout the land, water was pumped from the Kinneret, a freshwater inland lake better known outside of Israel as the Sea of Galilee. As a result, areas of the lake bed normally hidden under water became exposed.

The uncovered lake bed drew amateur archeologists Moshe and Yuval Lufan, members of the nearby Kibbutz Ginnosar, a collective settlement, in search of ancient remains. In January 1986 the two men came across the oval outline of a boat buried in the mud.

The brothers notified Mendel Nun, an expert on the Kinneret, of their find. He in turn contacted Shelley Wachsmann, a Texas A&M University archeologist who is the Inspector of Underwater Antiquities for the Israel Antiquities Authority. Wachsmann

described the events that followed in the September/October 1988 *Biblical Archaeology Review* and in the Fall 1991 *INA Newsletter,* published by the Institute of Nautical Archaeology.

To determine whether the buried boat was modern or ancient, Wachsmann carefully removed a small amount of mud from the boat's midship section. Beneath he found, secured by wooden pegs, mortise-and-tenon joints. A mortise is a notch or space cut in a piece of material to receive a projection called a tenon cut in another piece of material. Once the tenon is inserted into the mortise, a peg often is inserted through both, locking them in place.

The mortise-and-tenon method of boat construction came into existence in the Mediterranean as early as the 14th and 13th centuries B.C. and continued to be used through the Roman era, 27 B.C.–A.D.

By the second day of excavation, the boat dubbed the "Galilee Boat" began to emerge from the mud.

With the bow of the boat in situ, *the white plastic string delineates the planking seams. The fabric tags were later numbered to aid in recording the hull. Stainless steel welding wire was used to fasten the string and tags to the wood. Pinning them with straight metal pins was tried, but they quickly began to rust.*

395. The presence of the joints established that the newly found boat was ancient.

For two days, Wachsmann, accompanied by Nun and the Lufan brothers, probed small sections along the boat's length to determine its state of preservation and to try to narrow down its age. When they had done as much as they could, they reburied the boat to protect the site from looters and the curious until they could organize a proper excavation. As an added precaution, they dug two decoy excavations.

Two days later, to their dismay, newspapers carried reports of a wreck from Jesus' time in the Sea of Galilee. Media coverage rapidly escalated. Even worse, the Ministry of Tourism began promoting the "Jesus connection" to draw pilgrims to Israel. Soon rumors circulated that the wreck was filled with gold coins.

Little more than 48 hours after the story broke, the Lufan brothers noticed people with flashlights in the area of the boat. Wachsmann joined them in guarding the site overnight. The three agreed that they would have to excavate the boat soon or it would be found and destroyed in a search for nonexistent treasure.

An archeological excavation takes considerable time to prepare. Funds must be raised, team members recruited, and the details of housing, feeding, and transportion of the team worked out. The planning for excavations usually takes months, sometimes even years. Wachsmann and his colleagues took three days.

For advice, they raised money to bring to Israel an expert on ancient nautical construction, Professor J. Richard Steffy of the Institute of Nautical Archaeology at Texas A & M. For the rest of the team, they recruited people already in Israel. They planned to excavate the boat, study it *in situ* (in place) and move it to the Yigal Allan Museum at Kibbutz Ginnosar— if they were lucky—in one piece.

Before they could begin excavation, a new danger loomed: the lake threatened to once more cover the boat. Surrounded by a curious crowd, the team started work a week after the story broke in the newspapers. In a race with the steadily rising lake, they worked around the clock.

Using the light of gas fishing lamps, they removed the mud from the inside of the boat, being careful to leave a 6-inch layer of mud covering the water-soaked wood. The team realized that while excavating clumps of mud in the dark, they might miss artifacts (human-made objects). For that reason, they placed the mud in numbered plastic boxes and made a record of the mud's location on the boat.

Each part of the boat was tagged and numbered. White plastic tubing was used lengthwise to outline the layout of the boat's structure and to make it more easily identifiable in photographs.

When the partially excavated quarter of the stern (rear) on the starboard side (the right, facing forward) buckled because the team had dug too far without supporting it sufficiently, they feared that the boat would fall apart despite their best efforts.

To avoid touching the fragile wood while they excavated, the team built a series of metal bridges over the boat. In the beginning, excavators dug while lying prone on the bridges. As digging progressed, platforms bearing the prone diggers were suspended from the bridges.

Volunteers arrived from all over the country. Kibbutz Ginnosar "adopted" the excavation. After finishing their own day's work, kibbutzniks joined the excavation team for another 8–10 hours.

The Kinneret Authority, the governmental authority responsible for the lake, visited the site to investigate what they perceived to be a bizarre request: the Minister of Agriculture—in response to a suggestion by Wachsmann relayed by the Minister of Education—wanted them to lower the level of the lake by pumping water into reserve reservoirs. Instead of lowering the lake, Israel's main freshwater reservoir, the authority came to the rescue by having a crew build a dike of earthworks, a fortification of piled-up earth, and sandbags around the boat to block the encroaching lake. When at last Professor Steffy, the world's leading expert on ancient ship construction, reached the site, the team held its collective breath during his inspection. His first comment: "That's an old boat."

By the eighth day of excavation, the archeologists' task was completed and it was time for the task of

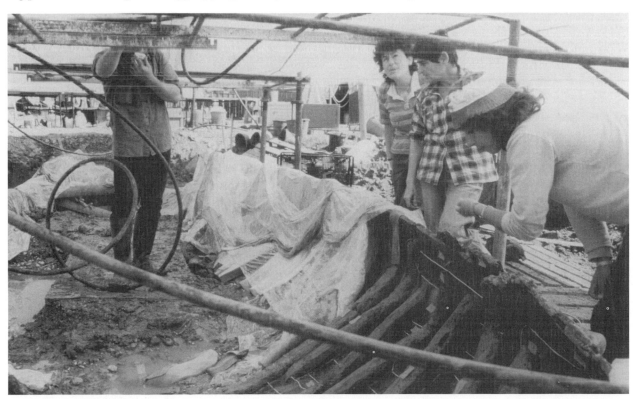

As the excavation progressed it was necessary to shade the boat from the sun's damaging rays with a tarpaulin stretched over a metal frame.

The Galilee Boat presented special preservation problems. Once the excavation was completed, the hull was covered with fiberglass and polyurethane to allow it to be moved to the Yigal Allan Museum for conservation.

preservation to begin. After centuries in the water, the cellular material inside the timber's wood cells had been replaced by water and had the consistency of wet cardboard. Any evaporation of the water from the wood would cause the cell walls to collapse. Therefore, Wachsmann brought in Orna Cohen, an archeologist-conservator, to cope with moving the boat 1,600 feet or so to the museum.

Cohen devised a method that had never been tried: She had frames of fiberglass/polyester laid down inside the boat. She then had the entire hull covered with fine plastic sheeting. Then a polyurethane foam was sprayed into the hull as a liquid. After it bubbled up, it solidified.

Next, Cohen's team excavated narrow tunnels in the mud under the boat. Fiberglass frames were molded to the outside of the hull and the tunnels beneath the boat were filled with polyurethane. The polyurethane strips hardened into supports for the boat, allowing the remaining clay and mud beneath to be excavated. Fiberglass trusses (support framework) were added, and the remaining areas were filled with polyurethane.

When the team was finished, the boat—wrapped in its protective cocoon—looked like a large, melted marshmallow. Water was pumped into the excavation pit until the boat floated. After a steam shovel cut a channel in the protective dike, the boat floated out onto the lake for the first time in 2,000 years. The

entire excavation had taken 11 exhausting days.

An equally exhausting task began after the boat was lifted by crane into a concrete pool built to serve as its conservation tank. Because some parts of the boat would strain to float and the stress would cause breakage, the pool could not be filled with water until the long, laborious task of removing the polyurethane casing had been completed. Yet, no matter how much water the team sprayed as they raced to strip away the boat's covering, parts already uncovered dried out at an alarming rate. Verging on the brink of disaster, the team finally finished its second excavation of the boat and submerged it.

The boat was to be treated by adding a synthetic wax called polyethylene glycol (PEG) to the water in increasing amounts. Simultaneously, the water temperature was to be gradually raised. Over a period of five to seven years, the PEG will penetrate the cellular cavities of the deteriorated wood and replace the water in the cells. Once the process is completed, the boat will be available for study in a dry environment.

Dating the Boat

Establishment of the boat's age took several directions. Seventeen identifiable pieces of ancient pottery were recovered from the Galilee boat and its surrounding area. The pottery pieces were not waterworn, so the archeologists could assume that they were deposited near the places where they were found. The pieces were comparable to types of pottery found at Galilean settlements at Capernaum and Migdal. Dr. David Adan-Bayewitz of Bar-Ilan University determined that the pottery was typical for the later part of the first century B.C. until about the year A.D. 70.

Since the pottery pieces are not a part of the boat and could have been in the region for unrelated reasons, a dating technique linked to the boat had to be used. Because the boat was made of wood, which contains carbon, wood from the boat could be dated using the radiocarbon dating method. This procedure depends on the fact that carbon exists in three forms called isotopes, which differ in the weight of their atoms, but not in their chemical behavior.

All living things absorb carbon, either from carbon dioxide in the atmosphere or by eating material such as plants that contain it. The most abundant form of carbon is carbon 12, but for every 10^{12} atoms of carbon 12 there is one atom of the heaviest carbon form, radioactive carbon 14. (Radioactive implies it decays to a stable nonradioactive carbon at a constant rate).

Carbon 14 is constantly being produced by the atmosphere. The amount of carbon in the atmosphere is assumed to be approximately constant, although scientists recognize that the amount of carbon 14 in the atmosphere has not remained constant through the ages.

As long as an organism is alive, it remains composed of the same proportion of carbon 12 and carbon 14 as the atmosphere. Once the organism is dead, replenishment of the supply from the atmosphere stops and the proportion of carbon 14 in the organism's remains falls at a steady rate.

For any particular radioactive isotope, it is possible to measure its "half-life." The half-life of carbon 14 is usually stated as 5,568 plus or minus 30 years. This means that at the end of 5,568 years one-half of the carbon 14 will have been lost. At the end of another 5,568 years, one-half of the remainder will be gone and so on.

Therefore, by measuring the concentration of the isotope, the approximate date of the death of the specimen can be calculated. In the case of the Galilee boat, Wachsmann and his colleagues assumed that the wood used to make the boat had been cut within a short time of the boat's construction.

Ten wood samples from different parts of the Galilee boat, each weighing several grams, were removed and sent to a laboratory. Using gas proportional counters, which count the radioactive decay events (when carbon 14 decays into nitrogen), the amount of carbon 14 in each sample was measured relative to the amount of carbon 12. The results indicated that the boat began its life as a fishing vessel on the Sea of Galilee some time between 120 B.C. and A.D. 40.

Professor Steffy's examination indicated that the boat had been built by a master craftsman, who had

The museum's conservator, Orna Cohen, thought that over water would be the best method of transporting the boat to the museum from the excavation site. Thus, after 2,000 years in mud, the boat floated 550 yards to be lifted ashore by a crane. Here, the Galilee Boat is being prepared for the lift.

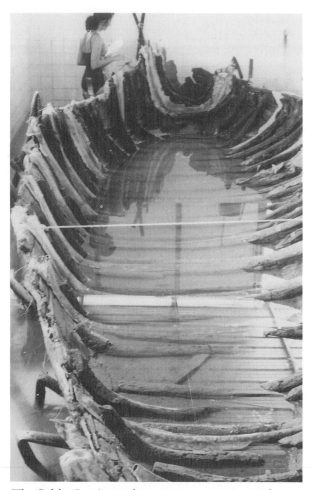

The Galilee Boat's new home is a conservation pool.

probably learned his trade in the Mediterranean or been apprenticed to someone who had. However, the boatbuilder had been forced to use timber inferior to that typically used on Mediterranean vessels. Moreover, many of the timbers in the boat, including those in the forward portion of the keel (the principal timber extending from stem to stern at the bottom and supporting the boat's frame) had been taken apparently from older boats. The boat had been repaired often, suggesting that it had had a long life. When it was taken out of service, someone had removed usable timbers, including the stem post (the upright piece to which the side timbers are attached) and stern post (the principal timber in the stern frame, joined to the keel, to which the rudder is attached).

Then the boat probably was pushed into the lake, where it sank into the silt.

The removal of the surplus parts and the discovery of two other boats and other wooden debris during the excavation suggested to Steffy that the area had been used for building and repairing boats. Old boats or trade-ins may have been brought to the shore, stripped of usable timber, and discarded in the lake. This possibility makes the site of interest for further excavations.

Wachsmann is asked often if the Galilee boat is of the type used by Jesus and his apostles or by Jews in the battle of Migdal, a revolt in A.D. 67 against the Romans, in which Jews were slaughtered. Details of the battle were chronicled by the first-century Jewish historian Josephus. Wachsmann believes the boats used by Jesus and by Migdal's defenders resembled the Galilee boat.

Wachsmann also is asked often if Jesus could have sailed with all the apostles in the same boat. He believes it is not possible to determine how many people took part in the voyages in the Gospels, since the Bible describes Jesus sailing with his disciples and he had many more disciples than apostles.

However, accounts by Josephus suggest that it would have been possible for Jesus to sail with his 12 apostles. In describing his sham fleet (boats intended to hide the small size of Jewish forces), Josephus noted that he brought on board with him seven soldiers. Together with a crew of five, that would have been 13. He also brought an unspecified number of friends, which means that there were at least 15 people in his boat.

The Galilee boat could have easily carried 15 first-century males—who averaged 5 feet, 4½ inches in height and probably weighed about 140 pounds—for a total of 2,100 pounds.

In short, the discovery of the Galilee Boat suggests that additional ancient vessels may be preserved in the lake's sediment. Indeed, the hulls of boats that took part in the battle of Migdal are still buried in the lake's bottom. Moreover, the Sea of Galilee's seafaring history extends back at least 5,000 years.

2

PLANTS AND ANIMALS

Change is Brewing in Systematics

With the development of new tools and the looming loss of many species of plants and animals, taxonomy has reclaimed the interest of young scientists. Taxonomy comes from the Greek word taxon meaning to order or arrange. Now called "systematics," it is the theory, principles, and process of classifying organisms into categories.

Biological classification not only shows the relationships between different groups, but also demonstrates the course of evolution. Yet tracing evolutionary paths is difficult. It requires interpretations of the connections between various characteristics. For example, a systematist might be forced to decide whether a flattened leaflike appendage is more or less primitive than a cylindrical rodlike one. The ultimate decision would depend on knowledge gathered earlier.

The names of species are of primary importance, particularly to systematists in museums who must trace specimens in their collection to existing descriptions. If an adequate description is unavailable, a systematist may publicize a purported new species that is not in fact new.

In his 1962 book *Naming the Living World,* Theodore Savory explained the value of a scientific method for naming organisms. He pointed out that many well-known organisms have common names that differ from one country to another—sometimes even from one village to another. An agreed-upon name such as *Pluvialis apricaria* provides not only a more definite name for the "small golden plover," it is less likely to be changed locally and more likely to

be helpful to ornithologists of many countries.

Before the 18th century, naturalists used an awkward naming system. To explain the system they used, Savory used dogs as an example—even though dogs all belong to the same species. A medieval author writing about dogs in Latin would have begun with *Canis,* a common word for dog. To distinguish between a bull terrier and a Manchester terrier he would have added description, perhaps calling one a "white dog" and the other a "black dog." However, if he had taken into account a third dog, a fox terrier, he might have called the bull terrier the "white dog with red eyes" and the fox terrier "the white dog with dark eyes."

Such a system rapidly becomes unwieldy. The buttercup now known to botanists as *Ranunculus bulbosus* once had four two-word descriptive phrases following *Ranunculus.*

The cumbersome system was laid to rest by Carolus Linnaeus (1707-1778), who began the systematic practice of two-part, or binomial, nomenclature (naming). His was not the first use of a two-part naming, but his was the first to gain wide acceptance. In June 1735 he became a physician, and in December of the same year he published *Systema Naturae,* a booklet on classification destined to become a classic. Eighteen years later, in the 1753 edition of *Systema Naturae,* he introduced his system of binominal nomenclature.

Linnaeus' acute powers of observation developed during childhood in his father's garden. He had a gift for classifying, an almost instinctive ability to choose

The plate, of Browallia, is from Hortus Cliffortianus, *a book by the father of modern taxonomy, Carolus Linnaeus, published in 1737. Linnaeus devised a system of classifying plants by the number of stamens and pistils. Each species was assigned to a genus, which is a group of related species.*

*Using a technique called microscope taxonomy, some late-19th-century scientists obsessively focused on minor physical variations to identify and label various "separate" species. Dr. C. Hart Merriam of Harvard University managed to describe an incredible 86 separate species of brown and grizzly bears in 1886. The one and only species of grizzly bear (*Ursus horribilis*) is a member of the brown bear family.*

the significant features among the characteristics of a group of plants or animals.

Using the system that began with Linnaeus and developed over the course of about a century, biologists in the field and in the laboratory study organisms and classify them with similar organisms into a group called a species. From species on up, groups of all sizes are called taxa (plural of taxon). Closely related species are grouped into genera (plural of genus); genera are grouped into families; families into orders; orders into classes; classes into phyla (plural of phylum); and phyla into kingdoms.

Every known organism classified is given its own unique two-part Latin name. For all organisms in the same genus, the first part of the name is the same. The second part of the name designates the species within the genus.

Linnaeus based his classification on visible characteristics of living organisms. Extinct organisms were brought into the scheme later. The 19th-century discoveries of paleontologists and Charles Darwin's analysis of evolution by natural selection encouraged systematists to assume their classifications reflected the historical record of life. They converted classifications into phylogenies, family trees of species or higher taxa.

Very few lineages from fossil organisms to living ones have been actually traced. Nevertheless, systematists hold that the truest classification is one that best reflects the relationship by common ancestry.

Too, reconstruction of evolutionary histories is not just dependent on the beliefs and decisions of individual biologists. It also depends on the availability of a fossil record. Many animals left no fossilized remains and many fossils have not yet been discovered. Therefore significant progress in paleontology can compel changes in classification systems.

Contrasting taxonomy with other sciences that simply discover and record facts, Savory wrote, "[T]axonomy is largely a summary of ideas and hopes [and] can best play its part in biology if it retains an elasticity which admits any changes and expansion due to advancing knowledge and developing interpretation."

The Impact of New Technologies

From the time of Aristotle until the middle of the 20th century, most scientists were content to divide the living world into just two kingdoms, plants and animals. In the mid-19th century, many systematists began to see that some organisms, such as bacteria

*Sometimes the American bison (*Bison bison*), or buffalo, are viewed as just shaggier, wilder second cousins to domestic cattle. But the buffalo is not a domestic animal and can be ferocious and unpredictable when confronted. The only animals that even try to prey upon bison are grizzly bears and timber wolves. When attacked the bison will form a circle, as would a wagon train, keeping the young in the center. The bulls will face out toward the predators with their dangerously effective horns.*

Living creatures were originally divided into two kingdoms, plants and animals. Eventually, fungi, such as mushrooms, were classified separately from plants.

and fungi, differ from plants and animals more than plants and animals differ from each other. From time to time, proposals were made for third and fourth kingdoms to accommodate them, but they were ignored.

Ernst Haekel (1834-1919), the German popularizer of Darwin's theory of evolution, made several proposals for a third kingdom of organisms. The boundaries of the kingdom he proposed fluctuated during his long career, but he consistently aimed to set the most primitive and ambiguous organisms apart from plants and animals. Within the kingdom he proposed, he recognized bacteria and blue-green algae as a major group called the Monera, distinguished by their lack of a cell nucleus, which is a small mass of protoplasm surrounded by a membrane that contains chromosomes and that functions in metabolism, growth, and reproduction.

Attitudes toward new kingdoms began to change in the 1960s. New biochemical techniques and the availability of the electronmicroscope unveiled affinities and differences on levels smaller than cells. Among a variety of proposals for multikingdom systems, a five-kingdom system proposed by R.H. Whittaker of Cornell University in 1959 gathered increasing support over the next three decades.

In 1982 Lynn Margulis of the University of Massachusetts in Amherst and Karlene Schwartz of the University of Massachusetts in Boston published *Five Kingdoms: An Illustrated Guide to the Phyla of Life on Earth,* a modification of Whittaker's system. Both

Whittaker and Margulis and Schwartz owed a significant debt to a 1956 four-kingdom model by Herbert Copeland of Sacramento City College in California.

The Whittaker system's five kingdoms are: **Prokaryotae** (Monera or bacteria); **Protoctista** (algae, protozoans, slime molds, and other less-known aquatic and parasitic organisms); **Fungi** (mushrooms, molds, and lichens); **Animalia** (animals with or without backbones); and **Plantae** (mosses, ferns, cone-bearing plants, and flowering plants).

Margulis and Schwartz recognize and describe 92 phyla, including 17 prokaryotic, 27 protoctist, 5 fungal, 33 animal, and 10 plant. They arrange based on the assumption that the simplest forms came earliest and evolved over time into the later, more complex forms.

As a rule the highest taxa within a kingdom—the phyla and classes—represent the most ancient divergences; the lowest taxa—the genera and species—represent the most recent. However, because the evolutionary arrangements of so many groups are not known, there are no absolute rules. Even though a common ancestry may not have been documented, many organisms are grouped in the same taxon because they have some distinctive trait in common. The phyla differ enormously in size. Some contain only a few species, others contain millions.

The recent revival of interest in systematics may be due to the introduction of new techniques, which make it possible to determine evolutionary differences at a level unimaginable a decade ago. The approaches hold promise for studying wild animals, while avoiding the trauma of capture. They also make it possible to provide forensic evidence needed to curb worldwide trade in endangered species.

One technique, the polymerase chain-reaction process, developed at Cetus Corporation in California, enables a scientist to separate the two strands of a deoxyribonucleic acid (DNA) double helix (the transmitter of the chemical code of hereditary pattern). With the aid of a chemical, a researcher can snip out a few molecules of a single strand of DNA. In a polymerase chain-reactions machine about the size of a microwave oven, heating and cooling cycles lasting about three minutes cause the DNA to replicate itself repeatedly, splitting and doubling in each cycle.

During an interview for a February 18, 1992 *New*

York Times article entitled "Sophisticated Tools Are Giving Taxonomy a New Lease on Life," Dr. William Alverson of the University of Wisconsin Herbarium in Madison explained that scientists on staff can receive an inch of leaf from the other side of the world one morning and have hundreds of millions of copies of a particular gene they want to look at by the next morning.

The technique is a major breakthrough, according to Dr. Steven Solheim, a botanist at the University of Wisconsin's Whitewater campus, who said, "For the first time it gets us out of a weird loop. In the past we used the characteristics to try to understand an organism's evolution, and then used the evolution to try to understand the characteristics, often not knowing for certain that we'd gotten the first part absolutely right."

Most systematists caution that technology cannot replace traditional taxonomy based on morphology (the form and structure of animals and plants without regard to function). One factor that limits the use of the polymerase chain-reaction technique is its prohibitive cost. Moreover, a scientist cannot walk around a forest and survey plants based on their DNA. The availability of the technique actually enhances the value of traditional taxonomic collections, since tissue from extinct animals can help to settle long-standing disputes.

Molecular studies for the most part have verified the past hypotheses of taxonomists. But the molecular approach can sometimes answer questions that observation alone cannot. Convergent evolution, in which two species evolving in similar environments have come to have similar characteristics, sometimes misleads biologists into believing that the two species have descended from a common ancestor. Molecular analysis can establish that they did not.

Choosing Up Sides

Unfortunately, new techniques cannot settle the field's intellectual and ethical debates. Plant taxonomists gathered from around the world in the Royal Botanic Gardens at Kew, just outside London, in November 1990 to grapple with two competing proposals to put all the world's higher plants into a computer data base. A computerized botanical library would help scientists engaged in improving the world's supply of food, fuel, and medicine, who need

The last ice age in North America killed off all hooved animals except for the buffalo. When the Europeans brought back the horse, no American Indians had ever seen them. For lack of a word for the animal, some simply elected to call the horse Big Dog.

to be able to determine quickly what is known about a plant.

The two proposals took different routes to creation of a data base. The Species Plantarum Project (SPP), conceived by Dick Brummitt, a plant taxonomist in the Herbarium at Kew, proposed to summarize all the botanical data on every known plant. Supported by Kew, the Missouri Botanical Garden, and five other institutions, SPP would offer: a taxonomic synopsis of all ferns and flowering plants with names and biological relationships verified by the latest scholarship.

The less-complex plan, the Global Plant Species Information System (GPSIS), would offer a checklist of acceptable plant names. The 21-volume *Index Kewensis,* begun a century ago by Charles Darwin, lists a million names for flowering plants. Since botanists agree that the number of plant species is only about 250,000, a data base that eliminated overlapping names would enable data base users to communicate without confusion.

A November 16, 1990 *Science* article entitled "The Name of the Rose, or Hunting for a Plant Database" presented the arguments of both sides. On one side Nancy Morin, head of botanical information management at Missouri Botanical Garden, said: "If you're a plant breeder, or an ecologist, the name isn't important. What's important is the biological entity you're dealing with. You want good biological information."

On the other, Frank Bisby, a senior lecturer in biology at Southampton University in England and an

Spiders are considered to be insects. However, along with mites and scorpions, they are classified in a separate genus, Arachnida. *This is the Lynx spider.*

organizer of an October 1990 meeting in Delphi, Greece on the GPSIS, insisted that users did not care what system was used as long as everyone used the same system. They simply wanted a list, without confusion.

After attending the Delphi conference organized by his opponent, Brummitt, the father of the SPP, seemed willing to admit that a checklist prepared in two or three years could have value, but he feared users would fail to recognize its limitations. Chris Leon, an ecologist working on a data base of poisonous plants for Kew, told *Science:* "There's no right or wrong in botany . . . We just want a set of names that will be fixed for 10 or 15 years." The lack of a data base is holding up international conservation efforts. Although the scientists seemed to be approaching consensus, lack of funding remained a formidable obstacle.

Lack of funding was the source of a controversy at Britain's venerable Natural History Museum in May 1990. The government, which provides a part of the museum's budget, insisted that the museum had to derive a greater portion of its funding from admissions charges. In response to the edict, the museum's director, Neil Chalmers, proposed to streamline research by concentrating on a half-dozen activities that

currently hold considerable popular interest. The areas were: biodiversity, environmental quality, living resources, mineral resources, human health, and human origins. Among a score of research departments the museum would scrap were: the evolution and classification of fossil birds and mammals, fossil plants, bees and wasps, and microscopic plants.

The decision to cut back on taxonomy drew widespread criticism. A May 1990 *Science* article entitled "British Museum in Turmoil" quoted Niles Eldredge, dean of the scientific council at the American Museum of Natural History, who said, "We just don't know what's out there. To cut back now is a disaster . . . There is no point in maintaining a collection if research is not being done on it."

Director Chalmer's view was at the other end of the spectrum: "With more than 30 million species on Earth, is it an attainable goal to try to classify them all? You have to leave gaps, so are you going to leave them on a random basis or because you concentrate on areas of perceived importance?"

Funding was not an issue in a rancorous dispute about ethical standards described in an April 28, 1992 *New York Times* article entitled "Rare Bird Illuminates Bitter Dilemma." Biologists working in Somalia captured the only known example of a new species of shrike, the robin-sized Buolo Burti boubou (pronounced BOO-boo), an insessorial (perching) bird with gray, black, and white plumage, a hooked beak, a shrill voice, and a long tail. Instead of preserving the only specimen of the bird, the Somalia biologists released it after keeping it for a year, hoping it would find a mate, breed, and produce offspring in the wild.

Left behind were photographs, blood samples, a handful of feathers and fuel for a battle over whether a very rare animal is more valuable dead or alive. Normally when a species is discovered, biologists choose one individual to represent the "type" as a standard to serve as a preserved model against which other individuals can be compared. Because it was the only specimen they had, the biologists in Somalia chose the boubou as its species type. To systematists, the idea of letting the species type, the only known boubou, fly off was almost criminal.

As species after species approaches extinction, the choice has become more common and the disagree-

Which of these two creatures is actually a descendant of the dinosaur? Until recently lizards were thought to be the descendants, but a controversial theory has arisen that says birds are the true descendants, including the whistling swan and the collard lizard.

ment between the two perspectives has become more heated. In letters to journals and in conversations among colleagues, preservation-minded biologists praised the release of the bird in Somalia, while other biologists, particularly museum systematists, called it short-sighted and sentimental.

Dr. Scott Lanyon, a population biologist and the head of the division of birds at the Field Museum of Natural History in Chicago, told the *New York Times* that small birds and mammals typically produce too many offspring to be supported by their environment; therefore, the removal of one individual is un-

likely to affect the fate of a species in the slightest.

In contrast, Dr. Jared Diamond, a research associate in the bird department of the American Museum of Natural History, declared Dr. Lanyon's logic to be flawed. He pointed out that some species have grown back to strength from a very few individuals. A breeding program with the Chatham Island Black Robin in New Zealand began with two females and five males and has climbed to 100 individuals. Such controversies may be doing as much as new technologies to keep young scientists interested in systematics.

Andromeda was used as a catch-all genus for many woody plants that were later separated into other genera, such as the Fetterbush (Pieris floribunda).

Sharks, Hunters of the Deep Threatened with Extinction

Sharks stir up such feelings of fear and dread in humans that environmentalists find it difficult to protect them. Yet humans may be on the brink of eliminating the global shark population. Not only do humans eat sharks in large quantity, they also kill them for their oil and skin. Some humans kill sharks for the thrill of boasting about the deed. Huge numbers of sharks are destroyed out of irrational fear. But the biggest threat is new fishing techniques. Commercial fishermen hate sharks because they damage fishing gear and destroy fish left in nets or on lines.

Although shark attacks can present a danger to anyone in marine waters, swimmers are more likely to die from drowning or a heart attack in the water or in a traffic accident on the way to the beach. Worldwide, there are an estimated 50–75 shark attacks annually resulting in 5–20 deaths. Most attacks occur in nearshore waters, typically inshore of a sandbar or between sandbars. Areas where food for sharks is plentiful, such as steep drop-offs, also are common attack sites.

Shark attacks were of little public interest until 20th-century communication increased public awareness. The press evolved from gathering local news to broader coverage of the world; therefore, knowledge of shark attacks became more common. Competition for readers led to "shock stories" about

Lemon shark mothers, 8 feet, 6 inches long and weighing 350 pounds, produce pups 2 feet long that weigh a little over 2 pounds.

sharks. Fictionalized shark attacks, in particular the 1973 book *Jaws,* later made into a movie, further heightened public fears.

World War II contributed to awareness of shark attacks. Air and sea disasters thrust pilots and sailors into tropical oceans, where they were likely to encounter sharks. Encounters with nonmilitary people increased following the war, because there has been a worldwide trend toward more intense use of marine waters.

Despite this, scientists have never confirmed stories that a shark actually consumed a person. The most common incidents are hit-and-run attacks in surf zones. The victim does not see the attacker and the shark does not return. Injuries are generally minor.

One theory about hit-and-run attacks proposes that the shark releases the person on discovering that it is not normal prey. Another theory holds that the shark's normal behavior is bite-and-spit, meaning the shark inflicts a massive wound and backs off to wait for the victim to die before returning to consume it.

Scientists suspect hit-and-run attacks are cases of mistaken identity, that is, a dark-suited diver or a surfer on a board resembles routine prey. Prey for the adult white shark includes marine mammals, such as harbor seals, sea lions, and elephant seals, all of which equal or exceed the size of humans. Unfortunately, knowledge about the white shark—responsible for most attacks on humans in areas such as central and northern California and southern Australia—is limited.

Less common are bump-and-bite attacks and sneak attacks. They usually involve divers or swimmers in deep water. In bump-and-bite attacks, the shark circles and bumps the victim prior to the attack. Sneak attacks take place with no warning. In both cases, multiple or sustained bites are common.

Sharks' lives are not a continual round of ambushing, pursuing, attacking, and feeding on prey. Recent evidence suggests that they feed intensively for short periods and fast for longer periods. The lemon shark, for example, is estimated to feed for about 11 hours and fast for about 32 hours. Compared to bony fish

Sea lions and other marine mammals are far more likely than people to be attacked by sharks.

and many other animals, sharks are light eaters. It takes them about a month to take in the equivalent of their body weight, while many bony fish consume their body weight in a few days.

Because they live in a concealing medium, sustained visual observation of many shark species has been impossible. Hence, many remain a mystery. One of the most intensely studied is the lemon shark of the Bahamas. In the North Sound of Bimini, more than 20 juvenile lemon sharks, fitted with internal ultrasonic transmitters, were tracked for periods of 12–39 days.

To track sharks scientists use telemetry, the transmission of instrument readings to remote locations through radio waves. Information gathered in this way on lemon sharks refuted a common assumption that sharks attack when they are defending their territory. Like all other sharks studied to date, lemon sharks appear not to be territorial. Although lemon sharks favor certain areas, their home ranges overlap and none has been observed defending a home range.

Eugenie Clark, professor of zoology at the University of Maryland, was the first biologist to gather data on sharks in the deep sea. From 1987 to 1990, she participated in 71 dives in deep-diving manned submersibles. To observe and photograph sharks in their natural habitat, Clark and her colleagues lured deep-sea sharks with bait. Between 1,000 and 6,000 feet, they saw many sharks. Beyond those levels—between 6,800 and 12,000 feet—they found no sharks, although they did find other cartilaginous (skeletons made of a tough elastic tissue) fishes.

If scientists and environmentalists can halt the slaughter of sharks and the sharks survive, the result might be breakthroughs in medicine. Recognizing this, Congress in January 1992 designated the Mote Marine Laboratory, a nonprofit research and education center in Sarasota, Florida, as the National Center of Shark Research. Work has been under way at Mote for more than a decade to determine the mechanisms that make sharks naturally resistant to cancer.

The blue shark is classified among the pelagic species that travel widely in the upper zones of the oceans. Other broad categories are: coastal species found inshore and along the continental shelf; deep-dwelling species that inhabit ocean basins and the continental slope; and coastal-pelagic that are found both inshore and beyond the continental shelf, but whose ranges do not seem to extend to mid-ocean or transocean.

Piecing What Is Known Together

To help its readers distinguish sharks from other fish, the American Littoral Society, a conservation organization, provided a taxonomic classification chart in its December 1990 bulletin entitled *Discovering Sharks.* The chart pointed out that modern jawed fishes with bone skeletons, such as herring, salmon, flounder, and mackerel, belong to the class *Osteichthyes,* which is Greek for bony fishes. Fish with skeletons made up entirely of cartilage, including sharks, belong in the class *Chondrichthyes.* Sharks are further distinguished as belonging to the subclass *Elasmobranchi,* a Greek reference to their flat, plate-like gills.

Because cartilage does not last long after an animal dies, the fossil record of sharks is skimpy. Nonetheless, scientists have traced sharks back 400 million years. About 320 million years ago, a warm bay called Bear Gulch in the foothills of Montana's Snowy Mountains served as a locale for nature's varied experiments in every possible way to make a fish. The remains of shark experiments are found in isolated teeth, scales, or fin spines. An abundance of 15-million-year-old white shark teeth fossils that measure nine inches along their cutting edge suggest that white sharks at that time ranged up to 40 feet in length.

Much remains unknown about the shark's role as a predator, an animal that preys on other animals for its food. When a mackerel is found in a shark's stomach, scientists seldom know whether the fish was alive or dead when it was consumed. Even if they know it was alive, they don't know whether it was healthy, and if healthy, whether its behavior was comparable to that of other mackerel. In other words, scientists do not know why a particular shark eats a particular mackerel.

If predatory capacities are viewed on a continuum, scavengers that feed solely on dead organisms lie on one end and superpredators that take prey at will, regardless of the prey's fitness, lie on the other end. In their predatory behavior, the majority of shark species lie somewhere in-between the extremes.

Sharks fill an ecological niche as the predator at the top of the marine food chain, by which scientists mean the feeding relationships that unite a biological community. Sharks are a key predator because they eliminate the weak and the sick among the species they eat, keeping the various species healthy, something neither scavengers nor superpredators do. If the world population of sharks is exterminated, scientists believe the shark's absence will upset the ecological balance of the ocean populations of prey species.

According to ecologists, the life history of an individual organism such as a shark is composed of customary patterns of behavior. The animal seeks and protects food and shelter and reaches maturity through a process known as differentiation—development of characteristics that distinguish one species from another—and produces offspring.

To talk about the life history of sharks is to talk about 350 or more different life patterns corresponding to 350 species. Within the 350 species, a range of adaptive variables have evolved. Each has been a trade-off between the cost of developing the variable and the benefits to be derived from possessing it.

Size is one of the most obvious of trade-off variables in the struggle to survive. The weight and length of living sharks extends from a few ounces to many tons. The Pacific dwarf shark is less than 12 inches. The filter-feeding whale, the largest fish in the sea, may reach 45 feet. Large sharks have no natural enemies except humans. However, it costs a lot in resources to maintain a large body. Small sharks need less in the way of resources, but they run the risk of being eaten by larger animals, including other sharks.

Sharks live almost everywhere in the ocean. Most are found in the tropics, but a few species inhabit arctic waters. Some live deep in the ocean, others in shallow shore currents, and a few live in freshwater rivers and lakes. Some sharks travel in packs. Others travel in schools only during certain times of the year. Some always travel alone, except when mating.

The course of a species' adaptation through evolution is called its "life history strategy. In an uncertain world, an animal wins the survival game as long as its offspring live long enough to have another generation of babies. Unlike bony fish, which all hatch from eggs laid in water, shark pups are born in a variety of ways. Some take 8–14 months to hatch in egg cases attached by long threads to coral or seaweed. Some hatch from eggs inside the mother and remain there until they are big enough to take care of themselves. One species, the Port Jackson shark, lays hard, shiny brown eggs shaped like corkscrews. Scientists speculate that the odd shape enables the slowly spinning eggs to dig themselves into the sand of the sea bottom, where they remain hidden until birth.

At least 350 million years ago, sharks evolved a reproductive strategy that favored a small number of offspring, which among many shark species are nurtured, protected, and nourished for varying lengths of time within the mother's body. Today biologists worry that this strategy may doom sharks in an ocean raked by mechanized fishing fleets, freezer ships, 100-mile-long nets, and thousands of miles of drifting gill nets designed to trap fish by entangling their gills in the mesh.

Sharks' Uniqueness

For many scientists, the sheer variety of sharks makes them marvels of adaptation. Cartilage is so supple that sharks easily make abrupt changes in direction. Cartilage is also lighter than bone, a factor important to sharks since, unlike bony fish, they lack an air-

filled bladder to provide buoyancy. Bony fish can remain motionless, but if sharks stop moving, they sink.

The absence of an air-filled bladder is an advantage for sharks because it means they are not confined to a narrow range of water depth. A fish like a large grouper cannot move far vertically without the risk of collapsing its bladder and sinking to the bottom or of expanding its bladder in a rapid ascent and ballooning to the surface. Some slow-moving sharks, like basking sharks or cookie cutter sharks, typically have large oil-rich livers that provide them enough buoyancy to maintain their position without much forward motion.

Scientists speculated for a long time about why the eyes of sharks remained undamaged when they attacked a prey. In time, research determined that many shark species have a protective membrane they close to protect their eyes during crucial moments.

The skin of sharks is structurally quite different from the overlapping scales of most bony fish. The structure of each scale resembles a small tooth. In sharks that are adept swimmers, the scales are shaped like mushrooms. The crowns of the scales have three to five longitudinal ridges arranged so that they run parallel to the water flow over the shark's body, a factor that probably reduces drag, the resistance that pushes in the direction opposite to the movement of the shark.

Scientists marvel at the shark's streamlined and efficient jaws. Most sharks look as if they could only bite something directly beneath them. However, in a swift transformation at the critical moment of capture, the shark's jaw thrusts forward and the teeth are extended, changing the whole shape of the head.

An advantage of the shark's underslung jaw is that it allows space for anchoring massive jaw muscles. The position of the shark's jaw muscles makes possible the transmission of large biting forces through short jaws and permits independent movement of the jaws with respect to the head.

The shark's mouth, which is on the abdominal side, is highly flexible. Food can be sucked up from the ocean floor and the mobile upper and lower jaws make it possible to pick up objects midwater and to carve out large chunks from prey too large to be taken at one bite. The weight of the shark's body sweeps back and forth like a saw to tear off a chunk of whatever is being bitten.

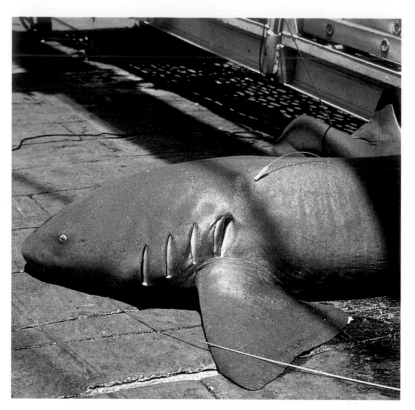

A recently killed nurse shark. The nurse shark, commonly found in the shallow, near shore waters of the southern United States plus tropical regions of the Caribbean Sea and the southwest Atlantic Ocean, is rarely considered dangerous. Slow-moving, they are a familiar sight to divers and fishermen. Because of their docile nature and capacity to survive in captivity, nurse sharks are included in many marine exhibits. All sharks are noted for their sense of smell, but their other senses, hearing, touch, even sight, are also acute. Sharks have had an unwarranted reputation for near-sightedness, due to such odd habits as occasionally attacking boats. The confusion seems to come from mixed sensory perception. Both boats and living creatures have weak electrical fields that the shark can detect. Sometimes the shark favors electrical fields over visual cues.

The shark is born with a complete set of teeth and is ready to hunt immediately. Additional layers of reserve teeth lie one on top of the other. Replacement teeth generally move into position within 24 hours of a loss, and most sharks grow and replace thousands of teeth during a lifetime.

Since no two kinds of sharks have exactly the same kind or size of teeth, teeth are an important means of identifying a shark. The teeth of a white shark can cut paper as cleanly as a razor blade, while the tiny teeth of the basking and whale sharks merely serve to strain plankton from the ocean water. In some sharks the upper teeth are triangular-shaped thin knives with sawtooth edges and sharp points, and the lower teeth are spikelike. The spikes hold a prey while the uppers cut into it. Sand tigers and mako sharks, which swallow a whole fish in a single gulp, have spikelike teeth in both upper and lower jaws.

The contents of captured sharks' stomachs have helped biologists to better understand their behavior. In addition to routine food items, such as two 6-foot sharks that were once found in the stomach of a 15-foot tiger shark, an array of extraordinary items have been found in sharks' stomachs. These have included: mud, coal, stones, cans, plants, a suit of armor, a roll of tar paper, a keg of nails, a carpenter's square, raincoats, goats, horses, sheep, reindeer, and monkeys. Many of the items may have fallen off or been thrown off ships. Presumably, the sharks could get rid of the strange items, if necessary, since sharks have the capacity to evert—turn inside out—their stomachs. Researchers have observed sharks in captivity evert their stomachs.

Several theories have been offered to explain the presence of strange items in sharks' stomachs. Sharks may simply swallow them along with other food. Or sharks' sensitivity to electrical fields may attract them to metal objects. Some observers believe that the indigestible items may serve as ballast in some sharks that have an excess amount of oil in their livers, which might make them too buoyant to dive or swim properly.

Sharks are elasomobranch fish; this means they have several gill slits, which are respiratory organs through which water is passed to the outside from the animal's pharynx, the digestive tract area that extends from the nasal cavities to the esophagus. On the water's route through the gill filaments, blood exchanges carbon dioxide for vital oxygen. Besides its role in respiration, gills may help regulate salt and have other functions.

Shark products include their hides for leather and their teeth for jewelry. But more important are biomedical uses. Sharks are almost totally immune to cancer. Nurse sharks exposed to carcinogens over a period of 10 years never developed malignancies. Shark liver oil—once used as a source of vitamin A—stimulates the action of white blood cells, which may contribute to the sharks' immunity. Another possible cancer fighter may be shark cartilage, which has been used in artificial skin for burn patients.

Most fish can supply their gills with water by simply opening their mouths while swimming rapidly—an operation called ram ventilation. Sharks use ram ventilation at slower swimming speeds. The importance of ram ventilation to sharks explains why they have multiple gill slits. Separate gill covers with control over their constriction makes possible fine adjustments in the movement of water through the various gill openings.

Because forward movement passes water containing oxygen over their gill surfaces, it was once thought that sharks had to swim constantly to breathe. It is now known that some sharks frequently rest on the bottom. Only sharks swimming over the abyss—the great depths of the ocean beyond the continental shelf, generally in excess of 3,000 feet deep—must remain in constant motion. The new insight came when researchers found resting sharks in caves in the Caribbean off the Yucatan Peninsula in Mexico. Sharks entering the cave waters seem to become tranquilized, almost lethargic. Fresh water high in oxygen, carbon dioxide and acidity seeps into the caves, which may reduce the need for motion to acquire oxygen.

Humans often hunt sharks for the oil from their livers. In some species, the liver approaches 10% of the animal's weight. The only support sharks have for

their liver and other internal organs comes from the pressure of water against the outside of the abdominal wall. Therefore, if a shark is removed from water, the abdominal skin sags and the internal organs are dislodged and damaged. Even if returned quickly to the water, the animal is likely to die due to intestinal injuries.

Many sharks return to the same area year after year. Scientists believe they are following Earth's magnetic fields. Their bodies have receptors called ampullae of Lorenzini, which are an array of pores (small openings), whose center lies in the mouth. These home in on Earth's magnetic fields. The ampullae serve other functions, including the initial location of prey. Moreover, when the shark gets too close to its prey to see clearly, the ampullae provide direction using the prey's magnetic field.

Who Is To Blame for the Decline of Sharks

Approximately 1.3 billion pounds of shark are landed worldwide each year. That figure does not include sharks caught as an "incidental bycatch" and thrown back dead   which might amount to another 6.5 million.

Samuel Gruber, a professor of marine biology at the University of Miami who heads the shark specialists group of the International Union for the Conservation of Nature and Natural Resources, asserts that although recreational fishermen have to share some of the blame, the major culprits are commercial fishermen. Most responsible are shrimp trawlers, longliners fishing for tuna and swordfish, and driftnetters, which harvest squid, salmon and other species.

Trawlers drag a large baglike net along the bottom of a fishing bank. Longliners put out long lines, to which a huge number of hooks are attached. Driftnetters use large gill nets constructed of 5- to 6-inch nylon meshes that hang as deep as 60 feet below the surface and extend outward for up to 100 miles.

Fish caught in drift nets try to swim through and get their heads and gills entangled and die. The January 1992 issue of *Discover* quoted Gruber's description of the fishing technique: "These nets kill everything, birds, marine mammals, sharks, and most are just thrown away."

The bycatch loss of sharks from all these methods is massive. The National Marine Fisheries Service

Organs found in some shark species, such as makos, enable the shark to maintain a higher temperature. The organs are called retia mirabilia *(retia meaning a network or mesh of veins, arteries or nerves, and mirabile meaning wondrous). Retia mirabilia pass oxygen-rich, cool arterial blood coming from the gills close to warm venous blood on its return from the shark's interior. The venous blood's heat transfers across the thin blood vessel walls to warm the cool arterial blood. The advantage of a higher temperature is an increase in the speed and power of muscle contractions, the rate of digestion, and the rate of embryo development.*

(NMFS) describes the number of dead throwbacks as extensive, but the agency notes that without on-board observers such tallies are only approximations.

According to NMFS data, longliners have depleted the shark populations of hammerheads, blues, and porbeagles in the Atlantic Ocean. Similarly dismal evidence is found in the world's other oceans.

In an interview for a January 1992 *Outdoor Life* article entitled "Predators in Peril," Dr. John Stevens of the CSIRO marine laboratories in Australia reported that 70 Japanese longliners that fished each of the last 10 years for bluefin tuna in the western Pacific used about 4.5 million hooks. Observer reports documented that a total of 43,500 blue sharks were taken.

After the sharks' fins were cut off, they were dumped into the ocean to certain death—if they were not already dead. Commercial interest in sharks' fins stems from the fact that in Asia shark fin soup costs as much as $50 a bowl and sharks' fins are valued as ingredients for tea, tablets, and aphrodisiacs (sexual stimulants). If the figures for the 70 Japanese longliners are extrapolated for hundreds of other long-liners operating legally and illegally around the world, the outlook for sharks is bleak.

Driftnetters have been dubbed the strip miners of the sea. A 1990 National Oceanic and Atmospheric Administration (NOAA) report, taken from drift-net vessel observer data, reported 81,956 blue sharks were killed incidentally in a 10% sample of Japanese drift-net fishing for the year.

To protect 39 species of sharks in the Atlantic, Gulf, and Caribbean waters, NMFS devised a shark management plan. The plan, entitled *Draft Secretarial Shark Fishery Management Plan for The Atlantic Ocean* (FMP), groups sharks into three categories: large coastal, small coastal, and pelagic (open sea). Each category is subject to season dates and weight quotas.

The plan requires no change for longliners, driftnetters, and trawlers—except that it asks for voluntary observation of incidental catch. Fins can be landed only when attached to sharks. A limit is set of two sharks per boat per trip for large coastal and pelagic species and five sharks per person per day for small coastal species. Experts believe NMFS should make an on-board observer program mandatory.

NMFS issued a proposed implementing rule for the plan on June 10, 1992. According to an NMFS news bulletin: "The proposed rule would regulate commercial and recreational shark fishing in the exclusive economic zone of the Atlantic Ocean, Gulf of Mexico, and the Caribbean Sea. The proposed rule addresses problems in the fishery, including overfishing, lack of management, 'finning' [harvesting of sharks for fins alone], and bycatch mortality."

After a 45-day period of public comments, NMFS expected to begin work on the final FMP and implementing rule. Since the fishing year specified in the plan is July 1–June 30, the FMP could be expected to go into effect July 1, 1993.

In a bow to conservation, many recreational fishing boats have adopted a "catch and throw back" policy. Whether a shark survives the throw-back experience depends on its size and whether it fights being captured. A small shark that lies quietly on the floor of the boat after capture may have a better chance of survival than a larger fish that thrashes after being landed.

In summary, the world's shark population does not have a promising future. Efforts at regulation seem too little and too late.

3

BIOLOGY AND SOCIAL SCIENCE

Brain Injuries, Major or Minor, Can Have Severe Consequences

Although in recent decades brain research has made great strides, little has been done to curb the high incidence of brain injury. The presence of injury to the brain is signaled by some change in mental state, including loss of consciousness, drowsiness, agitation, confusion, or "seeing stars."

The bony structure of the skull can sometimes be fractured without unduly harming its gelatinous inner contents. On the other hand, brain damage can occur without there being a blow to the head. Violent jarring from whiplash, a rapid change in direction, as when a child is shaken or a car stops suddenly, bounces the soft interior of the head against the rough protrusions of the skull's hard bone.

The whiplash-shaken-baby syndrome may be a much greater source of head injury than is generally recognized. Some physicians in the 1970s asserted that shaken-baby syndrome is widespread and called for a national education campaign to alert the public. An analysis of 20 cases reported in the February 1984 *Annals of Emergency Medicine* found that signs of the syndrome mimicked infections, intoxication, or metabolic abnormalities. Diagnosis depended mainly on a suspicion of abuse, a bulging fontanel—the soft spot in an infant's skull—head enlargement, and eye hemorrhage.

Of the 20 cases reviewed, three babies died and 10 sustained severe damage, including blindness, visual impairment, and delays in development. The called-for education campaign never took place and the syndrome remains virtually unknown to the public.

To provide the first reliable statistical picture of head and spinal cord injury problems in the nation's 48 contiguous states, a survey was made in 1974 by the National Institute of Neurological and Communicative Disorders and Stroke (NINCDS). The survey used a sophisticated method to sample hospital records, rather than attempt a total census of cases.

The survey had four goals:

• To determine how many new cases of head and spinal cord injury due to trauma were admitted to hospitals in America in a single year.

• To determine the number of old and new cases for one year, old cases being defined as injuries sustained from 1970 through 1973 that still required medical care in 1974.

• To secure statistical information about the effects of head and spinal cord injuries on subpopulations—age groups, sexes, races, and regions.

• To gather estimates of economic costs, and obtain statistical information to develop prevention measures.

Results of the survey were startling. It revealed:

• Motor vehicle accidents in a single year caused 49% of all hospitalized head injuries.

• The more severe the injury, the greater the likelihood that a motor vehicle accident was the cause.

• Male head injuries in 1974 were about twice the number for females.

• For all causes and for motor vehicles only, 15- to 24-year-old males incurred more new head injuries in a single year than any other age group.

• Head and spinal-cord injuries occurred most often on weekends, including Friday. Friday injuries far exceeded those on other nights. September appeared to be the most dangerous month, followed by April and August.

The statistics of the 1990s resemble those of the 1970s, with no national impetus to change them. In the National Institute of Neurological Disorders' publication *Implementation Plan: Decade of the Brain* (1990), the authors of the "Head Injury" section wrote: "While prevention is a very desirable goal, head injuries will continue to occur." Their statement implies brain trauma prevention is not a high priority.

Yet a greater attention to prevention seems called for. Traumatic brain injury (TBI) is the principal

Sports such as football, hockey, and particularly boxing, are closely associated with the incidence of brain trauma. Yet comparatively speaking, sports activities are not that high on the list of causes of head injuries. Automobile accidents, the single biggest cause, are responsible for more than half of all head injuries. Still, head injuries from sports are just as devastating and can be due to poor equipment, environmental factors, inattention, fatigue, poor coaching, or risk-taking.

cause of brain damage in young adults. Each year more than 2 million brain injuries occur in the United States and costs approach $25 billion. Annually, approximately 100,000 victims die, 500,000 require hospitalization, and 5,000 brain injuries result in epilepsy. As in the 1970s, young males aged 15 to 24 remain the most frequent victims.

Motor vehicle accidents cause more than half of the overall total, falls cause 21%, and assaults and violence cause 12%, with gunshot wounds being a common factor. The widespread presence of military assault rifles has increased the likelihood of wounds that result in death or severe brain damage.

An assault rifle bullet, with a muzzle velocity of 2,500 feet per second (compared to 800 feet per second for a pistol), creates shock waves that shatter bones or explode organs. A nick or graze from an ordinary gun's bullet may require only minor treatment, but the same type of wound caused by an assault rifle bullet can result in brain swelling and death within 12 hours.

Major Types of Injuries

Doctors group head injuries into two major categories: penetrating injuries and closed head injuries. Penetrating injuries occur when objects such as a bullet or fragments of an exploding shell rip the scalp, fracture the skull, enter the brain, and burrow through soft tissue. They can be caused by a steak knife or an ice pick, or even by do-it-yourself home-repair equipment such as a stud gun or power stapler. Their severity is related to the type of object, its force, and its path through the brain.

Much of what is known about penetrating injuries and their treatment comes from studies of the thousands of soldiers who received head injuries during World War II, the Korean conflict, and the Vietnam War. A Veterans Administration study of 1,000 head-injured men from World War II found that, despite neurological tests that deemed them healthy, few considered themselves "perfectly normal." Seven years after the trauma, 80% still had injury-related headaches.

Outside of war zones, closed head injuries are the most common type. A typical injury is one sustained when a person unrestrained by a seat belt or a shoulder harness is catapulted forward because a car stops suddenly. The soft brain colliding with the skull's hard bone may be twisted and squeezed. The blow also may injure the scalp and fracture the skull as well.

When a head smashes against an object such as a car windshield and the momentum slams the brain against the inside of the skull, brain damage most often occurs in one or more specific locations: in the frontal lobes at the point of impact; the temporal lobes (the temples); at the juncture of the frontal and temporal lobes; and in large veins above the ear, which may tear, causing subdural hematoma. (Subdural means beneath the brain covering and hematoma refers to bleeding in a confined space.)

Focal injuries—affecting a single, specific part of the brain—are of two types. Less serious is a contusion, the equivalent of a bruise, which occurs in almost 90% of cases. More serious is a hematoma that leaks blood into the brain or the dura.

A hematoma can be as small as a printed letter or involve a large part of the brain and can result in increased pressure on the brain, causing further injury. Extracerebral hematomas are those that occur between the brain and the skull—either above or below the dura. Intracerebral hematomas are those formed within the brain.

Diffuse injuries, as distinguished from focal injuries, involve several areas of the brain and are the result of billions of brain cells being twisted, stretched, and compressed. The damage may be temporary or so severe the cells die. Diffuse injuries fall into three categories: mild concussion; concussion; or diffuse axonal injury. In both mild and severe concussions, regions in the base of the brain—the brain stem—that control breathing and heart rate are temporarily disturbed, and parts of the brain that control memory are affected.

A typical mild concussion is one in which a tall person bumps his or her head against a low structure. Mild concussions happen frequently in sports. A blow to the head in a football game may cause confusion for a few seconds, and for 5–10 minutes the player may not remember the injury or the events just before it. With a more powerful blow, the player may have a longer period of confusion and forget events after the injury as well as before it. With a full concussion, the person loses consciousness and also loses the memory of events before and after the injury.

Diffuse axonal injuries involve a damaged brain stem as well as torn brain axons (the fiberlike projections from nerve cells that help transmit chemical messages from the brain to the body). In a severe diffuse axonal injury, many nerve fibers throughout the brain and brain stem are torn. With this type of injury, patients remain deeply unconscious for a long time. If they ever regain consciousness, they suffer extensive loss of intellect, sensation, and movement.

A head injury may be complicated by brain swelling, which is thought to be due to an increased flow of blood to the brain. The head injury appears to disrupt the routine action of the brain's blood vessels. In response, they expand and take up more space in the skull—a rigid container—compressing the brain and depriving it of oxygen.

Brain edema, the excessive accumulation of water and other fluids within the brain, also causes increased pressure within the skull with similar results. Much remains unknown about biological events that make the injury worse in the minutes and hours immediately following brain injury. Although most studies of head injuries focus on victims of auto accidents or weapons, two reports presented in April 1991 at the annual meeting of the American Academy of Neurology in Boston, Massachusetts concerned victims of assault. Dr. Anne Guyot, a neurologist at the Detroit (Michigan) Medical Center, who presented the research, said, "We found that assault victims have a high incidence of brain trauma, and that these injuries may often be difficult to detect with standard emergency room examinations."

Dr. Patti Peterson, chief of neurology at Detroit Receiving Hospital and Dr. Fernando Diaz, chairman of neurosurgery at the same hospital, reported that victims of unarmed attacks may suffer more damage than those struck in the head with a bat or a metal rod. A single blow from a bat or a pipe is generally all that is required to knock a victim out. Peterson explained why a beating is more lethal: "An assailant striking with fists or feet may have to strike the victim's head repeatedly to render him unconscious." Their findings concurred with other studies that have found repeated blows to the head are more damaging than a single blow from a weapon.

The assault-related head injury tends to result in a

diffuse axonal injury, one difficult to diagnose, even with computed tomographic (CT) scans. A report presented by Dr. Aashit Shah of the Detroit Medical Center questioned a current emergency room practice, which is to release head-injured patients if their skull X-rays reveal no fractures and they show no other signs of illness or injury. The study identified 30 patients injured by assault or falls who fit those criteria. Exams with CT scans found brain injuries in all 30 patients, two of whom died as a result of their injuries.

Such findings suggest that women who are victims of domestic violence, most often a beating, should routinely receive CT scans and be admitted to the hospital. Studies of such women also need to ask questions about the cumulative impact on the brain of such beatings and its effect on subsequent behavior.

Research Into the Consequences of Brain Injury

If and when survivors of severe head injuries regain consciousness, they are apt to find that their mental functioning has been forever changed. Many have temporary or permanent amnesia. For some, mustering the concentration needed to hold an ordinary conversation is impossible. Some lose their ability to handle language. Some become uninhibited, overtalkative, or short-tempered.

According to Dr. Nathan Zasler, director of Brain Injury Rehabilitation Services at the Medical College of Virginia, the degree of deficit following an injury and how long it lasts seems to have little correlation with the severity of the original injury. Researchers are discovering more and more that severe deficits may also affect the more than 500,000 annual victims of brain injuries categorized as minor. Minor brain injury is defined as either no loss of consciousness or unconsciousness for less than 30 minutes.

A February 3, 1992 *Boston Globe* article entitled "A 'Minor' Brain Injury Can Have Major Effects," described the case of Claire (a fictitious name), a 40-year-old nurse who was struck by a falling object while chatting outside her apartment. Following the blow to her head, Claire did not lose consciousness. An electroencephalogram (a recording of brain activity via electrodes attached to the scalp) and a CT scan failed to show anything wrong. However, after a few months back at work, it was obvious to Claire and

her supervisor that something was indeed wrong.

Before the accident, Claire lectured on nursing, jogged, skied, played tennis, and participated in an active social life. In the aftermath of the accident, she stutters, cannot think rapidly enough to work, gets dizzy in a crowd, reads only with enormous effort, cannot add two-digit numbers in her head, and takes hours to buy groceries because she cannot locate items on the shelves. According to Dr. Elaine Woo, director of the brain injury center at Spaulding Rehabilitation Hospital in Boston, the likely problem in Claire's case is that tiny nerve pathways throughout the brain were stretched or ripped by the force exerted by the falling object.

For most patients, behavioral problems connected to brain injuries prove more disabling than any physical handicaps they might have. University of Texas Medical Branch (UTMB) researcher Harvey Levin, Ph.D., has connected the effects on behavior to the presence in the brain of neurological damage. He also has established firmly that the victims of head injuries did not have the behavioral problems before the accident that friends, family, and medical personnel later observed.

Sensitive tests to challenge specific neuro-psychological skills (tests capable of demonstrating measurable deficits) often are not performed on head-injured patients, even when they complain of long-lasting problems. Because such patients are frequently involved in lawsuits, their physicians, family, and friends may suspect they are exaggerating their symptoms to win a settlement or to stay out of work. According to Dr. Woo, rather than being malingerers, most are desperate to rid themselves of the symptoms and return to their former selves.

Suspected of exaggeration, unable to perform at their former levels, and assured by physicians that nothing is wrong, these patients often become terrified. The worse the symptoms get, the more depressed and isolated they become. Hope for them may lie in increasing knowledge about the effects of brain trauma.

'Decade of the Brain'

Congress and President George Bush declared the 1990s the "Decade of the Brain." One of the loftiest goals of the decade is a functional map of the brain. James Watson, co-discoverer of the double helix that

Where head injury has affected physical function, patients may spend a great deal of time undergoing physical rehabilitation. But rehabilitation does not consist just of exercises to try to regain the use of muscles and the control of nerves. It also consists of occupational therapy. An Aids to Daily Living (ADL) board is used by head trauma (and other) patients trying to regain fine motor skills and relearn certain basic daily living tasks. Another aspect of trying to recover is to find alternative ways to do things, either temporarily or permanently. For example, when fingers are unable to handle buttons, pullover shirts may be a good substitute.

makes up deoxyribonucleic acid (DNA), said in *Discovering the Brain,* published by the National Academy of Sciences: "The brain is the last and greatest biological frontier, the most complex thing we have discovered in our universe."

The work of UTMB researchers and other scientists across the country has established that the extent of brain damage follows a roughly centripetal (moving toward a center) pattern. Current theory proposes that minor brain injuries are generally limited to the outer regions of the brain, while severe head injuries extend deeper into the brain, with the loss of a greater number of mental functions.

The link between an area of brain damage and typical abnormal behavior was made for Levin in 1974, when UTMB acquired its first CT scanner.

CT imaging makes it possible to see lesions that are invisible with less-sophisticated techniques. The T for tomography in CT refers to an X-ray technique that makes a film representing a detailed cross section of tissue structure at a predetermined depth.

In the 1980s, magnetic resonance imaging (MRI) further improved researchers' ability to see brain damage. MRI uses powerful magnetic fields to create images of soft tissue. To illustrate the value of MRI, Levin described a case in an Autumn 1991 *Biomedical Inquiry* article entitled "Aftermath: The Complex Puzzle of Head Injury." The patient had symptoms associated with damage to the brain's frontal lobes. CT images showed only diffuse injuries throughout the brain, but MRI images revealed the presence of the suspected frontal lobe lesions.

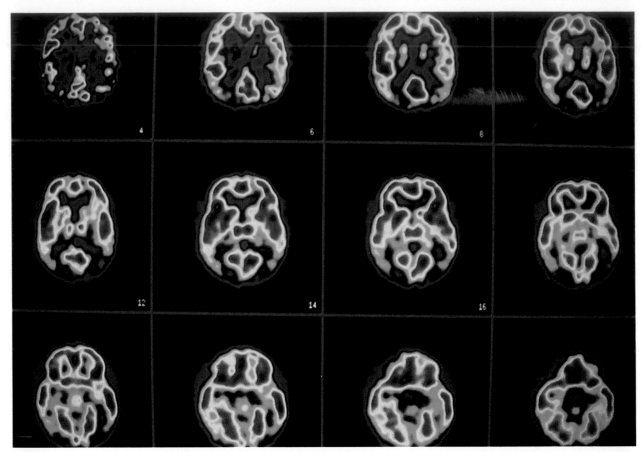

These PET scan images show different levels of the brain in a normal resting subject. They are images of regional cerebral glucose metabolism. The red and pink areas are those regions that have higher metabolic rates and the green and blue areas, lower metabolic rates.

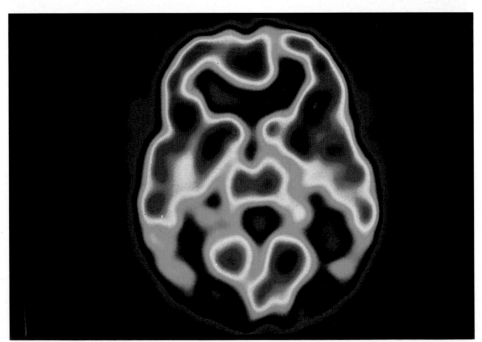

This scan is an enlargement of an image from the series of scans above.

Additional improvements in brain imaging have come from magnetoencephalography (MEG), which is similar to MRI but has advantages. MEG locates the area in a brain where electrical activity starts by detecting the brain's weak magnetic fields.

Positron emission tomography (PET) is still another device in the array of brain cartographers' tools. In a study that confirmed the reports of amnesiacs (people who have lost their memories), researchers learned that the hippocampus, a little seahorse-shaped structure deep in the brain, is critical in forming and retrieving memories. Glucose, the body's major source of fuel, is used for PET scan mappings. Volunteers are injected with radioactive glucose, which mixes with blood and wends its way to the brain. The more active the brain, the more glucose it uses. Heightened activity areas send data to computers that produce two-dimensional drawings of the hot spots.

An April 20, 1992 *Newsweek* article entitled "Mapping the Brain," described still another new device, the superconducting quantum interference device (SQUID), which senses tiny changes in magnetic fields. When neurons (nerve cells) fire, they create an electric current, which sets up magnetic fields. Magnetic field changes indicate neural activity. When New York University physicist Samuel Williamson and his colleague psychologist Lloyd Kaufman aimed a SQUID at a listening brain, they found that the brain hears loud sounds in a different place than quiet sounds. Moreover, the areas in which the brain hears tones are laid out in a pattern like a keyboard.

Each brain-scanning device has strengths and weaknesses. A CT scanner takes wonderful pictures of brain structure but cannot distinguish between a dead brain and a live one. MRI cannot detect brain functioning, but it can distinguish structures O.05 inch apart. PET accurately tracks brain function but

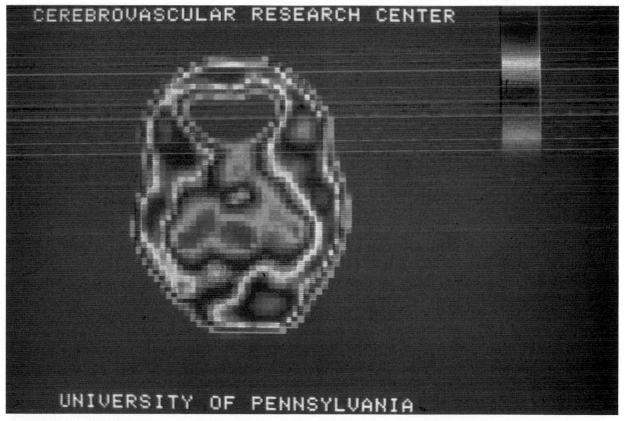

CEREBROVASCULAR RESEARCH CENTER

UNIVERSITY OF PENNSYLVANIA

In this PET scan, the left visual hemifield was stimulated with a slowly moving high-contrast black-and-white pattern of lines, as well as abstract color images. In this subject, there is asymmetrical glucose metabolism with the right frontal region (the pink spot) which probably represents increased metabolism in the right frontal eye field. This region of the brain causes a conjugate movement of the eyes to the left.

The positron-emitting isotopes used in PET scanners are produced by cyclotrons such as this one at Brookhaven National Laboratory.

cannot resolve structures less than 0.5 inch apart. The new imaging techniques enable scientists to peer into healthy brains. Earlier studies of patients with brain lesions, along with electrical stimulation of patients during brain surgery, pinpointed areas of specific activity, but they ran the risk of not being representative of normal-functioning brains.

Brain Cartography

Mapping the brain is overturning a lot of scientists' notions and helping to explain the wide variety of deficits suffered by patients following brain injury. An unexpected finding was that the area of the brain that learns and remembers faces is completely different from the area that learns and recalls human-made objects.

Scientists had long thought that to speak aloud a printed word, a signal had to be passed from the visual cortex to an area that decoded it and from there be shunted to the frontal lobe that pronounced it.

But PET pioneer Marcus Raichle of Washington University in St. Louis, Missouri found that the auditory areas of the brain are not active when one speaks. He told *Newsweek*, "You don't listen to what you say in the same way that you hear what others say."

PET researchers have found that brains are efficient. Once learned, the amount of energy needed to carry out an activity drops. The more intelligent the brain, the less it needs to do. Further, researchers suspect that more-intelligent brains get away with less work because they use fewer neurons or circuits or both. No one knows for sure, but they suspect that high intelligence may be a matter of "neural pruning." From birth to early childhood, a child's brain uses increasing amounts of glucose, until at age 5 it is using twice as much as an adult. Thereafter, glucose use and the number of circuits involved drop sharply. Highly intelligent brains may do more pruning, leaving behind more efficient circuits.

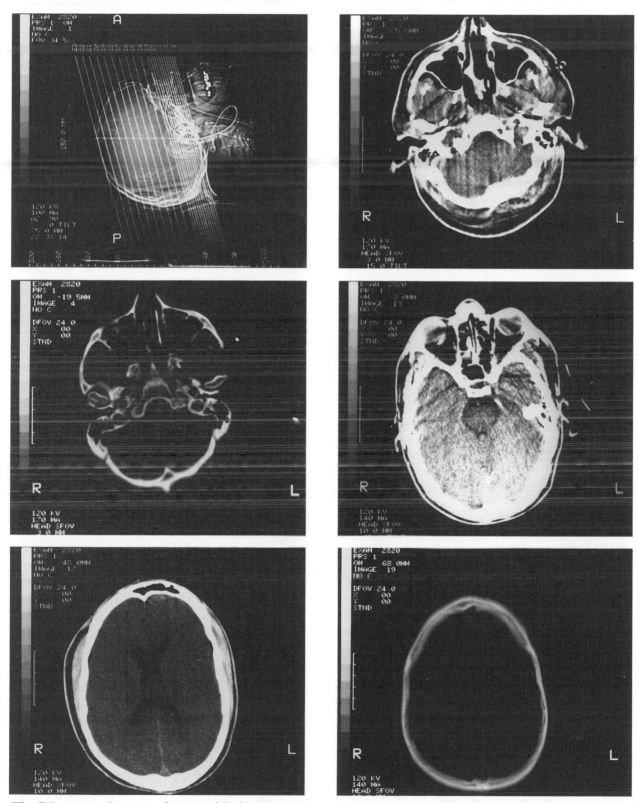

The CT scanner takes scores of images of the brain's tissue structure at various levels and positions, such as these few selected images from one patient's series of pictures.

Scans have revealed some of the brain's congregation of specialties. Separate zones scattered mostly around the back of the cortex contain fragments of a larger idea. These are brought together in what have been dubbed convergence zones. To reconstruct an image such as a silver candlestick, the convergence zone activates all the relevant storage sites simultaneously. From one site might come silver, from another cylinder-shaped, and from still another burns.

Clues to convergence zones have come from people with brain lesions who cannot name a famous face. A flicker of recognition is registered in their brains, but they cannot recall the face. The lesion apparently disrupts the links between the memories for the various parts of the face tucked away in storage, such as the shape of its feature and the tone of its skin. The convergence zone is unable to bring them together.

There are hopeful signs for the future. Twenty years ago most head-injury victims could expect to spend their lives in institutions, but research in rehabilitation has changed the outlook. Moreover, traditionally, scientists believed that damaged nerve cells in the brain were incapable of repair. Recently, they have shown that nerve cells from the central nervous system sprout new branches when they are in contact with supporting cells. This demonstrates that adult brain cells have the capacity for repair and growth. One of the goals of the Decade of the Brain is to investigate how this property can be used to repair damage to the brain's billions of nerve cell connections.

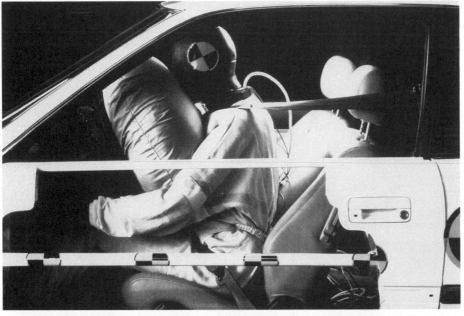

The most effective defenses against the possibility of head trauma, barring sobriety and basic safe driving habits, are the use of seat belts and air bags. Shown above is a crash test with a dummy. Shown on bottom is a Chrysler LeBaron convertible that crashed head-on into a full-size station wagon at a closing speed of about 80 miles per hour. The properly belted driver of the air bag-equipped LeBaron received injuries to her lower extremities, but no serious head, neck, or chest injuries. According to the National Highway Traffic and Safety Administration, the driver survived the crash because of the protection of the air bag.

Parapsychology: Scientists Disagree Whether It Is a Science

Parapsychology is defined as the study of phenomena, such as telepathy, clairvoyance, and extrasensory perception, not explainable by known natural laws. Fundamental to the controversy over whether parapsychology qualifies as a science is the subject matter parapsychologists choose to study. Parapsychologists' hypotheses assert that humans can acquire information or influence external events in ways that science is not yet able to explain.

Surveys have shown repeatedly that one-half to three-quarters of the American population claim to have had an experience they perceived as psychic. For over 2,000 years, people have been reporting experiences commonly referred to as psychic phenomena, or more simply as PSI. For almost as long, scholars have been trying to understand such experiences.

If parapsychologists' claims are correct, prevailing models in science may have to change, and the laws of physics may have to be rewritten. Although scientists' models are always in a process of being modified, and the laws of physics have been rewritten during the last century, parapsychology's area of interest makes some scientists profoundly uncomfortable—in some cases even angry.

J.B. Rhine, in the 1930s, conducting an experiment with the ESP cards developed at Duke University. The study of parapsychology could be described as being in a naturalist stage, comparable to 18th- and 19th-century medicine when much biological phenomena were observed and recorded but little understood. Surveys of the general public have found that most people either accept the reality of extrasensory perception or report that they have had such experiences themselves. Yet parapsychology continues to struggle to be accepted as a reasonable subject for investigation.

A classic ESP experiment is to position two people in different places and, at a set time, have one concentrate on an object while the other tries to "see" what that object is. The objects may be kept simple, such as the ball shown here. The results of such experiments highlight a problem that is not restricted to the study of parapsychology, the problem of inferential leaps. Such leaps can be unconscious, the mind leaps ahead to impose a thought or explanation beyond what it has truly perceived. Or the leaps can be conscious, deliberate attempts to guess or to extrapolate from the evidence available. For example, a psychic might discern the object as circular, but not discern it is a ball. Asked to guess, a psychic who has not had dinner might say an orange.

Parapsychologists assume as their responsibility the search for an explanation for psychic experience that fits within the known boundaries of science or that expands those boundaries. The first step in their analysis is consideration of how far ordinary or conventional mechanisms and knowledge can go in explaining psychic events. Investigators must take into account many factors, such as faulty observation, faulty memory, and deliberate deceit. If normal explanations fail to explain such observations, then what is left is an anomaly. When anomalies persist, they force scientists to revise their theories. Meteors and X-rays were once anomalies that forced such revisions.

Parapsychologists, as did their predecessors who were called psychical researchers, have chosen to confront some anomalies that seem to be closely connected with the operations of the human mind. To

do so, they have used descriptive categories such as extrasensory perception (ESP) and psychokinesis (PK) to serve as crude models of what they think might be happening.

ESP refers to the apparent ability of a human being to acquire information without using the ordinary senses of the body and without depending on logical inference. The "extra" implies outside of the sensory channels as they are now known. Perception refers to a range of phenomena, including vividly "seeing" or dreaming of an event, having a vague hunch, or obtaining information that never reaches consciousness but affects behavior.

The broad category of ESP encompasses a number of older, perhaps more-familiar terms, such as telepathy and clairvoyance. Telepathy refers to "mind to mind" contact, during which one mind receives communication from another without going through ordinary communication channels. In a typical experience a mother hears her child cry out. The child is physically miles or hundreds of miles away. Later, the mother learns that at the moment of her experience, the child had been involved in an accident.

Clairvoyance is the acquisition of information about an event, object, or place without using ordinary senses. Unlike telepathy, clairvoyance does not depend on direct contact with another person. One of the most famous examples involved the 18th-century Swedish scientist and spiritual leader Emmanuel Swedenborg, who reported to his host in Goteberg that he saw a fire raging in Stockholm 300 miles away. A courier from Stockholm later confirmed Swedenborg's visions precisely.

Telepathy and clairvoyance are assumed to take place at more or less the same time as the event that triggers them. However, ESP may involve a future event, a phenomenon referred to as precognition, that is, knowledge of an event before its occurrence.

Because telepathy and clairvoyance cannot be distinguished in laboratory experiments, parapsychologists seldom use those terms. Instead they use general ESP (GESP) to refer to both phenomena. The problem with separating the two is that no matter how scientists have designed experiments, for them to be checked for correctness, a target must exist at some point either as a written record or as an event. Therefore, it may have been picked up by either telepathy or clairvoyance (perhaps precognitively).

Psychokinesis involves the apparent ability of a human being to affect objects, events, or people around him or her without using the body's muscle system. The most familiar of these are flying objects, levitating tables, or the bending of metal. Derived from two Greek words, psychokinesis means "soul or mind motion" and is often defined as the direct influence of consciousness over physical systems.

Psychokinesis is reported much less frequently than ESP and seldom occurs spontaneously, apart from poltergeist activity or the occasional stopping of a clock at someone's death. Most contemporary research into PK involves the influence of consciousness on finely balanced electronic devices, an area that has come to be called micro-PK. Traditional PK is now referred to as macro-PK.

The Slow Advance Toward Acceptance

Although they constitute a significant body of data, puzzling reports of ghosts, apparitions, and poltergeists, once central to psychical research, have not constituted the mainstream of parapsychological research for much of this century. When J.B. Rhine, the father of modern scientific parapsychological experiments, began his experiments at Duke University in the 1930s with Louisa Rhine, his wife and colleague, he confined his study to events that could be experimentally controlled.

In 1938, just as parapsychological research at Duke University was becoming known, only 8% of the American Psychological Association's 352 members surveyed agreed that ESP was an "established fact." Two more recent surveys of scientists, each with 1,000 participants, found that view had changed. A *New Scientist* survey in 1973 found 67% agreed that ESP was an established fact, and a *Zetetic Scholar* survey in 1979 found 75% agreed.

In his 1991 book *Parapsychology: The Controversial Science*, Richard Broughton, Ph.D., Director of Research at the Institute of Parapsychology in Durham, North Carolina, raised the questions of why—if so many scientists consider ESP a possibility—parapsychology courses are not taught routinely in colleges and universities and why so few labs are engaged in research.

A 1981 survey conducted by University of Maryland sociologist James McClenon and published in his 1984 book, *Deviant Science: The Case of Parapsy-*

chology, suggested a possible answer. The survey was directed toward "administrative elites," members of the council and selected sections of the American Association for the Advancement of Science (AAAS). Among the elites, less than 30% believed ESP was an "established fact" or "a likely possibility."

Change does not come easily to science, which is structured to accommodate the steady accumulation of little facts. Periodically it is interrupted by upheavals. Minor revolutions such as acceptance of plate tectonics, the theory that Earth and its oceans rest on a cracked layer resembling the skim on a cooling pudding, happen all the time. Major revolutions, such as Albert Einstein's theory of relativity, happen less often. The prevailing scientific view does not give way to a challenger without a battle. The battle tactics are not confined to data and reasoned debate; they include ridicule, scorn, censorship, and exclusion from communication outlets.

Many scientific anomalies have come and gone without provoking a scientific revolution; therefore, parapsychology may in time disappear, leaving behind hardly a trace. However, sociologists of science see the hallmarks of a potential revolution in the activities and strategies of those who believe the claims of parapsychology to be fraudulent and in parapsychologists' efforts to win approval from orthodox science. About the struggle, Broughton wrote: "Frustrating as this struggle may be to those who champion the unpopular cause, we must accept that this is part of the give-and-take of normal science, the winnowing of the wheat from the chaff of human knowledge."

Who Are the Scientists?

Perhaps because parapsychology remains controversial, the number of researchers in the field remains small. In 1956 the Parapsychological Association (PA) was formed as an international organization to share information among professional researchers investigating PSI phenomena.

In 1969, when PA applied for membership in the august AAAS, Margaret Mead, renowned anthropologist, spoke on PA's behalf: "For the last ten years, we have been arguing about what constitutes science and the scientific method and what societies use it. We even changed the By-Laws about it. The PA uses statistics and blinds, placeboes, double blinds and other standard devices. The whole history of scientific advance is full of scientists investigating phenomena that the establishment did not believe were there."

In the mid-1960s, the Institute for Parapsychology in Durham, North Carolina was the world's leading producer of parapsychological research and the only major research center in the United States. It was joined in 1979 by a small but energetic group of researchers, under the leadership of Robert Jahn, dean of Princeton's School of Engineering and Applied Science. Researchers at Princeton regard the direct interaction of mind and matter as an engineering problem, and the lab is called the Princeton Engineering Anomalies Research, or PEAR, Laboratory.

When Jahn, a noted authority on aerospace engineering with a long record of work for the National Aeronautics and Space Administration and the U.S. Department of Defense, decided that some parapsychological problems were worth investigating, the university convened an ad hoc committee to oversee his research, a move unprecedented for a scientist of his stature. In a 1983 address to PA, Jahn said, "We have had commentary on our program from no less than six Nobel laureates, two of whom categorically rejected the topic, two of whom encouraged us to push on, and two of whom were evasively equivocal. So much for unanimity of high scientific opinion."

Another center for parapsychological research is the large contract research firm of SRI International, formerly Stanford Research Institute, which for more than a decade discreetly conducted ambitious research programs for a variety of contractors, including the U.S. government. Since the mid-1970s, a small research team at the Mind Science Foundation in San Antonio, Texas has produced a stream of innovative studies.

In Great Britain, there is a long tradition of small institutes that trace their roots back to the Society for Psychical Research (SPR), which began in 1882. The cornerstone of British parapsychologic research is the Parapsychology Laboratory of the University of Edinburgh in Scotland, endowed in 1983 by the writer-philosopher Arthur Koestler. A great deal of research is done by individual scientists pursuing modest programs in departments of psychology, physics, medicine, and others.

Methods: Case Studies, Field Investigations, and Experimentation

Case studies have a long history in parapsychological research. A case study, also known as the spontaneous-case approach, typically comprises a testimonial about an unusual experience that a person might label "psychic," plus some corroborating testimony, and the results of additional investigation by a researcher.

All case studies, whether done by social scientists, medical researchers, journalists, or any other kind of interviewer, carry built-in hazards. The most obvious are: faulty memory; embellishment; a natural tendency to mold perceptions to fit expectations; reinterpretation of memories; and fabrication. Nevertheless, there often is corroborating evidence—for example, a letter written and mailed before the death of a distant person.

After rigorous examination of thousands of cases, SPR investigators published in 1886 more than 700 of the best-documented cases in a two-volume work called *Phantasms of Living*, which remains a rich source of PSI phenomena. In 1951, the American Society for Psychical Research (ASPR) published a collection of 400 cases, gleaned from 1,200 reports received in response to a published appeal. In a similar fashion, University of Freiburg investigators in Germany put together a collection of 1,000 cases.

Because questionable cases always threaten to undermine their work, investigators for the British, American, and German collections took great care to validate the cases. But for her monumental collection, Louisa Rhine adopted a different approach to better reflect the diversity of PSI experience. She took for granted the reality of PSI experience; therefore she did not try to verify each case. Aside from making a first-cut inspection, which eliminated about half of the reports, she included in her collection any case that was intelligently written, appeared to be in good faith, and fulfilled the basic criteria for a PSI experience. She felt that the sheer number of cases would reduce any effect of less-valid cases.

Field investigations are uncommon in contemporary parapsychology. By their nature, spontaneous cases are one-time events. Obviously parapsychologists cannot be on the scene to investigate the experience while it is happening.

The story that Abraham Lincoln dreamed of his White House funeral has been repeated many times. Perhaps a little less well known is the report that Mrs. Ulysses S. Grant, on the day of the assassination, sensed some impending disaster and implored her husband to leave Washington immediately. The Grants, originally scheduled to attend the theater with the President and Mrs. Lincoln, left on an evening train. Grant was one of several people slated for assassination.

Field investigations are sometimes possible with types of PSI experiences that last for long periods of time, but they have pitfalls. Typically they are hurried and improvised. Frequently, conscious or unconscious fraud is a distinct possibility.

The experimental method, which unites all branches of science, has two major components: control and measurement. A psychologist who wished to determine how reading comprehension is affected by different printed type styles would hold constant (control) some variables, such as room lighting, visual acuity of the subjects, and degree of comfort in the chair. The experimenter would vary presentations of the independent variable, in this case the type style, to subjects. To measure the effect of the typeface, the experimenter would measure reading comprehension, the so-called dependent variable, using some kind of standard reading comprehension form. With the other variables controlled, the experimenter would assume that any measurement change was due to a change in the independent variable, the type style.

J.B. Rhine established the experimental method as his primary means for investigating PSI phenomena. He adapted a method used by Victorian psychic investigators. They had used ordinary playing cards to test for telepathy by having a person concentrate on a card, one at a time, and try to "send" the identity of the card to another, suitably isolated person. The odds of making a correct guess by chance alone with this method are 51-to-1. If a receiver can consistently guess correctly substantially more than 1-in-52, then something other than chance, such as ESP, can be surmised.

The playing cards have shortcomings. Even though a person might be able to correctly identify substantially more than 1-in-52, he or she will get most of the guesses wrong, which is demoralizing. To avoid discouragement, Rhine, with a Duke University colleague, designed new cards. They each carry one of five symbols and five of each symbol are included in a deck. Five was chosen because a 1-in-5 chance of success is sufficient to hold a subject's attention.

The five symbols are easy to tell apart, easy to remember, and are of roughly equal visual weights. The essence of Rhine's early experimental method was to have a subject guess the sequence of symbols in a deck of ESP cards. The deck was well shuffled to ensure randomness. In a typical experiment, many decks would be prepared and a subject would go through them deck after deck.

For a deck of 25 ESP cards, on the average, five would be guessed correctly by chance. To determine when a subject exceeded the boundaries of chance, Rhine turned to the field of statistics, then in its infancy.

In a typical experiment, a subject might guess his or her way through 10 decks of ESP cards. By chance he or she would get an average of about 50 correct "hits." Frequently by chance the subject might get 55 or 45 hits, and less often 60 or 40. Statistics would help the experimenter decide whether a score of 75 could be obtained by chance alone.

By standard convention in the social sciences, when the odds against chance for a given result are better than 1-in-20, chance is ruled out. Parapsychologists tend to be more conservative and hold out for higher odds. The odds against a score of 75 are less than 1-in-1,000, thus chance can be ruled out as an explanation.

A statistical test does not automatically demonstrate that ESP was demonstrated. Since ESP is defined as the acquisition of information without using the normal senses, the experimenter has to rule out any chance that the subject might have obtained information about the cards through normal means.

The Duke University labs worked out standard precautions. Some experiments were conducted with the subject and experimenter in one building and the experimenter with the cards in another building. A third experimenter received record sheets from each team independently. Different circumstances require different levels of control.

Apart from the fundamental control against "normal explanations," most parapsychological experiments are quite similar to ordinary psychological experiments. But critics' charges that experimenters have not ruled out all normal explanations keep parapsychology caught up in controversy.

The Mind-Matter Interface
and Random-Number Generators

At the close of the 20th century, research in PK is split into two camps that have little to do with each other. Traditional macro-PK research continues in much the same fashion that it did a century ago. Although the technology is far more sophisticated, the end result continues to be anecdotal. Nevertheless, the frequency of the anecdotes and the degree to which incidents are supported by witnesses make it impossible for mainstream parapsychology to completely ignore macro-PK.

Micro-PK, unknown 20 years ago, is the most robust line of research in parapsychology. Stringently designed experiments have yielded a rapidly accumulating data base of consistent evidence. Perhaps more important than a consistent data base is a strong possibility that parapsychology can make an important contribution to quantum physics, which has been struggling for decades with conflicting perspectives on the role of human consciousness in determining reality at the subatomic level. The hallmark of a mature science is when its knowledge can be applied to solve problems in other areas of science.

The scientist most responsible for the direction taken by micro-PK is German-born physicist Helmut Schmidt, who in the spring of 1969, while a senior research scientist at Boeing Scientific Laboratories in Seattle, Washington, refined an ongoing effort to automate ESP research. His original device (designed to test precognition abilities) chose a target, recorded a subject's guess, recorded the trials and hits on counters, and stored the sequence of targets and guesses on punched paper tapes. His method reduced the drudgery of recording, scoring, double-checking, and so forth. More important, it reduced opportunities for a subject to cheat.

The most important feature of Schmidt's design was the way the targets were generated. To shuffle the targets in his ESP tester, Schmidt made use of one of nature's elementary chance processes, the decay of radioactive atoms. He used a small sample of the isotope strontium 90 fixed to a Geiger tube that would respond to the irregular arrivals of electrons from the decaying atoms. Although it is easy to measure the average number of electron arrivals over time, it is impossible to predict the exact moment that an atom will decay and throw out an electron.

Over the years, Schmidt has designed a number of machines that incorporate similar principles. Perhaps the one that best demonstrates how his system works is a precognition device known as the four-button machine. The machine has four colored lamps in a row with a response button for each. The subject's task is to predict which lamp will come on by pressing the button below the lamp of his or her choice.

When the subject presses the button, a circuit is set up so that the next electron to hit the Geiger tube will stop a high-speed counter racing through numbers 1 through 4 at a rate of 1 million per second. The speed counter halted at a number will in turn cause the lamp corresponding to the number to light.

The act of pressing the button simply registers the subject's prediction and sets up the sequence that allows the next electron to stop the counter. The random timing of the electron's arrival selects which lamp will light. According to the current level of understanding, the process is completely random.

Many other researchers have duplicated Schmidt's various devices or developed similar ones. Collectively they are called random-number generators (RNGs) or random-event generators (REGs). Para-

psychologists use RNGs in dozens of different types of experiments.

In his next experiment, Schmidt tried to see if his subjects could control their ESP by aiming for a high score by guessing the lighted lamps correctly or for a low score by avoiding the lighted lamps. His subjects were able to hit or miss the lights just a little better

Individuals interested in psychic phenomena and involved in paranormal research have ranged from writers to scientists to politicians, including American Presidents Abraham Lincoln, Franklin Roosevelt, and Woodrow Wilson, as well as several British prime ministers. A.J. Balfour, (top left), prime minister from 1902-1905, was president of the British Society for Psychical Research in 1904. Prime Minister Winston Churchill (top right) is reputed to have had psychic hunches. One of his most famous came during a bombing raid on London during World War II. Churchill had a vision of the kitchen at No. 10 Downing Street (the prime minister's residence) being hit. He had the butler evacuate the kitchen. A few minutes later a bomb destroyed that room. Involvement of physicists in paranormal research is not a recent phenomenon. Physicist Balfour Stewart, who spoke of ""electrobiological power," and Sir William Barrett, who considered the possibility of a "magnetic sense," both served as president of the British Society in the latter part of the 19th century and the early years of the 20th century respectively. Involvement of physicians

in the study of humanity's possible psychic powers may seem more logical since their profession is based on observations of people. Harvard University's William James, a medical doctor (lower left), a respected investigator of mediums, helped found both the British and American Societies for Psychical Research and once served as president of the American Society. He is thought to have greatly influenced the tale of The Turn of the Screw *written by his brother Henry James.*

Other writers besides James have been attracted to ideas about psychic phenomena. Poet and playwright W.B. Yeats (lower right) studied mediums. One psychic, Geraldine Cummins, famed for automatic writing, scribbled down the plot of a play Yeats was then writing, a work of which she had no knowledge. Novelist Upton Sinclair's book Mental Radio *is a report of a series of experiments he and his wife Mary, a reputed psychic, carried out. Mary wrote a section in which she describes her attempts to "see" things. A far cry from the technicolor marvels created by Hollywood, her visions frequently consisted of a few lines against a gray background.*

The precognition tester has four colored lamps (red, yellow, green, and blue) with corresponding push buttons. By pushing the button corresponding to the appropriate lamp, the subject registers his or her prediction about which lamp will light next. This button activates the process by which the internal random-number generator selects a lamp to be lit. Two reset counters on top record the number of hits and misses. A pair of non-reset counters are connected to an automatic recorder, which stores the detailed sequence of buttons pushed and lamps lit.

than chance. Although the percentages were not large, the odds against them happening over numerous repeated trials by chance were more than 1-billion-to-1.

Although Schmidt's evidence for precognition—knowing which lamp would come on a fraction of a second in the future with an accuracy about two percentage points greater than chance—is hardly as dramatic as dreaming of an upcoming disaster, it functions as a vastly more acceptable demonstration of PSI phenomena to other scientists because it uses impeccable, repeatable methodology. In quantifiable terms, something happens.

Schmidt was bothered by the possibility that his subject might be using PK to cause the lights to match the button presses rather than precognition to predict the lights. He set up a third experiment in which a button press activated a punched paper tape of random numbers in another room to light the lamps. There was no way the subjects could use PK to influence the results. There were no appreciable differences among the experiments.

Schmidt left Boeing and went to work at the In-

stitute of Parapsychology in Durham, where he turned his attention to PK. In the summer of 1970, he began experiments in a room no bigger than a closet with no windows. In the room, the subject sat before an aluminum box about a foot square and several inches deep.

Nine lamps were arranged in a circle on top of the box, with a cable leading to the next room. Again using atomic decay, the system was set up so that some atomic particles caused the light to move to the next position clockwise, and other particles caused it to move counterclockwise. The subject was instructed to use PK ability to keep the light moving in one direction, clockwise or counterclockwise. Schmidt's designs have sparked the biggest revolution in parapsychology since J.B. Rhine designed the ESP cards.

Micro-PK's Potential Impact on Quantum Theory

In the forefront of those moving parapsychology into the broader realm of science are the scientists at Princeton University. In an August 1986 *Foundations of Physics* article entitled "On the Quantum Mechanics of Consciousness, with Application to Anomalous Phenomena," Robert Jahn, the Princeton dean, along with Brenda Dunne, laboratory manager at PEAR Lab, take the position that reality is constituted only in the interaction of consciousness with its environment. In their opinion, any conceptual scheme developed to represent reality must reflect not only the environment, but also the processes of consciousness. To pursue their theory, they make use of the concepts and formalisms of quantum mechanics.

Quantum mechanics, a mathematical theory in physics, assumes energy is not infinitely divisible. This means that energy is not absorbed nor radiated continuously but discontinuously in definite units called quanta (packets), the size of which are determined by the frequency (the number of times a phenomenon occurs during a specified period) of the radiation.

Quantum theory is a product of centuries of scientific speculation about the nature of light. After a long period of dormancy, interest in light was restimulated in the 17th century with the development of optical instruments like telescopes and microscopes.

Isaac Newton believed light to be particulate, meaning small particles of matter, but the Dutch philosopher Christiann Huygens ascribed to it a wavelike character. In 1873, James Clerk Maxwell theorized that light is a part of a broad spectrum of electromagnetic waves; and 1886 experiments by H.R. Hertz demonstrated that radio-frequency waves traveled at the speed of light and could be reflected and deflected. For a time, the evidence for the wave theory of light seemed overwhelming.

Serious doubt about the theory arose in 1905 when Max Plank postulated his "quantum theory," which held that radiation was not continuous but was divided into quanta, the size of which were related to their frequency. Einstein lent the theory support when he adopted it to explain the photoelectric effect, in which light striking metal can cause an emission of electrons.

In 1923 Louis de Broglie, in France, showed that a wave could be associated with every particle and related to its momentum, that is, the product of its mass and its velocity. In 1926 Edwin Schrodinger developed the concept further by expressing it mathematically and arriving at a compromise: matter could partake of both the nature of particles and waves. However, a wave does not precisely identify the position of a particular particle. It identifies the probability of a random event (the presence of a particle) taking place at a certain point.

In 1927 W.K. Heisenberg asserted his "uncertainty

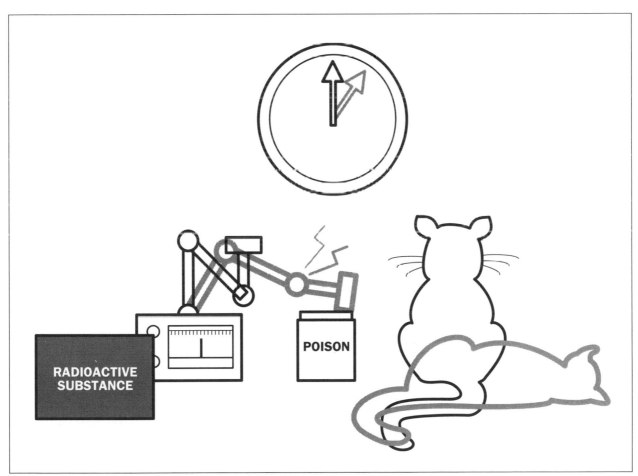

The Schrodinger's Cat Experiment: Will the cat live or will the cat die? An imaginary cat is locked in a room with a radioactive source that has an exact 50-50 probability of decaying within an hour. If it decays, a geiger counter registering the decay will prompt a hammer to strike a container filled with poisonous gas. At the end of an hour, according to the equations of quantum mechanics, the cat is not dead or alive but in a mixture of the states of being alive and being dead. However, when the experimenter opens the door and takes a look the cat will be in one of those states—dead or alive.

principle." By that he meant that it is impossible to define precisely both the momentum and the position of a particle at any instant in time: the more precisely one is determined, the less precisely the other is determined. His principle ran contrary to the universally accepted position set down more than a century earlier by Pierre-Simon Laplace, the great mathematical physicist. Laplace asserted that if the position and velocity of every particle in the universe were known at any given moment in time, its history and future development could be unequivocally determined. Heisenberg replaced Laplace's theory of certainty with a notion of probability. The question being raised by parapsychologists in PK experiments is whether some wavelike consciousness can affect the position of particles.

Reporting on experiments with REGs, Jahn and Dunne summarized the results of more than 50 million binary (two-choice) trials collected during seven years. The experiments involved long-term data collection with 33 "unselected" people chosen without consideration of PSI ability. Among their many findings, the researchers discovered that regardless of the device they were working on, some operators had "signature deviation patterns," that is, they achieved a consistent PK effect in a plus direction, a negative direction, both directions, or neither.

This finding has implications for engineering practices, which they, along with colleague R.D. Nelson, discussed in a 1987 *Journal of Exploration* (Vol. 1) article entitled "Engineering Anomalies Research." They wrote: "The results with the random-event generators raise the generic possibility of anomalous effects arising from conscious or unconscious interactions between human operators and any sensitive microelectronic information-processing devices."

They elaborate more fully in their 1987 book *Margins of Reality: The Role of Consciousness in the Physical World* in response to the frequently asked, variously phrased question, "What are nice folks like you doing in a field like this?" Among other motivations, they wrote: "From a cautionary standpoint, we must consider the possibility that a broad range of devices and systems similar to those employed in our research may likewise be responsive to the conscious and unconscious intentions of their human operators." In other words, the intentions of people oper-

ating certain microelectronic devices could influence how they function.

Remote Viewing

The scientists at PEAR refined precognitive remote perception (PRP) to make it compatible with their goal of carefully doing large numbers of trials. PRP also is known as remote viewing.

SRI International physicists Hal Puthoff and Russell Targ devised a series of experiments they called remote viewing based on a suggestion made by a subject, Ingo Swann. An artist with prior experience at the American Society for Psychical Research in New York, Swann was bored by psychokinesis experiments. He told SRI experimenters how much he had enjoyed some out-of-body experiments in New York, when he had been asked to describe the room next to him without physical moving to the room.

Swann wanted to take the experiments a step further by trying to move his viewpoint anywhere in the world. The results of preliminary trials convinced Puthoff and Targ and their funding sources that a full-scale investigation was warranted.

The director of SRI's Information Science and Engineering Division preselected a pool of 100 sites within a 30-minute driving range, sealed the site designations in separate envelopes, and secured them in a safe. Once the subject and the experimenter were closeted and cut off from communication with the outside world, one or more researchers and sometimes other SRI staffers selected one envelope from the pool of 100 and drove off.

Once away from the SRI campus, the team opened the envelope and drove to the designated site. There, they spent 15 minutes looking and wandering around.

Once the 30-minute travel time needed for the team to get to the site had elapsed, the experimenter would ask the subject to begin trying to view where the team was. Since the experimenter had no idea where the site was, he or she was free to question the subject for details. The impression session lasted 15 minutes and was recorded or videotaped.

The target team returned for an informal comparison of results and usually the subject was taken to the site for feedback. A typed transcript of the session was prepared for judging. The judges, SRI staff unconnected with the remote-viewing research, were randomly given unlabeled response packets. They visited all sites in the series and ranked all packets from best to worst against each site.

The rankings were summed and compared with what chance would produce. For example, an experiment involving nine sites could rank from 9, all best matches, to 81, all worst matches. The sum-of-ranks score for a former police commissioner, who felt his psychic ability helped him in his work, was 16, a score which included seven perfect matches. After correcting for the criticism that judges may not have received some of the packets in random order, several other laboratories reported significant success.

Imposing Controls
on Free-Response Experiments

Remote-viewing techniques benefited from procedures developed in earlier research in free-response—as distinguished from forced-choice—experiments. Dream research began in the late 1950s and continued in the early 1960s when researchers concluded that card guessing had run its course. A highly artificial and essentially boring technique, card guessing had provided scientific credentials for ESP, but it told little about how ESP worked in real life. New approaches were needed. Dream research was one new direction, particularly favored by parapsychologists who also were psychiatrists or clinical psychologists.

Dreams and ESP have been linked throughout history. Recent investigators have speculated that dreams unfold without the conscious mind's constraints on what is or is not possible. They speculate that a dreaming mind may fail to filter out extrasensory information normally screened out by an awake mind.

ESP dream research was facilitated by psychologist Nathaniel Kleitman's discovery that when people dream they exhibit rapid eye movement (REM) and that they have several dream cycles during the course of the night. Taking advantage of dream technology in 1964 was a team made up of Montague Ullman, then director of Maimonides Community Mental Health Center in Brooklyn, New York; Stanley Krippner, director of Maimonides Dream Laboratory; and City College doctoral student Sol Feldstein.

Since ESP card decks were not suitable as a target, the team revived an old method, the free-response approach, which has the subject respond freely, reporting whatever comes to mind in the form of images. In dream research, the subject recalls whatever he or she is dreaming about, no matter how strange.

The researchers randomly selected a target for each night and ensured that it was kept secret from the sleeper and the sleep lab personnel. The experimental design called for pens on a polygraph monitoring device to be hooked up to a sleeping subject. When the pens indicated the beginning of a REM cycle, a technician hit a button that sounded in a distant room. In that distant room, a researcher concentrated on the visual and emotional contents of the target, an art print, in an effort to communicate via ESP with the subject.

When REM stopped, the technician would wake the subject and ask for an account of what he or she had been dreaming about. Outside judges ranked the targets transmitted by the distant researcher and the dream contents on a scale 1–12, with 1 being a perfect match.

Work in the Dream Lab went on until 1978, by which time the researchers had completed a dozen formal studies, as well as screening data and pilot studies. Statistical analysis of the results found there had been 233 hits in 379 trials or an accuracy rate of 83.5%, where chance would be 50%. The odds against the matches being due to chance were 250,000-to-1.

Because dream labs are expensive to equip and operate, few parapsychologists replicated the Maimonides lab. However, they sought cost-effective ways to pursue ESP in states of consciousness other than the normal waking state. The most fruitful of these was developed in the mid-1970s by a former member of the Maimonides lab, Charles Honorton.

Honorton operated on the assumption that ESP is similar to a weak version of ordinary senses. He reasoned that ESP might operate more frequently than generally recognized but be overwhelmed by stronger signals from conventional sense organs.

The technique he developed is called the ESP-ganzfeld experiment, or simply the ganzfeld. The subject, relaxing in a reclining chair, is placed in a mild state of sensory deprivation (cut off from stimuli).

This quantum mechanical random-event generator at the PEAR Laboratory produces a random series of positive and negative pulses. The subject will try to influence the pulses.

In Honorton's original experiments, a subject did 15 minutes of relaxation exercises, while a co-experimenter in a separate room used a special computer program to select one set of pictures out of 36 sets and then one picture out of the set's four. The co-experimenter then placed a "judging set" by the door to the experiment control room and carried a replica to another building. Fifteen minutes into the experiment, as the relaxation exercises ended, the co-experimenter began a half-hour session of concentrating on the target picture. At the same time, the subject was told to describe whatever thoughts or images came to mind.

At the end of a half-hour, the experimenter collected the sealed envelope of four pictures and had the subject examine them and rank them according to how much they resembled what was going through his or her mind during the session.

During a decade and a half following Honorton's first ganzfeld experiment, more than 50 similar experiments were conducted in labs around the world. Not all were successful. Hardly any psychological ex-

periments work every time. However, they had sufficient success that many parapsychologists believe the ganzfeld technique may be the long-sought key to repeatable ESP experiments.

Reliable Performers

From the outset, parapsychologists have been preoccupied with trying to find consistent, reliable subjects. People who could score well in PSI tests turned up in their labs every so often, but the researcher could not predict who they might be.

Dozens of experiments yielded some impressions about personality traits linked to PSI ability. Those impressions were considerably strengthened by Charles Honorton, who became the head of the Psychophysical Research Laboratories (PRL) in Princeton, New Jersey when he left Maimonides. He had his staff systematically collect personality information about their subjects and test them in a uniform automated ganzfeld test environment. Besides a lengthy personal information inventory related to parapsychology, subjects were given a standard personality-assessment test, the Myers-Briggs Indicator (MBTI).

Honorton and his colleagues found four factors to be important for first-time participants. Those who did best had experienced what they thought were psychic events. They practiced or had at one time practiced a mental discipline such as meditation, biofeedback, or relaxation techniques. Extroverts did better than introverts. "Intuitives," those who are fond of abstractions and inferences, did better than "sensing" types, who are concrete and practical. The best subjects were "feeling" types, those good at understanding the feelings of others and analyzing subjective impressions, and "perceiving" types who are curious, open-minded, and flexible. Those who combined feeling and perceiving achieved a 55% success rate, where 25% is expected by chance. And those who had previously participated in PSI experiments did better than those who had not.

Four first-time subjects met the criteria of: prior psychic experience; mental discipline experience; feeling and perceiving personality traits; and prior PSI testing. They had a 100% success rate. Since subjects with prior PSI testing tend to be rare, researchers examined a three factor model as one more practical for most researchers. Twenty-eight subjects who had the other traits but had who had not had prior PSI testing had an astounding success rate of 64%.

In the light of PRL's findings, the Institute for Parapsychology examined data collected on 102 first-time ganzfeld subjects. They found that 28 subjects fit the three-factor model and had achieved a statistically significant scoring rate of 43%. Thus, they confirmed the PRL model of subjects who can be expected to be successful in the ganzfeld experiment.

The quarrel traditional science has had with parapsychology has been its difficulties in replicating specific findings of researchers in entirely independent experiments. Virtually no previous experiment had as closely replicated a tightly formulated prediction like that of Honorton and his colleagues as had the Institute for Parapsychology.

Meta-Analysis and Weak But Significant Effects

Some observers suggest that one of the reasons scientists, particularly social scientists, resist parapsychology is because it reminds them too much of weak-

nesses in their own sciences. Frequently psychological or therapeutic effects are discovered only to be discarded when other researchers are unable to replicate the findings.

Attitudes toward weak effects began to change in the social sciences in the mid-1970s when some statistical procedures were coupled with rules for combining studies in an approach dubbed meta-analysis. The technique has the capacity to question whether a collection of experiments demonstrates a real effect.

The results of any experiment consist of two elements: signal and noise. Signal is the effect on the data of the experimental factor under investigation. In a simple ESP experiment, the signal would be the number of correct guesses due to ESP-supplied information. Noise is everything else that appears in the data in which the experimenter has no interest.

The biggest component of noise in an ESP experiment is likely to be chance—correct guesses that would be there with or without ESP. Noise also includes factors that might cause a subject's ESP to vary or disappear during the experiment. Statistical tests provide an estimate of whether there really is something in all the noise.

The relationship of effect and noise is analogous to a radio listener who needs only a snatch of a strong signal to identify a familiar program but may have to listen long and hard to identify an unfamiliar, distant, weak signal. The more data that goes into a statistical estimate (the longer the listener listens), the better the chance of detecting the effect, if there is one.

If a subject could reliably use ESP to guess coin flips 5% of the time, then in an experiment of 20 coin flips with roughly 10 correct guesses, only one would be due to ESP. Provided the subject maintained the 5% ability, in 1,000 trials two-thirds of the tests would provide significant evidence of the subject's ESP, and 10,000 trials would virtually never fail to detect the subject's ability.

Many psychology and parapsychology experiments are of necessity designed around the constraints of available time and money, and hence are brief and likely to fail. The strength of meta-analysis is that it combines many short experiments into one long one. The methods of meta-analysis make it possible to make different experiments address the same statistically equivalent question, despite different experimental techniques, different subjects, and different results.

Besides a simple accumulation of results, meta-analysis can group studies according to factors—known as blocking—that might have something to do with different results. Studies can be coded according to the quality of the experiment, the number or type of subjects—whatever seems relevant. Meta-analysis also makes it possible to estimate the "file-drawer problem," studies never published because they failed to find the desired effect.

The results of meta-analyses in parapsychology have found that several lines of parapsychological research produce consistent, reliable effects that cannot be explained away as chance, poor methodology, idiosyncratic experimenters, or unusual studies. This research also has found that the effects are typically very weak—so weak they might have been missed in any branch of science that did not force its practitioners, as parapsychology does, to repeat the same experiments over and over.

Weak effect is not the same as no effect. To demonstrate how potent a weak effect can be, Broughton recalled the 1987 fanfare when a study of 22,000 subjects to determine the efficacy of aspirin to prevent heart attacks was halted because it was deemed unethical to withhold the treatment from the control group. There were 45% fewer heart attacks in the experimental group. Yet the effect size was only .03[11].

The actual effect of aspirin is so weak that if the study had been done on 3,000 subjects, the effect would not have been evident. By contrast, meta-analysis has demonstrated that the effects of parapsychological experiments range from a low of .0003 for the random-number generator research through .01 for dice, .02 for precognition, to a high of .29 for the ganzfeld work. Meta-analysis has made it possible for parapsychologists to make use of over a half-century of hard and frustrating work.

Parapsychology is in no danger of fading. Research is going on all over the world in an array of disciplines. Enhancement of PSI effects to a point where they might be consistently useful is likely to be difficult, but likely to be done because scientists with interests in the military, medicine, and quantum mechanics have a stake in parapsychology's future.

Research in psychokinesis (PK) had dwindled when J.B. Rhine began his dice-tossing experiments. The subject would try to influence the fall of the dice to show a specific number. Success was inferred if the subject achieved his or her goal more often than chance. For many years this was the only type of PK research.

4

CHANGING ENVIRONMENT

From Rio,
Principles for Sustainable Development

Preceded by five years of planning and two years of intensive preparation, the United Nations Conference on Environment and Development finally took place in Rio de Janeiro, Brazil June 3–14, 1992. Hailed as the second Earth Summit, the extraordinary meeting, held 20 years after the first Earth Summit in Stockholm, Sweden brought together more than 100 world leaders and 30,000 other participants. The decision to convene the second Earth Summit came in response to a 1987 report issued by the World Commission on Environment and Development that called for the world to shift to a course of "sustainable development."

The concept of sustainable development—a topic of bitter, ongoing debates—is essentially defined as a way of life that can adequately support the human population without depleting the Earth of resources needed by future generations. The 1987 report warned that putting the world on a course of sustainable development would require a reconstruction of cultures comparable to the agricultural and industrial revolutions of earlier centuries.

The first summit paved the way for the second by spurring not only the growth of thousands of grassroots conservation groups around the world, but also the organization of environmental agencies or ministries within the governments of 115 nations. A driving force behind the second summit was Secretary-General Maurice Strong, the seemingly tireless negotiator who chaired the 1972 Stockholm meeting.

During the 20 years that elapsed between the two summits, the world's environment drastically deteriorated. For example, air pollution, a major issue at Stockholm, worsened between 1972 and 1992. Even more critical, the two decades brought broad changes in the well-being of the atmosphere (the mixture of gases enveloping Earth).

One of the most serious changes was a continuing depletion of the stratospheric ozone layer about 12–15 miles above the Earth. That concentration of ozone protects the planet against incoming ultraviolet rays. Another alarming change was global warming due to a buildup of greenhouse gases, chemicals that prevent heat from escaping above the atmosphere, which sets up conditions for a chain of disastrous environmental effects.

Furthermore, according to the Washington-based World Watch Institute, during the two decades from 1972 to 1992, 200 million hectares (500 million acres) of the world's trees were lost. Moreover, erosion cost the world's farmers 500 million tons in lost topsoil (surface soil), which is the most fertile.

Politics has complicated the situation. The world in the early 1970s was divided by the threat of nuclear war into East and West blocs. Since the collapse of Communism, political conflict has increasingly been over environmental issues with the "North" (Europe, North America, and Japan) often aligned against the "South" (most of Africa, Asia, and Latin America), and vice versa.

Stark economic differences exist between rich and poor countries. With most of the world's wealth being concentrated in the Northern developed countries. Such sharp disparities between and within countries set up conditions of distrust and political unrest. Many Third World leaders blame the global

Earth rise as seen from the moon.

environmental crisis on the lifestyles of richer nations. When asked to stop practices that threaten the environment, such as the destruction of their rain forests, strip mining for precious metals that leaves behind barren soil, and the use of toxic chemicals, Southern developing countries direct attention to the extravagant consumption patterns of rich countries.

A June 1, 1992 *Time* article entitled "Rich Vs. Poor" highlighted the broad issues in contention. The North's developed countries are accustomed to lifestyles that use up a disproportionate amount of the world's natural resources.

The United States:
- has 5% of the world's population;
- uses 25% of the world's energy;
- emits 22% of the carbon dioxide that destroys the ozone layer; and
- accounts for 25% of the world's gross national product (GNP), the market value of all the goods and services produced by a country.

In contrast, India, where fuel is scarce:
- contains 16% of the world's population;
- uses 3% of the world's energy;
- emits 3% of the carbon dioxide; and
- accounts for 1% of the world's GNP.

To feed their burgeoning populations, many developing countries use irreplaceable global resources, such as their trees and water.

The stark economic difference between countries is mirrored by social structures in many Southern countries, where most of the wealth belongs to a tiny minority of people, who often use it or bank it in the developed nations. The indifference of the wealthy to the plight of the poor makes it difficult to pursue a goal of sustainable development. With no other resources, poor people worried about their next meal are not going to stop chopping down rain forests to make charcoal they can sell as fuel.

The issues that confronted the 178 nations in attendance at the 1992 Earth Summit included the globe's worst environmental woes:

- loss of biodiversity (a healthy balance of species);
- the erosion of coastlines;
- deforestation (chopping down forests and leaving a wasteland behind); and
- toxic waste dumping, particularly by the military.

Rio Principles

During five years of meetings leading up to the Rio summit a statement of 27 principles to be addressed by the conference was hammered out. Stripped of their excess language, much of which was needed to make them politically acceptable to the participants, the 27 principles are:

1. Human beings are entitled to a healthy and productive life in harmony with nature.

2. States (nations) have a right to exploit their own resources and the responsibility to ensure their activities do not damage the environments of other states or areas beyond their boundaries.

3. The right to development must meet developmental and environmental needs of present and future generations.

4. Environmental protection shall constitute an integral part of the development process.

5. Eradication of poverty to meet the needs of the majority of the world's people and to decrease the disparities in standards of living is indispensable.

6. The needs of the developing countries, particularly the most vulnerable, shall be given priority.

7. States shall cooperate to conserve, protect, and restore the integrity of the Earth's ecosystem. The developed countries acknowledge their responsibility for the pursuit of sustainable development in view of the pressure their societies place on the environment and because of the financial resources at their command.

8. States shall reduce and eliminate unsustainable patterns of production and consumption and promote appropriate demographic policies.

9. States shall support sustainable development by improving science, exchanging scientific and technological knowledge, and by adapting and transferring new and innovative technologies.

10. To encourage citizen participation, states shall make environmental information widely available and encourage public awareness.

11. States shall enact effective environmental legislation that reflects the context to which the measures apply. Standards applied by some countries may not be appropriate for others, particularly developing countries, given their economic and social costs.

12. States shall cooperate to promote an open international system to better address environmental degradation. Trade policy measures should not use the environment as a disguise to discriminate. Global environmental problems should, as far as possible, be based on international consensus.

13. States should develop national law about liabil-

As humanity searches for improved, nondamaging or less-damaging ways to use the environment, any good idea that can cut costs as well may be desirable. Here, Dr. John A. Heitmann, Jr., associate professor of wood and paper science at North Carolina State University, examines recycled newsprint for brightness. His enzymatic de-inking process could make recycling more efficient and economical.

ity and compensation for victims of environmental damage.

14. States should discourage the relocation of activities or substances that cause environmental damage to other states.

15. Lack of scientific certainty shall not be used as a reason for postponing cost-effective measures to avoid environmental degradation.

16. States should promote the use of economic accounting that includes the cost a polluter should pay, without distorting international trade and investment.

17. Environmental impact assessments should be made of proposed activities likely to have a significant adverse impact on the environment, subject to a decision by a competent national authority.

18. States shall immediately notify other states of any natural disasters or other emergencies likely to produce harmful effects on those states. The international community should endeavor to help such states.

19. States shall promptly notify other affected states with relevant information about activities that may have adverse transboundary environmental effects.

20. Women have a vital role in environmental management and development. Their full participation is therefore essential to achieve sustainable development.

21. The creativity, ideals, and courage of the world's youth should be mobilized to achieve a sustainable development and ensure a better future for all.

22. States should recognize and support the role of indigenous people and their contribution to a sustainable development.

23. The environment and natural resources of people under oppression, domination, and occupation shall be protected.

24. Warfare is inherently destructive to sustainable development. States should provide protection for the environment in times of armed conflict.

25. Peace, development, and environmental protection are indivisible.

26. States shall resolve all their environmental disputes peacefully and by appropriate means in accordance with the Charter of the United Nations.

27. States and people shall cooperate in good faith and in a spirit of partnership in the fulfillment of the principles embodied in the Declaration and in further development of international law in the field of sustainable development.

Although many of the principles had been watered down during the long and often heated negotiations, to arrive at this level of agreement was a remarkable achievement in and of itself.

Clashing Perspectives

Acrimony during the negotiations over principles reflected sharp differences in opinion over the reality and seriousness of threats to the environment. Bitter differences in opinion, a continuing battle ground during the two decades between summits, were not confined to those between countries but were also evident within countries. Environmentalists around the world, particularly in Brazil, the former Soviet Union, and the United States have been highly critical of their own governments' indifference.

In the United States, environmentalist William Ruckelshaus, the former head of the U.S. Environmental Protection Agency (EPA) expressed concern about the effects of environmental destruction on governments of the future. A June 1, 1992 *Boston Globe* article entitled "But Some Thinkers See It Differently" quoted Ruckelshaus: "People, when faced with a choice between chaos and authoritarianism, will inevitably choose the latter." In his opinion, environmental deterioration could encourage frightened citizens into accepting "green police," authoritarian governments given the power to enforce environmental survival measures.

Many conservative thinkers dismiss environmental concerns. John Shanahan of the Heritage Foundation believes that once having made some economic market adjustments in society—such as making polluters pay—a benign environment will evolve. In Shanahan's view, humans throughout history have repeatedly depleted resources and then found substitutes. And Murray Weidenbaum, former President Ronald Reagan's economic adviser, views suggestions that the world is facing an environmental crisis as hysterical.

For a long time, voices like Weidenbaum's and Shanahan's found an audience in parts of the American business community, particularly in the coal, oil, auto, and utility industries, which face the greatest transformations. But over the last four or five years, many business and political leaders in the United States and elsewhere have come to agree that there is a danger.

In May 1992, a group of leading industrialists around the world, collectively known as the Business Council for Sustainable Development, issued a 374-page report entitled *Changing Course,* which declared that the world is under serious threat and major changes are necessary. The founder of the council was Stephan Schmidheiny, a wealthy Swiss industrialist, recruited as an adviser in 1990 by Earth Summit Secretary-General Strong, a former oil executive.

To found the council, Schmidheiny used $10 million of his own money, an act that gave him credibility when he began recruiting chief executives of corporations to aid his cause. During an interview for a June 2, 1991 *New York Times* article entitled "Business Has Message for Rio Meeting," Schmidheiny said, "Environmental thinking is bringing a new industrial revolution. It is the most forceful trend in my lifetime. It will reshape business because it will redefine the rules of the economic game." His message to the Earth Summit on behalf of 48 international corporations that make up the council was that industry may be a big part of the problem but is also a big part of the solution.

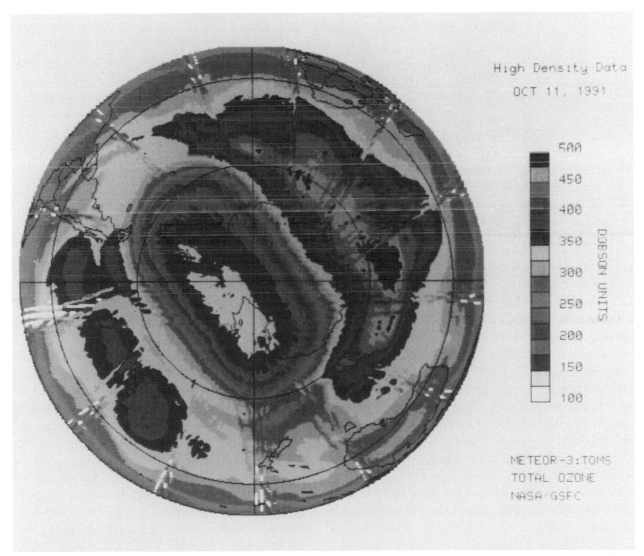

A major concern of the summit was ozone depletion in the upper atmosphere. Recently, atmospheric measurements have shown that thinning of the ozone layer has occurred over places besides the poles.

Many topics discussed at the summit relate to global warming. Of the two main greenhouse gases, the levels of methane (a gas 20 times more effective than carbon dioxide in trapping heat) seem to have stabilized, but the levels of carbon dioxide continue to grow. Carbon dioxide levels also fluctuate sharply with the seasons, reaching their highest point during the northern hemisphere's winter, a fact that may seem at odds with the crisp, clean smell of winter air. Carbon dioxide is removed from the air by plant photosynthesis. Since most of Earth's landmasses are in the northern hemisphere, during the northern hemisphere's winter, a majority of the world's plants are dormant.

Secretary-General Maurice Strong's Hopes

On April 5, 1992, the day following the last meeting of two years of negotiations by the Earth Summit preparatory committee, Maurice Strong addressed a dinner meeting of science writers. The occasion was a Rockefeller Foundation-sponsored media seminar entitled "Feeding the World, Protecting the Earth: Advances in International Agricultural Research."

Strong described the process of preparation for what he deemed to be "essentially a political meeting." His small United Nations secretariat staff had reached out for advice to professionals around the world, to other agencies of the U.N., and to scientific organizations, such as the International Council of Scientific Unions. Staff members also had sought advice from specialized groups such as women, youth, engineers, business executives, and indigenous peoples.

During the final five-week meeting of the preparatory committee, the committee agreed on 95% of the issues before it—but not without compromises. (One of those compromises was to change the name of the principles from the "Earth Charter" to the "Declaration of Rio.") Such a consensus was in stark contrast to the Stockholm summit, where it took until 5:00 A.M. of the final day of the summit to reach a comparable level.

Strong told the science writers that following the Rio summit, he expected there to be many naysayers. While he accepted many of their criticisms, he refused to adopt their gloomy perspective. He said, "I don't agree with those that suggest that nothing has been accomplished unless everything has been accomplished. That would be a recipe for disaster. That would be the surest way of not making progress on our agenda."

The secretary-general was gratified that the preparatory committee had reached agreement on 115 action areas because, in his opinion, "political will develops most rapidly during the home stretch." In other words, progress on difficult issues does not normally come until almost the end of negotiations. Controversial issues such as curbs on population growth and control on atmospheric emissions remained in "square brackets" (a device used in international negotiations to designate areas in which agreement has not been reached). Strong's last words to the preparatory committee were: "We cannot allow the future of our planet to be left in square brackets."

To reach agreement requires an evolution of political will and a mind set that puts environmental security on a list of global priorities. In Strong's opinion, many cost-effective measures can be taken in the developing world to protect its precious resources and to alleviate poverty without further degrading the environment. Indeed, such environmental controls are cost-effective in the developed nations. Japan, for instance, uses one-half as much energy as the United States to produce a unit of gross domestic product.

Financing global attention to protection and repair of the environment remains a stumbling block, but many of the channels through which funds will flow are already in place. The U.N.'s Global Environmental Facility is expected to expand, and develop-

Clean, available water is a global necessity. Repeatedly, it has been demonstrated that problems of water pollution need not be insoluble. The Merrimack River, in northeastern Massachusetts, was one of the filthiest rivers in the United States in the 1970s. Today it is clean enough to once again be a source of drinking water.

There are three goals in maintaining the world's food supply: preserving the environment in which the food is grown to maintain current levels of food production; increasing production to stay even with population growth; and reclaiming and repairing arable lands that have been lost.

Cassava, a crop that originated in South America, also is grown in Africa. To combat the cassava green mite, an unwanted immigrant to Africa, the mite's natural enemy was imported from South America. Above, Dr. Ann Braun, on the left, with Dr. Anthony Bellotti, both of the International Center for Tropical Agriculture (CIAT), examine cassava leaves damaged by mites. The inset shows a "friendly" mite feeding on the cassava green mite.

Small farmers in developing countries have trouble obtaining high-quality seeds. CIAT scientists have trained 58 specialists to promote local seed industries through farmer groups. Groups organize to supply seeds for their own crops and for surrounding villages. The farmers test, select, and market acceptable varieties. According to Dr. Adriel E. Garay of CIAT, "The systems are biodiversity-friendly; they make the best seeds of the best varieties, native or imported, for local conditions available to farmers."

The International Laboratory for Research on Animal Diseases (ILRAD) in Kenya conducts research with the goal of increasing resistance to diseases that cause heavy losses of African livestock. Embryo transfer technology is used for this research. The technique is valuable in the production of genetically defined calves, i.e., calves known or thought to possess a particular desired trait, such as resistance to a disease. Microscopic embryos can be frozen and transported relatively cheaply with negligible risk of transferring disease.

ing countries are likely to be given a greater role in its governance.

One of the channels of change will be so-called "Earth increments," conditions required of grant recipients. Such organizations as the IDA (International Development Association of the World Bank) Fund and U.N. development programs will require grant recipients to do something to improve the environment or, at the very least, to avoid damaging it.

Unfortunately, economic clout is lacking in private environmental groups or government ministries around the world. They also don't have influence on national policies related to areas that impact the environment, such as transportation, agriculture, or energy. Otherwise, they could direct attention to policy areas that provide subsidies for activities damaging to the environment. (Subsidies are grants of money by a government to support private enterprises consid-

ered to be beneficial to the public).

In the United States, coal, a major source of air pollution, is heavily subsidized. In many developing countries, heavy subsidies encourage overuse of fertilizers, which are deposited by the wind and runoff (drainage of water) into lakes, rivers, and oceans, where they disrupt plant and animal life.

During a question-and-answer period, a science writer from India asked Secretary-General Strong to comment on a problem that goes by various names but is most commonly known as "brain drain." Many young people sent by developing nations to college and/or graduate school never return home to live or, if they do return, leave in a few years to live in the country where they studied or in some other developed country. Thus "brains" are "drained" from developing countries, leaving them with a shortage of scientists and other professionals.

During the post-Columbus exchange of foods between the Old and New Worlds, the use of amaranth declined. Because amaranth has a near-perfect protein balance—as good or better than cow's milk—with a good mix of essential amino acids, it is being studied and is regaining its popularity. Moreover, amaranth adapts well to drought conditions. Its durability is reflected in its name comprised of two Greek words meaning "immortal" and "not withering."

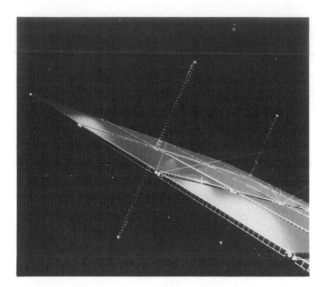

Some people suggest that imaginative, large-scale solutions are needed for some world problems. "Project Phoenix: Fire Replaced," designed by fourth-year and graduate students of the Institute of Design at the Illinois Institute of Technology in Chicago, consists of two macro-design proposals for confronting global warming. Both proposals focus on carbon dioxide. The first proposal would replace fossil fuel use with a power generation system in space, thereby reducing the amount of carbon burned and the amount of carbon dioxide entering the atmosphere. The second proposal would augment photosynthetic processes to increase the amount of carbon dioxide being removed from the air by the regreening of desertified areas and the construction of floating wetlands on the ocean. The power generation system would be a series of Solar Power Satellites, which by means of photovoltaic cells, would convert sunlight to electrical energy to be beamed to Earth via tightly directed microwaves. Shown is a computer rendering of a large solar panel, 1,200 meters (3,937.2 feet) to a side, that would be part of such a satellite.

The reasons for brain drain vary. Many professionals leave because salaries are low. Others leave because support for their work, both social and financial, is lacking. Still others feel stifled because they have few colleagues with whom to share ideas.

Such disparities between the North and South in access to professional advice made the summit preparatory committee's tasks more difficult. The developed countries came to negotiations accompanied by a bevy of experts, who themselves could turn for advice to other experts and institutions. The develop-

ing countries typically were accompanied by their few available experts, who had no backup.

Asked about the cost of full implementation of the principles of Rio, Strong estimated an average of $500 billion a year for developing countries, which would require a massive deployment of the South's resources. Developing countries also would need an additional $125 billion annually in subsidies from developed countries. Such subsidies could be funds diverted from activities that damage the environment and used to clean it up.

Getting Down to Work

One of the most disruptive issues for the Earth Summit was the biodiversity treaty, which U.S. President George Bush refused to sign. For months it looked as if Bush would not even attend the conference. During those months United Nations officials twisted arms and called in political favors in an effort to get the U.S. president to make an appearance.

The U.N. officials' dilemma and the reactions of other nations were described in a June 15, 1992 *Newsweek* article entitled "The Grinch of Rio." The author Sharon Begley wrote: "What would be the point of a conference on the future of the planet, after all, if the globe's only superpower stayed home. Rio's partisans got what they wanted. But when Bush shows up this week for a 40-hour appearance, even many of America's allies are going to greet him as the Grinch who stole the eco-summit . . . the White House weakened the climate-change pact . . . the administration refused to sign the biodiversity treaty, which is supported by more than 120 countries . . . and publicly snubbed its own delegate [EPA Secretary William Reilly] when he made a last ditch attempt to get the White House on board."

Because the United States had been a pioneer on many environmental issues, it was ironic to have the nation cast in the role of the villain. In the 1970s America created the Environmental Protection Agency, passed a Clean Air Act, and banned lead in gasoline. During the 1980s, the nation spent $800 billion on cleaning up the environment.

Yet American actions added to the confusion surrounding the conference. Until a few days before the opening ceremonies, Secretary Reilly was not told he would head up the American delegation. Moreover,

To construct such large satellites on Earth and launch them into space, even as pieces to be assembled, would be financially and logistically impossible. Therefore, the Project Phoenix plan proposes that the satellites be constructed in space, with parts manufactured in a Lunar Orbit Factory (above), from materials mined on the Moon. Solar-cell panels and structural elements of the satellites would be assembled in the vicinity of the factory before being towed by lunar shuttle to its operating position in geosynchronous orbit. There it would be outfitted with more equipment from Earth. There would be a large space station in orbit around Earth to facilitate operations.

Compared to coastal areas, midocean is comparatively barren of sea life. "Project Phoenix: Fire Reversed," proposes the creation of floating wetlands for transplanted aquatic and coastal plant and animal species. These floating coastal environments would: serve as substitute habitats for wetland-dependent sea life; reduce carbon dioxide; and become a potential source of food. Many species of animals and plants could contribute structurally to an island's skeletal base. The island's floating elements would be attached to a triangular grid of cables suspended below the ocean surface at a depth of 20 meters (65.62 feet). The power of waves, passing under breakwaters deployed for stability, would be harnessed for electric power. Strategically located pump islands (such as that shown) could supply the Floating Wetland with nutrients drawn from the ocean's surface waters.

the 47 members of the delegation were not notified that they were to attend until after the conference had started. By the second week of the summit, the conference verged on disintegration. Angered by Washington's refusal to sign the biodiversity treaty, several developing nations considered withdrawal of their support for the pact. Some spoke of reviewing their position on an agreement to combat global warming. Still, despite the squabbles and feuds, the participants ultimately pulled together to save the event. Their feat was described in a June 22, 1992 *Time* article entitled "Rio's Legacy."

Shortly before the 100 world leaders were scheduled to arrive for the grand finale of treaty signings, delegates seemed to recognize that the animosity had to stop. The conference was widely perceived as the last chance to save the planet. With the world looking on, no one had anything to gain from a dismal failure.

Stemming a revolt among the developing nations, the delegation from India, the source of many of the most provocative comments about the shortcomings of developed nations, announced that it would sign the biodiversity treaty. A tacit accord was reached between family-planning advocates and the Catholic church to permit developing nations to take more effective steps to curb population growth.

Implementation of the Earth Summit's proposals will be difficult. Obstacles will include:
- psychological denial that there is a problem;
- nonrecognition of global interdependence;
- resistance by those who hold orthodox theories of economic growth; and
- a continuing worldwide equation of personal well-being with an ever-greater use of resources.

Despite rancorous disagreements, the Earth Summit was a landmark effort in the drive to protect the planet. Most summit participants agreed that the best hope for the future lies in changes in values. Spencer Beebe, president of the American environmental group Ecotrust, said it best: "Saving the planet has never been an issue of money but rather a matter of resourcefulness and motivation of individuals."

The Pacific Electric Railway (PE) was once the world's largest trolley and interurban transit system, but Los Angeles abandoned the PE in 1938. Today the city has hired a Japanese contractor to build a new mass transit system because none of the American companies that submitted bids met the specifications. Meanwhile, cars are a big source of carbon dioxide in the United States and industrialized nations. The U.S. population of cars has grown far faster than the country's human population. America's love affair with the automobile has sometimes been encouraged by unethical means. Although some once-existing transit systems shut down because they were no longer financially viable, numerous transit systems were purchased by people with financial interests in the automotive industry and eventually closed.

War Leftovers

The 1991 Persian Gulf war, officially known as Operation Desert Storm, was launched to force Iraq to end its occupation of Kuwait. Although militarily successful, the war turned out to be another example of the lengthy and costly cleanup and restoration that follows armed conflict. Enormous damage came from oil dumped into the Persian Gulf by retreating Iraqi troops, who then set fire to oil wells.

Scientists who had theorized about the possibility of extensive oil fires in the event of a war speculated that the smoke might rise into the stratosphere, about eight miles above Earth. Once there, the smoke would be picked up by jet streams and carried around the world. Some scientists feared that such windborne smoke might disrupt the rains carried by the monsoon (southwest wind of the Indian Ocean). The result would be widespread drought in India. Others feared the smoke might cause a global drop in temperature by blocking the sun.

To assess the global threat of the smoke, which kept many Kuwaiti cities in darkness, researchers from Britain's Meteorological Office spent 10 days in March 1991 flying at different altitudes and distances from the burning wellheads. They concluded that most of the soot and gases were remaining close to Earth and their impact would be mainly regional.

On a local level, the fires were fearsome. A June 25, 1991 *New York Times* article entitled "Environmental Toll Mounting in Kuwait As Oil Fires Burn On," described one fire burning 30 miles southwest of Kuwait City: "The wellhead is buried inside a towering cone of coke that blazes with a furious roar, emitting charcoal-black smoke so dense that it feels like liquid soot in the eyes and on the tongue. For acres around this mound of flame, a congealing puddle of spilled oil belches incandescent gas and flickers with a thousand lesser fires."

A major obstacle to coping with the fires was finding and removing thousands of land mines scattered by Iraqi troops. To put out the raging oil field fires, scientists, inventors, and entrepreneurs around the world competed to create novel strategies. The new ideas included robots that launched flame-eating chemicals and portable factories that spewed supercold foam.

The imaginative methods of Houston, Texas-based Boots and Coots, one of three U.S. firefighting companies hired by Kuwait to battle its blazing fires, were described in a September 1991 *Popular Science* article entitled "Fire Over Kuwait." Blowout specialists typically bring an oil fire under control by detonating explosives above the well.

Among war's leftovers are soldiers. When a war ends, many soldiers return to civilian life at a time when business may not be able to immediately absorb them into new jobs.

The faces and terrain may change with each war, but the problems of refugees remain the same. Displaced, they are people who have no place to go and no means of sustaining themselves. They need water, food, clothing, and shelter for indefinite, extended periods of time. In the top photo are Kurdish refugees of today. In the bottom photo are a Greek mother and child from 1920.

However, to use explosives, firefighters need a large quantity of water. First, the water keeps the explosives cool while they are being put in place above the well. And second, the explosives only extinguish the fire for an instant; the water prevents the superheated metal pieces from re-igniting the blaze.

With only a few thousand gallons of water available, instead of the huge reservoir needed with explosives, Boots and Coots put into practice a technique that had long been suggested but never tried. They placed a vertical steel pipe over the spout of burning oil and pumped in nitrogen heated to a gaseous state. The nitrogen displaced the oxygen and thus smothered the fire.

Even more difficult than putting out a fire is shutting down the well. Once the fire is out, oil rains down on the workers. The smallest spark can turn the area and the workers into an inferno. Nevertheless, despite the risks, by November 6, 1991, four months ahead of schedule and 10 months after the 732 oil well fires were started, the last was extinguished.

Attention then turned to the damage inflicted by the oil spills. Beginning January 18, 1991, the spill poured roughly 300 million gallons into the Persian Gulf, an amount estimated to be 25 times larger than Alaska's 1989 Prince William Sound oil spill. Airborne pollution from damaged wells carried by the winds as soot or fine oil mist, thought to have ended up in the water, probably doubled the total.

Although enormous ecological damage from the oil spill was immediately obvious as thousands of animals and birds died from contact with the oil, the long-range effect may not be known for years. Many of the airborne particulates (tiny solid particles) are known carcinogens.

To assess the impact, the U.S. National Oceanic and Atmospheric Administration (NOAA) research vessel *Mount Mitchell* left Norfolk, Virginia January 15, 1992, under the sponsorship of the United Nations, for a six-month investigation. The *Mount Mitchell* has a crew of 50 and can carry 24 scientists. By the end of the trip in June 1992, about 150 researchers from 18 nations had participated. Because the livelihood of 40,000 Iranian fishermen depends on the gulf, approximately 12 Iranian scientists joined the investigation.

The scientists found oil damage extensive in crucial marine breeding grounds in the intertidal zone (between high and low tide) along hundreds of miles of Saudi Arabian beaches and coastal shallows. They hoped to determine how much petroleum pollution the gulf waters could hold without being permanently damaged. A May 26, 1992 *New York Times* article entitled "Most Marine Life in Persian Gulf Thrives Despite Huge Oil Slick," reported that in deeper waters, damage was not so evident.

Interpretations of what biologists found is hampered by a lack of scientific knowledge about the conditions in the gulf prior to the war. More cautious than some scientists who marveled at the gulf's resilience, Dr. Sylvia Earle, NOAA's former chief scientist, told the *New York Times,* "It is a permanent change. It will recover, but it will be different. We don't know what is missing."

Many of the airborne particulates from the oil fire, in addition to adding to the water pollution, may also have been inhaled by U.S. Desert Storm troops. An August 3, 1992 *Boston Herald* article entitled "Toxins Eyed in Mystery Gulf Vet Ailments" reported that an emerging body of evidence suggests dozens of New England Desert Storm veterans and possibly hundreds nationwide suffered from a variety of ailments the veterans believed to be due to environmental and chemical exposure during the war.

The Pentagon insisted that the veterans' maladies were stress-related and not due to exposure. Veterans groups, military personnel, and private environmental-health experts disagreed.

Dismantling Destructive Weapons

The destruction of unused weapons is one of the many residuals of war. And much of this destruction is technologically unsophisticated.

United Nations troops in the Persian Gulf war were not only exposed to smoke from the oil well fires, some were exposed to chemical risks by their participation in a mass demolition of Iraqi weaponry. Between June 30 and July 7, 1991, troops, under the United Nations auspices, destroyed 62 Iraqi missiles, support equipment, warheads, and fuel trucks. The main technique was pulverization by a bulldozer with a huge steel bucket.

Unused weapons are far more costly to keep track of and dispose of than to produce. The task goes on long after those who planned and fought the war are

What is not left after a war also is important. The Cambodian war so decimated the adult population that 600,000 hectares of land used for growing rice has been left fallow. Malnutrition is up sharply in a land that until the late 1960s, exported rice and now must import it. Those children not old enough to take on many tasks are heavily dependent upon a small population of adults and older children who can work. Beyond needing workers to farm the land, Dr. Harry Nesbitt of International Rice Research Institute (IRRI) reported: "Most of the qualified agriculturists fled or perished during the Pol Pot regime." To aid Cambodia to regain its agricultural capacity, IRRI sent a team to Cambodia in 1990 to introduce basic principles of integrated pest management (IPM)—the best mix of pest-control tactics to maintain high yields with minimal use of ecologically disruptive pesticides. Techniques include growing rices that are resistant to pests and diseases and controlling pests with predators, parasites, and pathogens rather than insecticides.

With the breakup of the Soviet Union has come agreements to dismantle weapons systems. This is the inside of a U.S. Titan II missile silo after the deactivation of the 308th Strategic Missile Wing. The silo is about to be destroyed, but the debris will be left in place for verification according to international agreements.

dead. Unexploded bombs buried following World War I are regularly unearthed by Belgian farmers.

After nearly a half-century race to develop nuclear bombs, designers and arms-control experts from the East and the West came together in December 1991 for a week-long meeting in Moscow to examine ways to destroy the fruits of their labor. The aim of the conference was to develop rules for counting, disabling, and destroying thousands of nuclear warheads.

Interviewed for a December 17, 1991 *New York Times* article entitled "Nuclear Designers From East and West Plan Bomb Disposal," Dr. David Watkins, a designer at the Los Alamos National Laboratory in New Mexico, said, "Soviet society is falling apart. It's in our interest, in their interest, in everybody's interest, to get these stabilized as soon as possible. It would be a terrible thing, down the road, if we lost some of these weapons."

Americans remain concerned that the former Soviet Union's widely dispersed weapons, perhaps 15,000 of a total of 30,000 nuclear weapons, might fall into unfriendly hands in distant republics of the dissolved country, now decentralized and known as the Commonwealth of Independent States. Indeed, some Western experts suspect that even the top officials of the former Soviet Union may not know how many weapons were deployed.

The American delegation in Moscow promoted the idea of sealing the weapons and putting a unique tag for identification on each, while they await transport to dismantling facilities. One simple system would be to wrap each in a fiber optic cable illuminated at one end. The unique light "signature" visible at the other end would be photographed. At subsequent inspections, new photographs could be taken and compared with the original signatures for signs of tampering.

The United States is downsizing its armed forces, but certain military items, particularly ships, are too expensive to destroy or sell and later replace. They are stored, in a manner designed to preserve them for possible future need. Four decommissioned battleships await that possibility.

The best disposal method would be to disable the warheads in place, an option available for several American weapons. Russian experts have suggested that retired arms might be incinerated in nuclear blasts deep beneath the ground.

Missiles, which are objects designed to strike targets, also are a treacherous disposal problem. For a half-century, rocket experts built increasingly bigger and more efficient missiles to transport armed warheads. Many of them are now racing to find ways to tear down the missiles or divert them to peaceful uses.

A September 17, 1991 *New York Times* article entitled "New Methods Sought to Dispose of Rockets With No Harm to Earth" included an interview with research scientist Cheryl Rofer, who heads a Los Alamos National Laboratory project to develop harmless methods of destroying solid-rocket fuel. In an understatement, she said of the effort, "There are a lot of people scratching their heads, trying to think up innovative technologies."

But their task is difficult. Missiles are large tubes filled with toxic chemicals, explosive fuels, and exotic alloys (a mixture of two or more metals or of a metal with something else). If they get too old or are handled roughly, they can blow up. Their conversion for use in launching satellites would be technically difficult and costly. Moreover, their exhaust fumes might damage the ozone layer in the upper atmo-

Several ground-launched cruise missiles awaiting destruction.

sphere that shields the Earth from damaging ultraviolet rays.

Much of the impetus for the search for new ways to destroy missiles was spurred by public protests following a test-firing in Utah to destroy Pershing missiles. The 35-foot-long Pershing is filled with the standard type of solid fuel made up of a dense, rubbery binder containing 20% aluminum particles. The test produced an exhaust containing aluminum oxide, hydrochloric acid, and asbestos, which blew across the desert into Salt Lake City.

One deactivation approach the Los Alamos researchers have tried is the use of a reactor comparable to a pressure cooker, which heats and destroys solid-rocket fuel in a cloud of dense steam. The trick is to

Civilian employees use a plasma-arc welder to cut through the body of a ground-launched cruise missile at the missile-dismantling and destruction site. Tests will determine the most economical and efficient way to dismantle the missiles.

The SR-71 and the U.S.S. Gurnard, after having broken through the Arctic ice, illustrate data-collection abilities. Spy agencies are still collecting data of interest to scientists, and some of it has been released. Officials are trying to devise ways to balance secrecy about information-gathering abilities with the needs of scientists.

put the sensitive chemicals into the reactor and not have them blow up. The Air Force research has had success with a technique using special breeds of anaerobic (needs no oxygen) microorganisms, which digest components of rocket fuel. The digestion leaves behind a simple salt.

Life After the 46-Year Cold War

The Pentagon's little-known research agency, the Defense Advanced Research Projects Agency (DARPA), more than any other government agency, has had a remarkable record of inspiring innovation. Because the agency has assumed that a healthy industrial base and vigorous research are critical to national security, its technologies have found civilian as well as military use. DARPA paved the way not only for the Persian Gulf war's smart (self-correcting) weapons, but also for the personal computer industry.

DARPA has always been a streamlined agency. It has no laboratories of its own, no research staff, and no study centers. An October 22, 1991 *New York Times* article entitled "Pentagon Wizards of Technology Eye Wider Civilian Role" reported that DARPA is perceived as the "lean, mean wizard of high technology."

The agency operates by looking for promising research and then paying companies and universities to work on high-risk, high-payoff areas. Since its founding in 1958, DARPA has contributed to a string of successes. Among them are: stealth aircraft (difficult to detect on radar), cruise missiles, tiny satellites, and fundamental advances in computers, electronics, robotics, new materials, and artificial intelligence, that is, machines that can learn functions normally associated with human intelligence.

In the mid-1960s, DARPA pioneered packet-switching, the technique that breaks computer information into billions of tiny bits and sends it to distant destinations via the fastest route available. By the early 1970s, DARPA had created ARPAnet, a defense department network that inexpensively linked hundreds of military computers. ARPAnet was followed by a flood of civilian networks.

At a time when it could be most useful to civilian science, DARPA may fall prey to political ideology. Many Democrats view DARPA as the potential savior of America's faltering high-technology industry.

But many Republicans view it as government meddling in a free-market economy.

A New Kind of Peril

On the other side of the world, following the breakup of the former Soviet Union, research devoid of connections to the civilian world was revealed. The world learned of the existence of 10 hidden cities that had formed the heart of the Soviet military-industrial complex for the design and production of nuclear arms. A federal intelligence report estimated that the nuclear complex employed some 900,000 people, about 2,000 of whom know how to make nuclear arms.

Disintegration of these previously secret cities has the potential to disperse scientists and materials into the hands of terrorists or governments intent on war, resulting in a new kind of international peril. A January 14, 1992 *New York Times* article entitled "In Russia, Secret Labs Struggle to Survive" reported two opposing views of the risk involved. One view is that of the Russian government, whose officials dismissed any risk as scare tactics on the part of scientists who wanted to guarantee their salaries. Other observers pointed out that Russian nuclear experts already had received job offers from Iraq and Libya.

Some former Soviet Union bomb makers are striving to find new ways to make money at home. The Natural Resources Defense Council, a private Washington, D.C.-based group with ties to weapons scientists in the former Soviet Union, has mounted a crash effort to finance a shift to environmental research, which would include ways to clean up the mountain of nuclear waste in Russia, the largest of the former Soviet republics.

Dr. Thomas Neff, a Massachusetts Institute of Technology (MIT) physicist who attended a December 1991 conference in Kiev, Ukraine on warhead dismantlement, proposed to the *New York Times*, "The U.S. should hire all of them and put them to work on some hard technical problem. It would be cheaper than buying a battleship." Dr. William Sutcliffe, a senior physicist at Lawrence Livermore Laboratory, a federal center for nuclear-weapon design in California, calculated that for as little as $10 million a year the United States could finance the work of 10,000 important nuclear experts in the former Soviet Union.

Defense Spinoffs

Some war equipment does not require disposal. Great enthusiasm greeted an announcement by the Air Force at the May 27, 1991 annual American Astronomical Association meeting that it would declassify research done on ground-based lasers. (A laser converts input power into an extremely narrow intense beam.) The ground-based lasers were a part of the Strategic Defense Initiative, popularly known as star wars, whose purpose was to develop ways to track and destroy enemy missiles.

It was learned that defense research scientists faced a problem common to astronomers. Turbulent currents of warm air in the atmosphere diffuse and weaken laser beams, a phenomenon that blurs the images of targets. Blurring by turbulent warm air is familiar to sky-viewers as "twinkling." Fortunately, the Air Force developed a technique to eliminate blurring. Other techniques for coping with distortions already were available. For example, mirrors that can be deformed—so-called "adaptive optics"—have been built into telescopes for some time.

The system created by the Air Force makes use of adaptive optics. An artificial "guide star" is projected high above the ground and positioned as close as possible to the object of interest. The guide star consists of light scattered or emitted by atoms in the upper atmosphere when they are hit by a laser beam aimed through the telescope. Up to 1,000 times a second, sensors (devices that receive and respond to signals or stimuli) connected to the telescope compare an image of the laser light going up with an image of the distorted light returning through the atmosphere from the artificial star.

The sensors feed the comparisons into a computer. The information enables the computer to send continuous commands to mechanical devices that slightly change the deformable mirror mounted in the path of light on which the telescope is focused. The mirror corrects for each distortion as it arrives.

The European Southern Observatory's New Technology Telescope (NTT) in Chile uses adaptive optics in which real stars are used as a guide for assessing distortion and making corrections. But often an astronomer's target does not lie near another star bright enough to serve as a guide star. Thus, the laser system's ability to create an artificial star opens up a wealth of new possibilities for astronomers.

Environmental researchers may also benefit from formerly secret Cold War satellite data. After reading that environmental scientists were unable to gain access to Navy data on polar ice, Tennessee Democratic Senator Albert Gore—now vice president—and a dedicated environmentalist, began lobbying in early 1990 to have the data released. Following a meeting in March 1990 of civilian scientists and Navy officials, the Navy released large quantities of formerly classified data gathered by its nuclear submarine fleet.

On behalf of the environment, Gore also approached Robert Gates, director of the Central Intelligence Agency (CIA). In early 1992. Gates agreed to allow access by ecologists to reconnaissance data collections. Perhaps inspired by Gates' action or in response to environmentalists' lobbying, President George Bush, a former CIA director, signed a directive in May 1992 ordering all the government's space-based equipment, civilian and military, to be evaluated with the goal of improving the nation's abilities to detect and document global climate changes.

Data collected by spy satellites has an obvious limitation: a narrow field of focus, which a June 23, 1992 *New York Times* article entitled "Spy Data Now Open to Study Climate" likened to viewing the world through a soda straw. On the positive side, radar satellites can see through clouds and all kinds of obstructions. One experimental radar aboard a satellite in 1981 penetrated the surface of the Sahara Desert to a depth of 16 feet, revealing traces of an ancient river.

Among data sources expected to be helpful to civilian researchers are the powerful telescopes and cameras of orbiting craft like the KH-11, which have, among other things, photographed missile silos in the former Soviet Union season after season. Measurements of snowfall from such data may provide clues to global climate change.

In addition to taking photographs to track military activities, spy planes have taken air measurements, which may provide assessments of levels of methane and carbon dioxide, factors in global warming, and of chlorofluorocarbons, chemicals that damage the ozone layer, the planet's protective shield against damaging ultraviolet rays.

While sailing the world's oceans, U.S. Navy vessels collect data on currents, temperatures, salinity (the quantity of dissolve salts in sea water), and ocean chemistry. Such records may hold clues to ocean pollution and global climate change. U.S. submarines' measurements of the thickness of the Arctic ice cap taken to locate safe routes of passage beneath the ice may reveal shifts in temperature over time.

Making Way for Peace

With the Cold War at an end, experts expect that over a six-year period, 1.3 million people can expect to lose their jobs in the U.S. defense industry and military services. Seymour Melman, chairman of the National Commission for Economic Conversion and Disarmament, wrote an opinion article critical of U.S. conversion efforts for the February 1992 *New York Times*. He asserted that the White House, the Pentagon, the Congress, and the corporate managers of defense production are blocking proposals for conversion to a civilian economy.

Melman pointed out that at the close of World War II, U.S. planning for conversion to peacetime industry was already in place. He attributed the planning to the efforts of David Prince, a General Electric vice president, who on April 28, 1943 wrote to the War Production Board to point out that without prior planning the nation would find itself confronted by a great many people that industry would be unable to put to work for two years.

Prince wrote: "The very least time during which a product can be conceived, models made and tested, and pilot plant production initiated is of the order of two years." The War Production Board accepted his advice, and planning for conversion became national policy. Industry, unions, and the government appointed officials to spur the program.

In Melman's opinion, military bases can be converted to industrial parks, schools, hospitals, airports, and recreational facilities. The scientific staff of military laboratories can turn their attention to societal needs, such as renewable energy and pollution prevention. Factories can produce products now purchased abroad. Such conversion is critical to creation of a full-employment economy. To make it work, peacetime will take a lot of effort.

5

HEALTH AND MEDICINE

Emergency Trauma Centers: an Overwhelming Dilemma

Trauma is the leading cause of death in the United States for those under age 44, killing more than 140,000 people each year. Battlefield medicine, practiced in two world wars, the Korean War, and particularly the Vietnam War, has demonstrated that many lives can be saved if emergency care by a trained staff begins immediately, rather than waiting until the patient arrives at a hospital. When basic life support is provided to a seriously injured victim within four minutes and advanced life support within eight minutes, 50% of the victims survive.

The delivery of rapid-response care varies widely throughout the United States. The quality of care is affected by the type of vehicle used and the training of the personnel who staff it. A community's size, which governs the funding tax base available to pay for care, explains many of the differences. The adequacy of planning and management explains the rest.

At one end of the rapid-response scale are "prehospital emergency vehicles," which cost $75,000–$100,000 to purchase. Insurance, maintenance, and staffing add another $300,000 in expense each year.

A fully equipped ambulance carries advanced life support technologies (ALS), including heart monitors, high-tech communication, intravenous fluids, defibrillators to restart a stopped heart, and, if state regulations permit, paramedics qualified to administer drugs. Some physicians propose that ALS ambulances also should carry video cameras to enable a physician in the emergency room (ER) to give advice.

Some communities' systems are even more elabo-

rate and hence more costly. Helicopters are a part of some fleets. Ambulance personnel in Tulsa, Oklahoma are linked by computer to mini-medical records services. Fort Worth, Texas, according to an April 1988 *Technology Review* article entitled "Fastest Care in the West," purchased an advanced tracking system for its ambulance fleet at a cost of $250,000.

At the other end of the rapid-response scale are many small communities with few, if any, ALS vehicles. The vehicles they do have are usually operated through municipal police or fire departments and staffed by emergency medical technicians (EMTs). Unlike paramedics who receive advanced training, some EMTs are not permitted to administer drugs or read electrocardiograms.

In hopes of saving money, some communities turn to private ambulance and fire services companies, but small towns seldom can attract such companies. Two private companies, MedStar and Rural/Metro, provide services to Las Vegas, Nevada patients at no charge, because health insurance usually pays the bill. Other private companies offer low bids to cover emergency services to win the higher-profit, nonemergency business of transferring patients to and from hospitals and nursing homes. Some fail to deliver on emergency care.

Even if patients get to an emergency trauma center rapidly, problems may begin once they get there. Overburdened, understaffed, and underfinanced, emergency rooms across the United States struggle to deliver high-quality, high-tech care. In 1990 they treated 90 million patients, more than twice the

Emergency medicine owes a debt to the armed forces. The experiences and practices of military medical units have been adapted to the civilian trauma center.

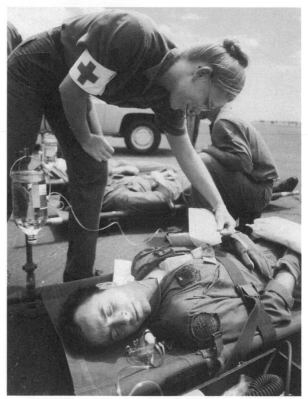

number treated in 1960. Some 110,000 physicians, nurses, technicians, social workers, and paramedics, employed by roughly 5,700 ERs, endeavored to keep pace.

In large urban centers, personnel treat an average of 200 patients in the course of a single, brutal 12-hour shift. Given the availability of automatic weapons, many routinely treat wounds normally seen only in war zones. Yet the crisis in emergency medicine is ironic, given major advances in the delivery of emergency care made in the last couple of decades. Lessons learned on battlefields taught that speed was as critical as skill in taking advantage of the "golden hour," a time immediately following trauma before shock sets in, when lifesaving treatment is most likely to succeed.

With the golden hour in mind, states in the early 1980s began organizing into trauma networks and setting up tailored programs for physicians interested in emergency care as a specialty. The networks improved paramedic training, integrated ambulance services, and diverted critical patients to hospitals that provided specialized services, such as limb reattachment or spinal injury treatment, or specialized facilities such as burn units.

The advantages to patients were evident almost immediately. In the year following the setup of a trauma network, traffic fatalities in Peoria, Illinois

dropped by 50%. In Orange County, California, deaths among non-head-injured traffic-accident victims plunged from an estimated 73% to 9%. However, since 1986, some 60 designated trauma centers have closed their doors, leaving about 370 nation-

On-the-scene treatment is a major factor in the reduction of deaths from trauma. But all the gains of recent years are at risk of being whittled away. According to data from the National Association for Hospital Development, by the year 2000, an estimated 40% of the nation's 2,200 acute-care hospitals will be closed or converted to other uses.

wide. In Chicago, four out of 10 centers shut down. In Dade County, Florida, every hospital except one dropped out of the trauma network, leaving only Jackson Memorial to serve more than 2 million residents.

The Sickest Patients Often Can't Pay

By enhancing emergency care capacity, hospitals hoped that most accident victims would be well-insured middle-class sources of revenue. They failed to realize that patients most likely to need such treatment are least likely to be able to pay for it. The poor work in menial jobs where accidents are likely to happen or they live under conditions of immense risk, such as having no home or a home in substandard housing located in a high-crime, high-density area, where the likelihood of becoming a crime victim is great and illnesses spread rapidly.

The average trauma-patient bill in 1989 was $13,000, and the average loss on each case by hospitals was $5,000. Hospitals have always balanced their books by spreading the cost of nonpaying patients across the bills of those who paid. Private hospitals keep the number of poor patients low by refusing to admit them unless they have insurance or can make an initial payment.

Transfers by private hospitals to public hospitals of patients who have used up their insurance and still need expensive treatment is not unusual. Although some of these hospitals are operating in the red and cannot afford to keep such patients, some are just reluctant to make less profit than usual.

In the 1950s, many private American hospitals obtained low-cost building loans from the U.S. government for expansion and renovations. The terms of the loans required the borrowers to provide their communities with an amount of free care based on a small fixed percentage of their average annual income.

Much of the private hospital free care was delivered as outpatient care to the poor. It relieved some of the burdens of public hospitals. But once the loans were paid back in the 1970s, much of the free care was withdrawn. Then the poor turned to emergency rooms for their routine health care. Fortunately, a 1986 federal law forced private hospitals to pick up some of their share of the community's health care needs. The law prohibits hospitals from turning away poor patients at the ER before they are stabilized.

While trauma centers were expanding in the early 1980s, government support for health care was shrinking. To curb health care costs, the federal and state governments tightened controls over hospital charges for Medicare patients. Private insurers followed suit and restricted charges for their subscribers. The result has been that patients often are discharged too soon. Many return to ERs, sicker than when they went home.

Other cost-containment measures have contributed to the ER crisis. In the early 1970s, health care planning councils urged hospitals to contain their costs by eliminating under-utilized beds. Among the beds cut over the next two decades were some in intensive-care units (ICUs), where costs are high because of the need for intensive monitoring by nurses. ICUs receive many ER-admitted patients.

A May 28, 1990 *Time* article entitled "Do You Want to Die?" described one result of ICU cuts. Dr. Albert Lauro, director of emergency medicine at Charity Hospital in New Orleans, Louisiana, said: "They sit in the emergency room hours and days trying to get into the intensive-care units." One man in need of neurosurgery waited eight days, a woman with a stroke waited four.

An August 22, 1989 *New York Times* article entitled "Crowding Causes Agonizing Crisis in Intensive Care" included an interview with Martin Strosberg, a Union College professor of management, who had spent a year visiting ICUs around the country. Strosberg said, "Most ICUs are filled to the brim, much more than they were five years ago. That means that other patients may be denied intensive care. The unseen victims are the people dying outside the unit

on the hospital floor."

In some hospitals, if the ICU is full and no one can be moved out, the intensive-care staff might care for new patients for a day or two in the emergency room, the postoperative recovery room, or even in a regular hospital room by recruiting extra nurses and moving in life support equipment like a ventilator. But because of the furious pace in ERs, some critical care directors refuse such arrangements. Instead, they divert ambulances to other hospitals.

ERs As Substitute for Primary Care Providers

Health care can be thought of as divided into three levels:
• Primary care, which is routine outpatient care, such as that given by a family physician.
• Secondary care, which is routine inpatient care given at a local community hospital.
• Tertiary care, which is specialty care, such as that given at burn units or trauma centers.

For many of the nation's 37 million uninsured people, many of whom are poor, ERs are their only source of primary care. ERs could once reroute those in need of primary care to walk-in health clinics, but funding for such clinics was curtailed in the early 1980s and many closed their doors. Even in neighborhoods that still have clinics, people with menial jobs may not be able to take time off to go a clinic when it's open.

The crush of people seeking care in ERs continues to lengthen the time patients wait to be seen. An August 28, 1991 *Journal of the American Medical Association* carried two articles that examined patients who left without being seen. Some previous studies had suggested that those who left were impatient people with minor complaints.

The studies indicated otherwise. They found that those who left after waiting hours to be seen were just as willing to wait as those who stayed. But they were forced to leave due to obligations, such as child care, or due to circumstances such as transportation difficulties, conflict with work schedules, or because they were too sick to wait any longer.

The median wait for those who left was three hours. The longest was 17 hours. On the average, those who stayed waited another 52 minutes before being seen by a physician. Of the 15% who left, 27%

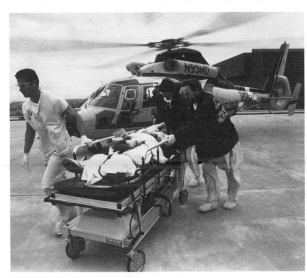

Although helicopters are used in the city and in remote areas, they are a particular boom to rural areas. They cut hours off a trip to take a patient to a distant emergency facility. But they are expensive.

subsequently returned to an ER and 4% had to be hospitalized.

ERs are poor substitutes for reliable primary care providers. Because of the long waits, the grim settings of emergency rooms, and the hordes of very sick people waiting, many people put off treatment as long as possible. When they do finally appear in the ER, they are sicker than they would have been had they been treated earlier in a primary care setting, hence they require longer hospitalizations, tying up scarce beds.

The problems of the nation's hospitals are magnified in New York City, which has the world's largest municipal hospital system. A May 19, 1990 *Economist* article entitled "Lost Weekend" outlined some of the issues. Until the 1980s, New York's hospital system was considered one of the nation's best. It continues to have dedicated staff and to teach one in seven of America's medical students.

The system has 10,000 beds in 11 acute-care facilities and five long-term institutions. On the average, each year it handles 260,000 inpatients and 3.7 million outpatients. The special dilemmas of the nation—AIDS, drug abuse, and the homeless—are present in much greater numbers. Three-quarters of the system's income comes from private insurance and from Medicare and Medicaid (the federal and state health care programs for the old and the poor). The rest comes out of the city's budget.

But cost-cutting has been a constant theme. When bed occupancy fell below 80% in 1982, authorities cut 15% of the bed capacity over the next five years, even as demand was growing.

The Impact of Occupancy Rates

For flexibility, a hospital needs some empty beds. An occupancy rate of about 85% is ideal. The concept of a bed in a hospital setting implies more than just a piece of furniture in a room. The bed is located in a room with the capacity to provide a full range of services, including special wiring, outlets for oxygen, nurses to provide bedside care, and a communication system connected to a nurses' station. Operating costs, such as nurses' salaries, continue whether the bed is empty or full. Hence, cost-cutting usually strikes at beds first.

When a hospital's occupancy rate is 100%, patients in the emergency room in need of hospitalization cannot be admitted. ERs often resort to putting patients to bed in hallways. The beds are given numbers such as H1, H2, and H3. Thus, occupancy rates often rise above 100%.

Patients who are sicker when admitted stay longer. The president of the Greater New York Hospital Association, Kenneth Raske, told *Time,* "The longer the length of stay, the higher the occupancy rate, and the more the pressure on the emergency rooms."

Support for Raske's assertion appeared in an article entitled "The Emergency Department as a Pathway to Admission for Poor and High-Cost Patients" in the October 23, 1991 *Journal of the American Medical Association.* By conducting interviews over a six-month period with 20,089 patients at five different hospitals, the study contrasted patients admitted through the ER with patients admitted by their private physician. Uninsured patients were 3.1 times more likely to be admitted through the ER than patients with private health insurance, and ER-admitted patients required substantially more resources than nonemergency patients.

The researchers made adjustments for age, income, severity of illness, and diagnosis related group (DRG). DRGs are payment classifications of patients by admitting diagnosis or surgical procedure based

Those who practice dangerous professions are dependent on high-quality trauma centers. When people think of dangerous professions, they usually think of police work and firefighting. But other occupations have their dangers. Miners risk cave-ins and explosions. Truckers are at great risk of motor accidents. Fishermen fall victim to squalls. Sugarcane cutters frequently lose a toe or a foot to a machete. Farmers' tractors pose a danger because they are top heavy.

on the notion that treatment of similar diagnoses should generate similar costs.

The study concluded that because hospital reimbursement for care is based on the national Medicare DRG system of fixed payments, hospitals with high occupancy rates tend to limit delivery of emergency care. In other words, they keep their beds filled with patients with insurance admitted by private physicians. Thus, the DRG system of payments has the effect of limiting access to care for the poor and the elderly.

Social factors are escalating the woes of ERs in New York and across the country. The proportion of New Yorkers classified as poor rose from 15% in the mid-1970s to 25% by the early 1990s. Once-dormant diseases like tuberculosis and measles have reappeared. At Bellevue Hospital on Manhattan's Lower East Side, a survey found that 40% of the inpatients were homeless, and in the psychiatric wards, 70% were homeless.

Once patients are admitted to Bellevue, physicians are reluctant to discharge them if they are homeless or have no family physician to take over their care. The psychiatric emergency room at Bellevue resembles a bus station waiting room because people wait there for days until a bed becomes available.

Staffing Presents Special Problems

To hang on to staff despite the working conditions, some pioneering hospitals, such as George Washington University (GWU) Hospital in Washington, D.C., treat emergency medicine as a high-status specialty and work to attract physicians. They point out that despite the high stress, the hours are regular. Moreover, there is an opportunity to see a wide variety of ailments. Dr. Michael Bourland of GWU told *Time,* "I think generally people see what goes on down here as either stress or excitement. Those who interpret it as stress burn out and those who see it as excitement don't."

One of the factors that complicates the delivery of care in ERs and ICUs is an ongoing national shortage of nurses that shows little sign of abating. In New York in 1990, about 5,000 registered nurse's jobs were vacant, about one position out of every six.

Even if cost were not a factor, because ICUs are staffed mainly by nurses whose labor is intensive, expansion of ICUs would be difficult. Like ERs, ICUs can be exhilarating or emotionally exhausting places to work, depending on how many people are rescued from the brink of death or how many people die. For example, ICU nurses engage in such an intimate relationship with their patients that they are apt to feel responsible for those who don't live. An ICU filled with too many people too sick to survive can demoralize its staff.

ERs also wear people out. The pace is relentless. Most ER staff members eat a large meal before going on duty because they will have no breaks once they start.

The potential for error is enormous. An October 14, 1991 *Newsweek* article entitled "State of Emergency" began with a vignette of a young man who was stabbed. The ER residents on duty at Brooklyn, New York's King County Hospital treated the man for one wound but for 45 minutes allegedly failed to note a second wound. The man died later in surgery due to blood loss. As the Brooklyn district attorney's office began an investigation, a weary hospital official told a reporter, "It was just a very, very busy night."

One result is that the extraordinarily high risk of malpractice suits drives many ER staff members out of the field. Dr. Elisabeth Rosenthal of New York Hospital told *Time*, "You have to work quickly during an emergency, with a lot of angry people, in a climate in which lawsuits are used by people to express their anger."

Weapons and drugs also make ERs difficult places to work. A veteran ER nurse at the Elmhurst Hospital Center in Queens, New York, told *Time* that drug addicts were once quiet and easy to handle. But, she said, "With crack, it's overwhelming. They're wild, they go after patients, they swing from IV packets, they jump out of stretchers. They become paranoid. And they have enormous strength."

Dr. Peter Moyer of Boston City Hospital told *Time* about treating a young man wounded in a shootout, presumably over cocaine staff found in his underwear. The man was accompanied by a huge bodyguard, who kept a hand on a bulging object inside his jacket. The bodyguard refused to obey security guards to leave. When they threatened to call the police, the wounded man climbed off the treatment table, the bullet still in his arm, and left with the bodyguard.

In a health care system battered by efforts to contain costs, gunshot wounds seem like the last straw. A study reported in the November 25, 1988 *Journal of the American Medical Association* examined the out-comes for 131 patients admitted to San Francisco General Hospital in California in 1984. The hospital costs ranged from $559 to $64,470, with an average cost of $6,915.

Because San Francisco ambulance drivers were required to take all gunshot wounds to San Francisco General, the researchers reasoned that they could extrapolate their findings to the nation as a whole. They estimated that in 1984, 62,075 people were hospitalized for gunshot wounds at a cost of $429 million.

Gunshot and stab wounds were once mostly confined to ERs in inner-city areas. Now virtually every hospital sees them. Dr. E. Jackson Allison, Jr. of Pitt County Memorial Hospital in Greenville, North Carolina, told *Time*, " Sometimes, this place is like a M.A.S.H. unit," referring to the military's mobile army surgical hospitals. His colleague, Dr. Herbert Garrison III, added, "We have people come in here carrying weapons who are out of their heads. Sometimes we have police officers with shotguns in our parking lot."

Their rural Southern experience differed little from the inner-city experience of Dr. Eric Stirling, director of the ER at Highland Hospital in Oakland, California, whose description of his work as "trench medicine," was quoted in a February 21, 1989 *New York Times* article entitled "Epidemic in Urban Hospitals: Wounds From Assault Rifles." In 1987 and 1988, Highland treated 700 gunshot victims at a cost of $10.5 million.

Dr. James Haughton, the medical director of Martin Luther King/Charles Drew Medical Center in Los Angeles, California offered his ER as a training ground to the U.S. Army to train battlefield surgeons. His offer was accepted.

Perhaps the major difference between the more rural trauma centers and ones in the inner cities is sheer volume. Paramedics call the busiest periods "medical gridlock." They cannot unload their ambulances because the emergency room is full and the hospital has reached 100% occupancy. At that point, the hospital may go on "bypass," asking that the ambulances be sent elsewhere. Hospitals that once went on bypass once a year, may now do so once a week. It is difficult to take advantage of the golden hour when hospitals are on bypass.

Although most suburban hospitals have been

spared a lot of the urban crises, many rural hospitals are swamped because farming, fishing, and forestry are among the nation's most dangerous occupations. Moreover, like inner-city trauma centers, they too must contend with the effects of poverty on health. The 1990 census reported that of the nation's 31.5 million people living below the poverty line, 41% lived in the South and 22% in the Midwest.

Dr. John Johnson, president of the American College of Emergency Physicians, directs emergency services at Porter Memorial Hospital, a 350-bed hospital in Valparaiso, Indiana, 45 miles from Chicago.

Crack has not been a problem there. The entire county had only about 10 cases of AIDS and among 33,000 emergency visits in 1989 there were only about 1,000 severe injury cases. Yet at one point in January 1990, 17 emergency patients had to wait for beds.

An October 1990 *Esquire* article entitled "Trauma Cases," quoted Dr. Johnson: "People put on blinders . . . and say 'That's a big-city problem, I don't have to worry about that in Middle America.' They're wrong."

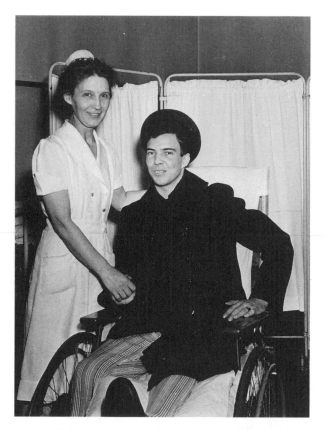

The building remained after a fire in one of Boston's favorite nightclubs, the Cocoanut Grove, took the lives of 429 people. On the night of November 28, 1942—from the scene of one the nation's worst fires—vehicles of every type and description rushed hundreds of injured to the emergency rooms of Boston City Hospital (BCH) and Massachusetts General (MGH). At BCH, the dead lay stacked on one side of a hospital hall, while the living awaited treatment on the other side. At one point, a victim was arriving every 11 seconds. Many died at the scene from smoke inhalation and carbon monoxide poisoning. Most of the severely burned did not live long enough to receive treatment. Those who lived owed their lives, in great part, to round-the-clock nursing. Among them was Coast Guardsman Clifford Johnson shown here with his nurse Mercy Smith. Johnson escaped from the club but almost immediately went back inside to pull others out. He continued his rescue efforts until he was enveloped in flames. Burned over 45% of his body, Johnson was in a coma for a couple of months. No one in history had ever survived such extensive burns. Despite the loss of 60 pounds and many complications that should have killed him, Johnson lived, to die a decade later in another fire. Lessons learned in treating Johnson and other Cocoanut Grove victims greatly advanced burn treatment. Medical personnel realized that burns could affect every organ. They evolved a mapping technique to estimate the percentage of the body burned. Physicians gained extensive experience in doing skin grafts.

The Life and Death Impact of Global Discrimination Against Women

Discrimination against women around the world is so common it is taken for granted. Social, cultural, and economic barriers cause and worsen many of women's health problems; and their low social status contributes to a lack of interest in their health among care givers and researchers.

When American women working in the civil rights movement in the 1960s found their participation limited to making coffee, typing letters, or being sexual partners, they resurrected the feminist movement that had won women's suffrage in 1920.

Echoes of American women's experience in the 1960s came in the wake of the liberation of Eastern Europe in 1989. The May 1992 *World Monitor* reported an angry conference held in Dubrovnik, Yugoslavia that brought together women from Poland, Bulgaria, Hungary, Ukraine, Czechoslovakia, and the former German Democratic Republic (GDR). These women, who had helped to bring about their nation's respective revolutions, found themselves ignored by male former dissidents now in government. Their story of discrimination is a familiar one.

Sexual Harassment on the Job

Discrimination takes many forms. One of them is sexual harassment. Sexual harassment on the job is seldom mentioned in assessments of physical or psychological threats to women because it seldom ends in physical violence. But, by its nature, sexual harassment keeps many women psychologically under constant threat because they fear the harassment might end in a physical assault or in the loss of their job.

Sexual harassment practices are varied: lewd conversations and/or lewd posters; sexual items like condoms left in a woman's locker or desk; remarks about the size, shape, or quality of her body; touching her body without permission, particularly on the breasts or buttocks; and requests for sexual favors, some coupled with the threat of demotion or promise of promotion.

Although American women have been complaining about sexual harassment at least since the last century, their complaints seldom have been taken seriously. Change came in October 1991, during U.S.

Senate hearings on whether Clarence Thomas should be confirmed as a Supreme Court justice. University of Oklahoma law professor Anita Hill testified before the Senate Judiciary Committee about alleged sexual harassment by Thomas 10 years earlier. Thomas had been her supervisor from 1981 to 1983, initially at the U.S. Department of Education and later at the Equal Employment Opportunity Commission.

Questioned by the 14 male members of the committee about why she had remained on the job or failed to complain, Hill said she feared she would be squeezed out of good assignments and possibly lose her job. Judith Resnick, a professor at the University of Southern California Law Center, characterized Hill's testimony as a paradigm (typical model) of a sexual harassment case.

Questions by some senators implied that Hill had been scorned by Thomas and that her testimony represented an attempt to get even. It became clear from testimony that Hill had not offered to testify; she had done so only after a statement she had been requested to make to the FBI had been leaked to the press by senators' staff members.

Thomas was ultimately confirmed. But the issue of sexual harassment was not closed. As the hearings were broadcast across the country and around the world on television—C-Span and C-Span 2 carried them in their entirety—the attitudes of some members of the Senate Judiciary Committee toward Anita Hill incensed many women viewers.

Following the hearings, worldwide debate about sexual harassment went on for weeks on TV and radio talk shows and in stories carried in print media. A flood of new complaints were filed with the various U.S. government agencies charged with investigation of sexual harassment.

To many women, the all-male Senate Judiciary Committee seemed incapable of understanding the psychological impact of sexual harassment and its economic effect on the course of a woman's career. An October 14–20, 1991 *Washington Post National Weekly Edition* article entitled "The Men Just Don't Get It, Do They?" quoted Democratic pollster Celinda Lake as saying, "What is startling is how what seems clear to women seems so unclear, or murky, to men."

An October 21, 1991 *U.S. News and World Report* article entitled "Harassment: Men on Trial," reported that two female police officers in Long Beach, California had won a $3.1 million verdict after three years of sexual taunts from colleagues. The stress of the harassment led to the breakup of one woman's marriage and both women had left their careers in law enforcement.

Many women were galvanized into joining political campaigns for the first time to defeat some of the senators who had been hostile toward Anita Hill. Other women were inspired to run for public office. More women ran for Congress in 1992 than ever in history. Two women won the senate primaries in California.

In part because the Senate hearings were broadcast around the world on C-Span and C-Span 2, then rebroadcast often, the impact of the Hill-Thomas conflict continued to reverberate in other parts of the world. Charges of sexual harassment were raised in several countries. Japanese management hurriedly began to offer courses in proper behavior for businessmen toward their women peers and subordinates.

A study reported in a November 22, 1991 *New York Times* article entitled "Sexual Harassment: It's About Power, Not Sex" found that harassment is most frequent in occupations and work places where women are new or in the minority. Dr. Nancy Baker, a psychologist in Los Angeles, California, conducted in 1989 a study of 100 women working in a factory. Women machinists, nontraditional jobs, reported far more harassment than women on traditional assembly-line jobs. On a 28-item scale ranging from lewd remarks to sexual assault, women machinists had the highest scores. The same relationship is true in white-collar jobs. The more nontraditional the job the greater the incidence of sexual harassment. Women surgeons and investment bankers rank among the most frequent targets for harassment.

Research Falls Short in Women's Health

For years women complained to no avail that they were routinely excluded from major health studies, including aging, heart disease, and AIDS. Finally in 1986, the National Institutes of Health (NIH), the

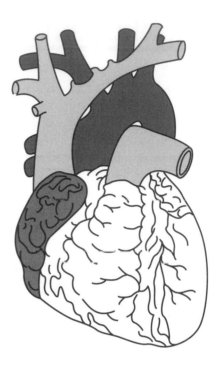

The onset of heart disease in women generally comes later in life than it does in men. Because heart disease often is perceived as primarily a man's disease, women often are not diagnosed early. State-of-the-art diagnostic techniques and treatments typically don't reach a woman until she is much sicker than a man. Lacking early treatment, women: are more likely to die within one year after the first attack; more likely to have a second attack; more likely to have bypass surgery late in their illness; and three times more likely to die on the table when they do have it. Black women are 1.5 times more likely than white women to suffer fatal attacks, for reasons as yet unknown.

principle source of U.S. biomedical funding, mandated the inclusion of women in their research guidelines.

Nevertheless, in June 1990, a representative of the General Accounting Office (GAO), the investigative arm of Congress, testified in a congressional hearing that several major studies under way excluded women and that NIH had failed to follow its own policies by tracking the number of women enrolled in studies.

Researchers offered a variety of reasons for not including women, such as men are easier to recruit, and women could become pregnant while taking experi-

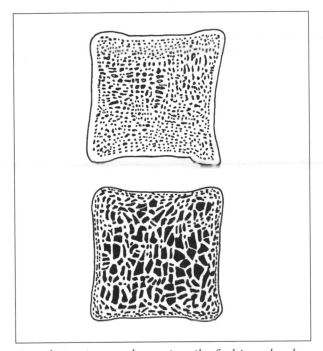

Bone, living tissue made up primarily of calcium phosphate crystals and the protein collagen, is constantly broken down and rebuilt. The top drawing is a cross-section of a normal slice of a spinal vertebra. The lower drawing is a cross-section of a slice of vertebra affected by osteoporosis. Vertebrae contain large proportions of trabecular bone, which has a honeycomb structure. Note how the walls of that honeycomb break down and disappear in the bone with osteoporosis. Women's bones are more vulnerable than men's because they are smaller and thinner. One difficulty in finding a successful treatment for osteoporosis has been that the body has two kinds of bones. Spongy bones are predominant in the spine, and compact bones are the main source of strength in the pelvis and the long bones of the arms and legs. Some treatments have proved disappointing because they built up one kind of bone at the expense of the other.

mental drugs that might harm the fetus. In the case of heart disease, they argued that women do not get heart disease until they are older.

The National Institute on Aging's largest study from 1958 until 1978 excluded women. A study of 22,000 doctors that began in 1981 to determine whether aspirin could prevent heart attacks excluded women because their inclusion would have increased the cost. Such reasoning failed to consider that conclusions applicable to only half the nation's population are even more expensive.

Experts on women's health criticize the men-only approach to research because the results of such studies are used to make decisions about the diagnosis and treatment of women's health problems, even though physiological and hormonal differences between men and women may make them inappropriate. In September 1990 the near-total omission of women from U.S. biomedical research became such an embarrassment that the government promised to launch a $500-million, 10-year study to explore such issues as menopause.

Menopause is strongly linked to heart disease. Menopause also is linked to osteoporosis, which is responsible for an estimated 1.5 million broken bones annually in the United States. Osteoporosis is a loss of bone mass that renders bones vulnerable to fractures. The so-called dowager's hump, a bent-over rounded back, in elderly women is a familiar example of osteoporosis, the end result of years of small, unnoticed fractures of vertebrae (spinal bones).

Worldwide, approximately 200 million people—including 20 million American women and 800,000 Canadian women—suffer from the affliction. Each year, about 240,000 American women who have osteoporosis fracture their hips; 19,000 of them die of complications within six months. As a result, in 1990 NIH announced the opening a newly created Office of Research on Women's Health, headed by Dr. Vivian Pinn.

Breast Cancer

Although most women's diseases tend to be neglected, some—because of their sheer numbers—have received recent attention. But even in this area of study, women's concerns have been ignored. For years, women have complained that surgeons remove more tissue than necessary when they amputate cancerous breasts, a process called a radical mastectomy. For some women, the loss of a breast has an enormous impact on their feelings of sexual attractiveness.

Surgeons' typical response has been that they want to be sure to remove every trace of cancer. But over the years, in small increments some surgeons reduced the amount of tissue removed. Eventually, some began performing a procedure called a lumpectomy, which removes the cancerous lump with some surrounding tissue and some lymph nodes under the arm.

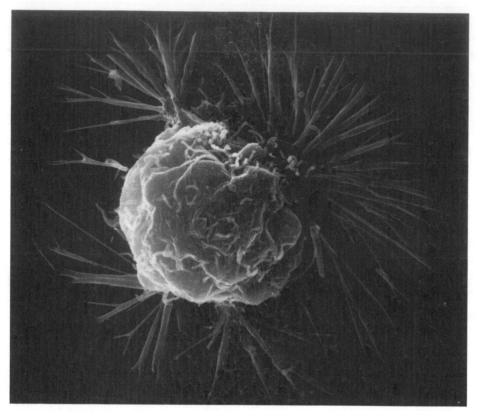

A breast-cancer cell. Treatments that may improve or prevent one condition may increase risks of another. Estrogen-replacement therapy is frequently prescribed for women whose family medical history reveals them to be at risk of developing heart disease or osteoporosis. But if a woman also is at an elevated risk of developing breast cancer, estrogen therapy may increase that risk.

A panel of specialists convened by NIH in 1990 concluded that for most women with early cancer, a lumpectomy plus radiation is a preferred method of treatment, because it is equally effective as a mastectomy and it preserves the breast. Nevertheless, the chances of a woman in the United States receiving a lumpectomy vary depending on the region of the country in which she lives.

To some surgeons, the two procedures are essentially equivalent. But in a January 20, 1992 *Boston Globe* article entitled "In Many Cases, Lumpectomy Is a Better Choice," Dr. William Wood, chairman of the NIH panel of specialists, defined their difference: "If we can do equal procedures, one involves amputating your leg and the other doesn't, no one would consider those equal."

Despite three decades and hundreds of millions of dollars spent principally by NIH and the American Cancer Society, breast cancer is still the number two killer of women over age 50—second only to heart disease—and the leading cause of death among women ages 30–50. On average, 135,000 American women develop breast cancer annually.

Certain factors can put a woman at higher risk: early onset of menstruation, having children late or not at all, a family history of the disease, and abortions and miscarriages at any age. But many women who get breast cancer do not fall into any category of known risk. Despite numerous studies on the causes of the disease, experts still disagree about the potential influence of external factors.

A suggestion that those who favor the influence of external factors might be looking in the right direction came in the fall of 1991 when golfer Heather Farr became the fourth woman on the professional golf tour in two years to have been diagnosed as having breast cancer. Experts wondered whether harsh chemicals used on golf courses might be responsible.

Even more pressing than the lack of agreement about the causes of breast treatment is the lack of consensus about treatment. An April 24, 1988 *New York Times Magazine* article entitled "Breast Cancer: Anguish, Mystery and Hope" detailed the findings in a January 1988 GAO report to Congress on various therapies. GAO found that one-third of American women who should have been getting chemotherapy were not and that many physicians who prescribed chemotherapy did not prescribe enough.

But not everyone agrees that high dosage is proper. I. Craig Henderson of the Dana Farber Cancer Center in Boston, Massachusetts told the *New York Times,* "My own personal bias is that dosage is a fairly small factor. Higher dosages are more toxic. I may be wrong. Who knows." Answers on dosages are expected to come some time between 1993 and 1996 from a federally funded study of dosages.

In 1991 another concern about mastectomies erupted. Beginning in the early 1960s women began to have silicone breast implants. By 1992 about 2 million women had received silicone implants and the annual rate was 100,000–150,000. About 80% of the women had the surgery because they wanted larger or better-shaped breasts. The remaining 20% sought reconstruction after removal of a breast for cancer.

The implants are essentially small plastic bags of a semiliquid silicone gel, first used as a lubricant or sealant in Navy ships. The implants have been linked to chronic inflammatory disease and sometimes to a painful hardening of surrounding tissues. A few studies in animals suggest a link with cancer.

A January 7, 1992 *New York Times* article entitled "F.D.A. Acts to Halt Breast Implants Made of Silicone" reported that several officials of the Dow Corning Company, the manufacturer of the implant, had warned management in internal memos that studies to assess the safety of silicone gel were needed. Their warnings had been ignored.

Many women's groups criticized the U.S. Food and Drug Administration (FDA) for having so long ignored safety hazards that began to be reported in the early 1980s. On the other hand, some women who were happy with their implants and some physicians who felt 30 years of use provided safety data were clearly unhappy with the decision.

An Epidemic of
Women's Deaths in the Third World

Although scientists and health care providers are generally challenged by complexity, they have been uninspired by the complexities of women's health problems—many of which are related to their reproductive hormonal cycles—including menstruation, osteoporosis, breast cancer, and child bearing. Nowhere does the lack of interest have more dire consequences than among the billion women of childbearing age living in the Third World. If current practices do not change, deaths due to reproductive causes will double by the end of the century. Almost all of them are preventable.

At least a million Third World women die each year and more than a hundred million suffer disabling illnesses from childbirth, unsafe abortion, and pregnancy complications. Moreover, nonpregnancy-related reproductive-tract infections kill more than a million women a year and maim another hundred million.

Throughout the Third World, women are last in the receiving line for medical care, according to the results of a worldwide survey announced in June 1991 by the Washington, D.C.-based Worldwatch Institute, an independent, nonprofit research organization. The survey compiled studies done by the World Health Organization and the World Bank and by independent researchers in Latin America, Africa, and countries such as India and Brazil. The researchers found that women receive care only after other priorities are met, such as the care of men and children and population control.

The Worldwatch report's senior researcher, Jodi Jacobson, concluded that maternal mortality, though routinely overlooked, is as important a measure of a nation's health care as infant mortality rates, the index health care specialists generally use. Infant mortality rates are nine times higher in the developing world than they are in industrialized nations, but maternal mortality rates are a hundred times greater.

In most Third World nations, the complications of pregnancy, childbirth and abortion are the leading cause of death for women of reproductive age. Botched abortions account for 20%–40% of the deaths, but unsafe childbirths account for even more. Sixty percent of maternal deaths could be avoided if developing nations spent $1.50 per woman per year on prevention.

"The statistics on maternal deaths are the most obscene differences in health statistics around the world," in the opinion of Sheldon Segal, a distinguished scientist at the New York City-based Population Council, who was quoted in a July 15, 1991 *Boston Globe* article entitled "Third World Medical Care: An Epidemic of Maternal Deaths."

What makes the women's epidemic all the more poignant, according to Jacobson, is that the obvious solutions are rarely implemented. The solutions are: greater access to more contraceptive choices and safe, legal abortions; training of midwives for safer, cleaner childbirths; and screening for reproductive-tract infections.

Women regularly bleed to death, particularly in remote villages, following delivery or a poorly performed abortion. Sepsis, fatal infections, also are routine after deliveries or abortions due to health care workers' unclean hands or instruments. Toxemia, untreated high blood pressure related to pregnancy, often leads to convulsions and death.

Frequently, when a cesarean-section delivery is unavailable, obstructed labor results in a mother's death because the uterus ruptures. In parts of Asia and Africa, obstructed labor is perceived as a sign of a woman's infidelity and help is often not sought until a woman "confesses." Even if a woman does not die, obstructed labor is likely to result in tears in the tissues separating the vagina from the bladder and rectum. The result is retention of urine or feces and an odor that may lead to a woman's abandonment by her husband.

Dr. Allan Rosenfield, dean of the School of Public Health at Columbia University, published in 1985 a pivotal paper in the British medical journal *Lancet*, which asked "Where is the M in MCH?" (MCH refers to maternal, child health.) When women's needs are considered at all, Rosenfield asserted, "it's as a mechanism to improve child health."

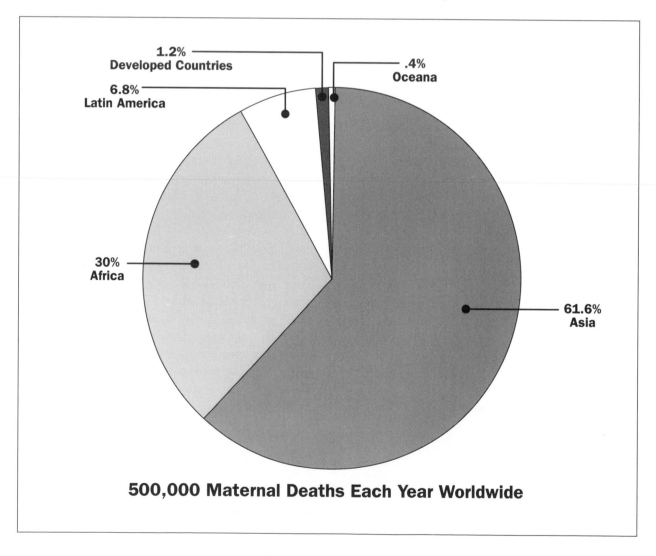

500,000 Maternal Deaths Each Year Worldwide

Even family-planning programs, once seen as a way to help women as well as children, have sometimes damaged women's health. In Brazil, family planning cut the average number of children born to each woman from 5.8 in 1970 to 3.3 in 1990 by relaxing restrictions on oral contraceptives. Other contraceptive alternatives such as condoms, diaphragms or intrauterine devices (IUDs)—implanted to block the uterus—remain largely unavailable.

Brazilian women flocked to pharmacies for "the pill," obtainable without prescription. Most pharmacists did not warn women who smoked that they had an increased risk of stroke. Stroke has become the leading killer of reproductive-age women in Brazil.

Not all failures to meet the special needs of women end in death. Nonfatal reproductive-tract infections cause enormous suffering. In India, the government's recent family-planning emphasis has been on IUDs. Promotion of IUDs, "not always on a voluntary basis," has contributed to the spread of reproductive-tract infections. An IUD inserted under sanitary conditions in a woman who does not have a vaginal infection is safe, but such conditions are rare in the Third World.

Eight infectious organisms account worldwide for 250 million new sexually transmitted infections a year. Although men and women both suffer from such infections, women face more severe medical consequences. Chlamydia and gonorrhea can spread to the upper reproductive tract, causing permanent disability and even death.

Annually, cervical cancer related to human papillomavirus, a sexually transmitted infection, kills 354,000 women, and AIDS kills another 100,000 women. Estimates for deaths related to sexually transmitted diseases are considered conservative because they do not include deaths from pelvic inflammatory disease or a variety of sexually transmitted diseases for which no mortality figures are kept.

Reproductive-tract infections often result in infertility for women. If a woman is infertile, she may get thrown out of her home, although the disease may have been transmitted to her by her husband. In Africa, traditional healers perpetuate the myth that sex with virgins is a cure for a man infected with a sexually transmitted disease.

Sixty percent of pregnant women and 47% of nonpregnant women in most developing countries are anemic, a condition that vastly diminishes their chances for healthy lives and pregnancies. Anemia is more likely to be found among the poor, who often do not get enough to eat.

Maternal deaths in the United States are not as high as they were at the turn of the century—when they were comparable to those now found in Third World countries. But for poor women the change has been less significant. Economic discrimination in the work place, sexual harassment, domestic violence, and little or no child support for single mothers make women more likely to be poor. Poverty by itself appears to be an independent factor in poor health.

Violence Against Women

Violence daily threatens the health and lives of women around the world. In the United States, a woman is beaten by her husband or boyfriend every 15 seconds, and 3–4 million women are battered each year. Every five minutes a woman is forcibly raped.

In 1990, 102,555 rapes were reported. U.S. law enforcement experts believe for every reported rape 3–10 go unreported. That could mean in 1990—along with the 102,555 reported rapes—there may have been an additional 300,000–1 million unreported rapes.

From 1965 to 1990, assaults against women in the United States rose by 50%, while assaults against men declined. Murder is overwhelmingly a male offense. Of those arrested for murder in 1989, 88.6% were male. Males mostly killed other males; however, nine out of 10 women victims were killed by males. When a woman kills, the victim is often a husband or boyfriend who has been beating her for years and whom she believes intends to kill her.

The September/October 1990 issue of *Ms.* focused attention on violence against women. In an article entitled "Femicide," authors Jane Caputi of the University of New Mexico, Albuquerque, and Diana Russel of Mills College, described the experience of Canadian novelist Margaret Atwood when she asked a male friend why men feel threatened by women. The man answered, "They are afraid women will laugh at them." She then asked a group of women why they felt threatened by men. They answered,

Some diseases, although not gender-specific, do seem to be gender-oriented. More women than men suffer from migraine headaches and arthritis. Eight to 10 more women than men suffer from systemic lupus erythematosus, an inflammatory disease of the connective tissues. Fewer girls than boys have asthma, but girls are: less likely to "outgrow" the disease, more likely to have severe cases, and more likely to suffer lasting deficiencies in lung function. Women are 21% more likely than men to be hospitalized for asthma and 25% more likely to die of the disease. Age can affect the onset of some diseases. Such elements as race, ethnicity, and nationality often are likely to be medical factors insofar as the availability of treatment and preventive measures are concerned.

"We're afraid of being killed."

In other parts of the world, conditions are even worse. For example, women who belong to some ethnic groups in India have been picked up and jailed on flimsy grounds and raped while in custody. Further, Japanese women activists have been responsible for directing attention to sexual slavery practiced by Japanese organized crime, the yakuzu, who entice rural women in Pacific Rim countries into leaving their homes based on a promise of a well-paying job. The jobs are in brothels. The yakuzu bosses confiscate the women's passports so they can't escape and take whatever money they make.

In some countries, a woman's vaginal canal by custom is closed with a clasp or sutures to limit intercourse. If pregnancy does occur, the canal does not permit labor to proceed and the woman often dies. Obstructed labor also is caused or exacerbated by the practice of female circumcision (clitoridectomy), the cutting out of all or parts of the genitals. Worldwide, approximately 84 million women and girls have been circumcised.

If American researchers had access to women in other countries, their findings probably would mirror those of a study conducted by Dr. Lisa Goodman of the American Psychological Association, reported in the October 1991 *American Journal of Orthopsychiatry.* Goodman extensively interviewed 100 poor women about their childhood and adult lives. Fifty were mothers or pregnant women with housing. They were compared with 50 closely matched homeless women. Goodman found that as a child, more than half of all respondents had experienced physical abuse and almost half had experienced sexual abuse. About two-thirds were victims of physical spousal abuse. Overall, 90% of the homeless and 88% of the housed respondents reported some form of physical or sexual abuse during their lifetimes.

'The Grim Mystery'

Not only are women oppressed around the world, apparently many are eliminated early. From the moment of conception onward, females have a better survival rate than males, although more males are

Women's work often is undervalued. Yet in most parts of the world, without it food would literally never reach the table. Most of the world's home gardens are tended by women, in addition to the farm work they do in the fields.

conceived and born. Therefore, there should be more women in the world than men. However, demographers have discovered the grim statistic that an estimated 60 million women are unaccounted for.

In the developed countries, where lower fertility means fewer children in the population and better medical care means longer lives, there are roughly 106 women for every 100 men. In the developing nations of Africa and Latin America, a higher fertility rate and a shorter life expectancy are reflected in a roughly equal ratio of males and females. But in many Asian countries there are less than 95 women for every 100 men.

Quoted in a February 3, 1992 *Boston Globe* article entitled "The Grim Mystery of the World's Missing Women," Joan Vanek, coordinator of the United Nations Statistical Office, said, "There are clearly cultural patterns operating and operating in very complicated ways to favor young boys rather than young girls."

In some areas, prenatal tests or ultrasound screening are being used to discover the sex of fetuses, and girls are being aborted. A study in Bombay, India found that of 8,000 abortions, only one fetus was a male. Some demographers suspect that female infanticide has had a resurgence in China. And there continue to be reports of deaths among newborn girls in India.

In societies where girls appear to be missing, some studies have shown that young girls receive less food than boys. One Bangladesh study found that boys received about 809 calories daily as opposed to 694 for girls, despite the fact that girls worked longer than their brothers. Other studies have shown that young boys receive more medical care.

Education makes a significant difference in women's capacity to cope with discrimination. Harvard economist Amartya Sen told the *Boston Globe:* "The more female education, the less discrimination . . . when you earn an income that is visible."

PART TWO

EARTH AND SPACE SCIENCE

The year 1992 saw another showcase of Tall Ships. The ship above, the Amerigo Vespucci, *was one of more than 200 Tall Ships from 34 maritime nations that took part in the Grand Regatta Columbus '92 Quincentenary. This ship, along with the* Cristoforo Columbo, *was built in Livorno, Italy in 1930. The* Amerigo Vespucci *is now the Italian Navy's oldest ship on duty. Her sister ship was presented to the former Soviet Union after World War II. But the whereabouts of the* Cristoforo Columbo *is unknown. Maritime training and oceanographic research are two of the primary uses of these oceangoing vessels under sail. Maritime training is as important to ocean researchers as it is to navies and coast guards.*

Events and Trends in Earth Science

Possible connections between global warming and the weather continued to preoccupy many scientists in 1992. Hurricanes that meteorologists rate as Category 4 or Category 5 often are called 100-year storms because the storms' fury is assumed to happen only once or twice in a century. Yet three such storms recently battered the North American continent.

In 1988 Category 5 Hurricane Gilbert pounded Jamaica and Mexico's Yucatan Peninsula. In 1989 Category 4 Hurricane Hugo smashed South Carolina. And in 1992 Category 5 Hurricane Andrew flattened areas of South Florida and Louisiana. Still, scientists don't know whether these storms are statistical flukes or harbingers of storms to come in the wake of global warming.

Weather and Climate

Hurricane Andrew began as a parcel of hot air over West Africa. When Andrew became a tropical depression, the U.S. National Hurricane Center (NHC) in Dade County, Florida began watching it closely. A tropical depression becomes a storm center in an area of low pressure when water picked up by the hot air is given off by evaporation. Three days after NHC began watching it, the storm, located 1,000 miles off the Leeward Islands, 1,250 miles west-northwest of the main Hawaiian islands, continued to gather strength, and NHC meteorologists named it Andrew.

During the next two days, it churned itself up past Category 3 to a Category 4. Andrew struck Barbados at 11:00 P.M., August 30, 1992, moved on to the South Florida coast at 3:00 A.M., Monday, and then cut a swath across the Gulf of Mexico to slam into the Louisiana coast south of Baton Rouge at 11:00 P.M., Tuesday.

Andrew's toll of 27 deaths was low given the storm's fury. Laxity in building codes during the 1980s, however, resulted in enormous property damage: 63,000 homes were destroyed in Florida, and 44,000 were left homeless in Louisiana. Florida's damage was estimated to be $20 billion, and Louisiana's, $300 million.

Coming on the heels of Hurricanes Gilbert and

Hugo, Andrew raised questions about whether global warming is increasing the intensity of storms. A September 7, 1992 *Newsweek* article entitled "Was Andrew a Freak—Or a Preview of Things to Come?" reported that some computer climate models suggest that global warming—caused by the existence in the atmosphere of heat-trapping gases—could escalate a Category 3 hurricane into a Category 5.

The engine that drives a hurricane is water vapor rising and cooling, which releases its heat into the air. Extra heat strengthens the forces that contribute to the hurricane's formation. If the greenhouse effect warms the tropical ocean by two or three degrees, the area of tropical ocean that spawns hurricanes will spread out. As a consequence, locales where hurricanes seldom strike will experience them.

Unfortunately, researchers cannot predict what impact global warming will have on hurricanes because they don't know precisely what turns a storm into a hurricane. Meteorologist Kerry Emanuel of Massachusetts Institute of Technology (MIT) told *Newsweek:* "We are virtually helpless to say anything about how the frequency of hurricanes will change with climate."

Some computer models suggest that, instead of increasing hurricanes, a warmer climate might reduce them. This reasoning is based on the fact that a warmer atmosphere would produce wind patterns that are different from patterns now familiar.

If climate models were able to predict that Category 4 or 5 hurricanes would occur more often, then laws governing building codes and zoning laws would require a massive overhaul. Whatever happens with climate models, in estimating the costs associated with global warming, economists will need to begin factoring in the possible costs of an increase in hurricanes that can produce $20 billion and more in damage.

Earth and the Ocean

Seeing by "daylight sound," the acoustic counterpart of natural daylight, was the subject of a series of experiments carried out by scientists at the Scripps Institution of Oceanography at La Jolla, California and

Florida Atlantic University in Boca Raton. Their work was described in an April 21, 1992 *New York Times* article entitled "Using Natural Sounds, System Tries to 'See' Objects Deep in Ocean."

The system under study uses the constant hiss of noise radiating throughout the world's oceans. The noise is mainly due to the oscillations (variances back and forth between two values) of tiny bubbles near the ocean surface. In much the same way that objects above the water are illuminated by the scattering or absorption of daylight, objects below the ocean surface are illuminated by the so-called "white ambient" (surrounding) noise of the ocean.

Dr. Michael Buckingham and his colleagues focused scattered underwater sound using an acoustic mirror similar in principle to light-gathering mirrors used in astronomical telescopes. The 4-foot-diameter mirror is shaped parabolically (U-shaped) and coated with thick neoprene, which is synthetic rubber resistant to weathering and various chemicals. A microphone, shielded against sound coming from directions other than the reflector, is mounted at the focus of the parabolic dish, where it measures the intensity of sound concentrated at that spot.

The scientists were able to locate three submerged boxes they had set up as test targets. The experiment was not intended to produce a complete picture but simply demonstrate that the idea could work. The scientists obtained the equivalent of one pixel, the smallest picture element of an electronically coded image. In other words, they obtained a single cell of a computer image that was digitized, that is, converted into numerical values.

In the next phase, the scientists planned to mount several hundred tiny microphones at varying distances from the focus of the parabolic reflector. Each microphone would measure sound coming from a slightly different direction and generate a single pixel. Assembling all pixels in their proper relative positions should yield a recognizable picture of the original object.

Earth in the Past

Fossil discoveries in China in 1984, which took several years to come to the attention of scientists elsewhere, provide a glimpse of strange creatures that populated Earth in the early stages of the Cambrian geological period, 570–500 million years ago. From what was once a sea floor, paleontologists have unearthed specimens of 70 species of trilobites—creatures composed of three lobes—including worms, sponges, and various ancestors of crustaceans, spiders, and insects.

The discoveries demonstrate a swift, dramatic transformation of life from single-cell organisms to complex, multicell forerunners of modern animal life, called fauna. The conversion was more sudden and widespread than scientists had imagined earlier. They are uncertain about what touched off the proliferation of life forms, following 3 billion years during which life forms never became more complex than rudimentary bacteria, primitive worms, and algae, which are mainly aquatic one-celled or multicelled plants, such as seaweed, that contain chlorophyll.

An April 23, 1991 *New York Times* article entitled "Spectacular Fossils Record Early Riot of Creation" described paleontologist Dr. Jan Bergstrom's perception of the Cambrian transformation as "a revolution perhaps more than an evolution." Bergstrom is with the Swedish Museum of Natural History.

Most of the Chinese fossils resemble species found in the Burgess Shale, the 530-million-year-old fossil beds located in the Canadian Rocky Mountains, which have been the main source of knowledge about the period. Similarities between the fossils found in the two sites make it possible to conclude that diversification and proliferation of new life forms at the outset of the Cambrian period must have been rapid.

Most of the change took place within the first few million years of the period, a fraction of a second on a geographical and evolutionary time scale. Bergstrom speculates that it might even be possible for the formation of an entirely new type of animal within a time frame of mere thousands of years.

The fossils were found in Chengjiang in the southern province of Yunnan. They stretched 30 miles in one direction and 12 in another on the sea bottom, or just below or above it along a broad continental shelf beneath shallow waters.

Even some animals without hard skeletons or shells were preserved, a rare event. The fossil record worldwide is 99% animals with skeletons. One possible explanation is that a violent storm stirred up the sea bottom with the result that mud settled over a large area, cut off the animals' supply, and preserved them.

Despite their great age, a majority of the fossil species found at Chengjiang belong to animal groups that still exist.

The Stars and the Universe

Asteroids, craggy leftover from the creation of the universe, are too faint to be visible to the naked eye. They were discovered in 1801 by an Italian monk named Guiseppi Piazzi working at a Palermo, Sicily observatory. By the end of the 19th century, more powerful telescopes were tracking hundreds of asteroids, which are found in a loose belt between Mars and Jupiter.

An asteroid found in 1932 raised concern because occasionally its orbit deviates from the normal and brings it across Earth's path. Nevertheless, scientists did not begin to systematically search for Earth-crossing asteroids until recently. An April 7, 1992 *New York Times* article entitled "Asteroid Defense: 'Risk Is Real,' Planners Say" reported the number of Earth-crossing asteroids at about 150, with two or three new ones discovered each month.

The largest found is approximately five miles wide. Computer predictions projected well into the 21st century do not foresee any known asteroid hitting Earth. Nevertheless, a government-appointed team of nearly 100 scientists suggested in the spring of 1992 a $50-million plan for a warning system.

Critics denounced the plan as "make-work" for astronomers and weapons makers to offset funding cuts in the wake of the end of the Cold War. The authors of the plan insisted that it drew on a large quantity of data generated by astronomers, geologists, and biologists over the last decade.

The plan called for an asteroid census and the placement of six ground-based telescopes around the world to scan the heavens. The telescope would issue warnings, sometimes decades in advance, allowing time to work on interceptors to deflect the danger.

The team estimated that the telescopes might find 1,050–4,200 Earth-crossing asteroids that are at least 0.62 miles in diameter, a size sufficient to create a tremendous impact on the climate and agriculture. The enormous speed of even small rocks is sufficient to generate, on impact, heat comparable to the release of multiple nuclear explosions. After slamming into Earth at a speed of about 16 miles per second, a large asteroid could explode with a force equivalent to a million hydrogen bombs. Pulverized rock, crushed into dust, would block most sunlight resulting in darkness that might last for months and lead to starvation of a billion or more people.

In response to criticism, Dr. Richard Binzel, an asteroid expert at MIT, told the *New York Times:* "Although the threat is small, it's not zero. There's probably a 1-in-7,000 chance that an impact with global repercussions could happen in a person's lifetime . . . It's really a political decision as to whether the threat is judged big enough to warrant investigation . . . This does not fall within our ordinary experience, so it takes some getting used to."

Evidence of the danger, while circumstantial, is extensive. Robot spacecraft exploring planets have found a large number of impact craters. Geologists during the last two decades have begun to recognize that numerous craters exist on Earth. New discoveries are being made on an average of about five or six each year. The largest is in Ontario and measures 124 miles from rim to rim. For centuries craters on Earth were thought to be due to volcanoes. Many have been eroded by Earth's atmosphere and oceans.

Additional evidence comes from research of supporters a theory proposed in 1980 by University of California Nobel Laureate Luis Alvarez based on the records of fossils and ancient stone. Alvarez hypothesized that 65 million years ago an asteroid created a global veil of dust that resulted in the mass extinction of many life forms, including the dinosaurs.

Further evidence comes from a handful of observers, whose modest efforts have produced large numbers of discoveries. Since the late 1980s, Dr. Tom Gehrels of the University of Arizona has scanned the skies with a Kitt Peak telescope using an advanced electronic detector and found swarms of small asteroids zipping past Earth at uncomfortably close distances.

Scientists are unsure about the source or sources of cosmic rays. They hypothesize that cosmic rays are born of cataclysmic celestial activities such as supernovas. In supernova 1987A, as seen through the Curtis-Schmidt telescope at Cerro Tololo on March 2, 1987, the star appears as a very bright object in the Large Magellanic Cloud.

6

The Stars and the Universe

Cosmic-Ray Shower Detection Has Once Again Become a Frontier of Science

Arrays of detectors are aimed at the sky in a massive search for elusive traces left by cosmic rays that rain upon Earth from the Milky Way and from stars hundreds of thousands of light-years away. Scientists believe that cosmic rays—charged with energies of up to 100 billion billion electron volts—are created during violent celestial events. Such events include supernovas, which are stars that become extremely bright as they blow up, and collisions among galaxies, which are huge aggregates of stars, dust, and gas.

Powerful enough to travel billions of light-years across the universe, the deadly radiation of cosmic rays—fortunately for humans—is absorbed quite efficiently by Earth's protective atmosphere. Cosmic rays are elementary particles, such as protons, electrons and the nuclei of atoms, largely hydrogen, that impinge on Earth from all directions with nearly the speed of light. Showers of cosmic rays result when a single cosmic ray causes the simultaneous appearance of many ionizing particles on a downward course of secondary radiation, which includes gamma rays.

Cosmic rays come in two forms. The majority are ions, electrically charged atoms or molecules. (A charge may be positive or negative or zero.) A small number are photons, uncharged particles of radiant energy. Most cosmic rays are individually charged nuclei; about 90% are single protons or hydrogen nuclei, with the other 10% including a sprinkling of everything from helium to lead.

Astronomers' struggle to understand the consequence of colossal events in the sky is linked to the particle physicists' struggle to understand the minia-

ture architecture of atoms. The structure of the atom became clear to scientists between 1911 and 1913. They learned that most of the atom's mass and all of its positive charge are concentrated in a tiny central region called the nucleus, which is surrounded by negatively charged electrons.

By 1919 New Zealand-born, British-trained physicist Ernest Rutherford had determined that the nucleus of atoms is made up of several elements and contains positively charged particles of matter identical to the nucleus of hydrogen, the lightest atom. Rutherford argued that these particles are found in all nuclei. He named them "protons."

In 1932 British physicist James Chadwick discovered the neutron, an electrically neutral particle only slightly heavier than the proton. With the exception of hydrogen, in which the nucleus is a single proton, neutrons and protons together form the atomic nucleus of all elements. The parts of the nucleus are bound together by the so-called nuclear force.

In a typical atom, the protons and neutrons reside in the dense central region of the nucleus, where they make up more than 99.9% of the atom's mass—technically its resistance to acceleration—but only a minute percentage of its volume, or the amount of room the atom takes up in three-dimensional space. The vast majority of the atom's volume is taken up by lightweight electrons that orbit the nucleus at relatively long distances.

In any atom, the number of electrons, which determines the chemical properties of the element, exactly balances the number of protons in the nucleus.

The role of the neutron is to dilute the repulsive electric force between the protons and thereby prevent the nucleus from flying apart. The larger the nuclei, the greater the number of neutrons necessary to counteract the electric force. In the heaviest nuclei, the number of neutrons greatly exceeds the number of protons.

Some configurations of protons and neutrons are completely stable. Others that are unstable, referred to as radioactive, change to more-stable structures through spontaneous emission of radiations. Such radiations can be in the form of alpha particles (helium nuclei), beta particles (electrons), and gamma rays.

A gamma ray, or high energy photon, is typically emitted by a nucleus in transition between two energy states. A photon, as a unit of electromagnetic energy with no charge or mass, has momentum and behaves as both a particle and a wave. Photons carry the energy of gamma rays and X-rays. The quantities of energy released in shifts from unstable to stable structures, referred to as transmutations, are millions of times greater than the quantities involved in chemical reactions.

Cosmic rays are no longer intact by the time they reach Earth. The primary rays collide with air atoms and splinter into showers of secondary particles. Some of the secondary particles careen into other air nuclei creating more particles.

The whole collection of shower particles travels toward Earth in what is sometimes described as an ever-enlarging pancake. The shower arrives within a few millionths of a second. By then, the pancake is about 100 yards in diameter and contains as many as a billion particles. Most of the particles are electrons, but some are muons, which are short-lived, highly penetrating particles similar to electrons but about 200 times as massive.

Attention to Cosmic-Ray Research Has Fluctuated

Scientists' search for evidence of cosmic rays began in western Europe with two independent experiments. In 1919, Father Theodore Wulf, a Jesuit priest and amateur scientist, found atop the Eiffel Tower in Paris, France that radiation was higher in the atmosphere than it was at ground level. Aloft in a balloon

at heights that exceeded 16,400 feet, Victor Hess, a young Austrian physicist, found that radiation levels above 5,000 feet steadily increased in intensity. At 17,500 feet, the balloon's maximum altitude, the intensity was several times that of ground level. In 1925, the radiation found by Wulf and Hess was named cosmic rays by the American physicist R.A. Millikan.

Prior to the experiments of Wulf and Hess, laboratory experiments had demonstrated that energetic radiation strips electrons from atoms in a gas, thereby making them able to conduct electricity. Wulf and Hess carried the laboratory experiments into the atmosphere using electroscopes made up of two gold leaves.

An electroscope's gold leaves are suspended from a common point inside a gas-filled, electrically insulated container. An initial electrical charge stored on the surface of the leaves causes them to repel each other and move apart. As incoming radiation ionizes gas inside the electroscope, the charge dissipates on the leaves and they come back together.

Because cosmic rays are charged, they get bounced around by magnetic fields in the galaxy, tracing an erratic route to Earth. Therefore, by the time they reach detectors, they seem to be coming from everywhere and nowhere. In the years since cosmic rays were discovered by Wulf and Hess, a variety of cosmic-ray sources have been proposed; supernova explosions remain a favorite.

During the 1930s and 1940s, the study of cosmic rays operated as a frontier of science. In the 1930s, American physicist Arthur Compton sent 60 researchers to look for cosmic rays in various parts of the world. After climbing icy mountain peaks, scientists spent weeks huddled in snow-covered huts. When two researchers died on Mount McKinley, Compton retrieved their instruments to include their data in the research analysis.

The collective work of the mountaintop scientists created an assembly of new elementary particles. (A particle is smaller than an atom and is not a composite of other particles.) After contributing heavily to the growth of the field of particle physics, the study of cosmic rays went into a decline.

Particle accelerators are machines that smash atoms at high speeds to break them into particles. As

The Gamma Ray Observatory, placed into orbit in April 1991, was photographed as it passed over western Africa.

these became standard equipment throughout the 1950s and 1960s, high-energy physicists confined their work to laboratories, leaving unanswered the fundamental question of the origin of cosmic rays.

A revival of interest in cosmic-ray astronomy in the 1970s was sparked by the reports of the few physicists who had never abandoned mountaintop research that the most energetic cosmic rays in space slam into atomic nuclei with considerably more impact than anything produced in human-made accelerators. The mountaintop detectors had recorded cosmic rays 1 million times more energetic than any produced in the Fermi Laboratory in Batavia, Illinois, the world's most powerful atom smasher.

The collisions in space do not seem to obey the laws laboriously developed by physicists in accelerator labs. Understandably, not all physicists welcomed the mountaintop findings. A September 1989 *Discover* article entitled "The Case of the Cosmic Rays" quoted University of Wisconsin physicist Francis Halzen: "Most physicists just wish the whole thing would go away. That way they wouldn't have to worry about it anymore."

A stepped-up search for cosmic rays—particularly high-energy cosmic rays—has brought astronomers and particle physicists together in a common pursuit. In a May 11, 1991 *Science News* article entitled "Catching Some Cosmic Rays," University of Chicago physicist Leslie Rosenberg explained the new relationship between the two fields: "Particle production and decays [gradual reduction of factors such as current, magnetic fluctuation, charge, or phosphorescence] have been the exclusive domain of particle physics . . . [But] at sufficiently high energies, particle physics and decays become prominent features of astrophysical sources [explosions of stars and collisions of galaxies], and the two fields of study intertwine."

Current Research Sites

On April 6, 1991 scientists lofted the 17-ton Gamma Ray Observatory into an orbit 268 miles above Earth. Their goal was to detect gamma rays directly rather than being forced to infer them from Earth by the presence of secondary particles. The observatory has more than lived up to expectations. Astronomers had expected gamma-ray showers to be confined to the vicinity of the Milky Way, but they have discovered that they come from all parts of the sky.

The Gamma Ray Observatory's greatest value lies in its capacity to identify areas of the sky most likely to emit high-energy photons. However, the Gamma Ray Observatory has limitations.

The observatory can study only "medium-energy" gamma rays, those with energies up to 10 billion electron volts, or 10 GeV. At energies greater than 10 GeV, the shower of photons and charged particles is reduced to a trickle. Therefore, the limited collecting capacity of space-orbiting devices makes detection of high-energy gamma rays virtually impossible.

Several types of instruments now in use in the United States are tailored to track the activity of gamma rays of different energy levels. The instruments share the principle that they are designed to see the light that results about 12.5 miles above Earth when the self-destruction of photons creates pairs of oppositely charged ions.

One cosmic-ray tracking device located atop a hill at the U.S. Army's Dugway, Utah Proving Ground is set up with 67 cylindrical detectors. Each detector is fitted with a mirror that focuses light into several photomultiplier tubes. This arrangement permits analysts to reconstruct particle trajectories, or flight patterns. Every detector surveys a different section of the sky looking for a faint, bluish glow that indicates that the most energetic cosmic rays—from 100-bil-

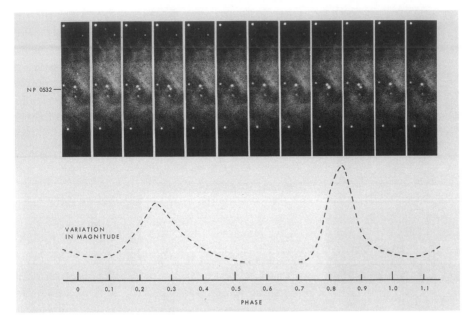

VARIATION IN MAGNITUDE

PHASE

Pulsars also are thought to be a source of cosmic rays. This sequence shows the visible light variation of the pulsar at the center of the Crab Nebula. The photos were taken by a NASA-developed instrument called the "Pulsar Hunter" via the 2.1-meter telescope at Kitt Peak National Observatory. The pulsar's light has a regular cycle of 30 times per second.

lion-GeV to 100-trillion-GeV particles—have collided with nitrogen atoms, resulting in fluorescence (the flow of some sort of energy).

A smaller collection of detectors two miles away is designed to record fluorescence emitted at altitudes of up to 6.25 miles. Known as Fly's Eye I and II, the multimirror arrays, designed at the University of Utah in Salt Lake City to mimic the compound eyes of insects, can operate only on dark, moonless nights. Working together, the two Fly's Eye detectors help to distinguish between cosmic gamma rays and other light sources.

Several other detectors located at the Dugway site detect lower-energy gamma rays. Surrounding Fly's Eye II is the Chicago Air Shower Array, a collection of 1,089 plastic scintillators, materials that emit optical photons in response to ionizing radiation. Night and day, the scintillators monitor cosmic showers induced by gamma rays of about 100,000 GeV to 10 million GeV.

At these lower levels, the gamma rays do not have enough energy to make nitrogen glow. However, they do induce a stream of secondary particles that create a flash when they strike the plastic scintillators. The angle and intensity of the incoming showers enables astronomers to identify the gamma rays' source in the sky.

A group of underground detectors, designed by researchers at the University of Michigan, Ann Arbor,

is located 9.8 feet below the Dugway site, where it counts muons during cosmic showers. The detectors occupy a 299,000-square-yard area.

A joint cosmic-ray venture known as CYGNUS is located at the Los Alamos National Laboratory in New Mexico. In addition to the Los Alamos researchers, the project includes scientists from the Argonne (Illinois) National Laboratory, the University of Maryland at College Park, the George Mason University in Fairfax, Virginia, and the University of California at Irvine and Santa Cruz.

CYGNUS has a set of 202 scintillators spread over 101,660 square yards atop a Los Alamos plateau. The scintillators survey gamma rays at the same low energy levels as those surveyed by the University of Chicago array at Dugway. The project includes muon detectors buried at the site under six feet of concrete.

The proximity of the New Mexico scintillators to those in Utah provides a distinct advantage. With two experiments observing the same source in the same area of the sky at the same time, comparable findings recorded by each cannot be dismissed by other scientists as statistical flukes.

Set up atop Mount Hopkins in southern Arizona is a detector sensitive to the lowest-energy gamma rays that can be indirectly detected on Earth. On clear, moonless nights, the Whipple Observatory telescope's 32.8-foot-wide dish of 248 mirrors focuses incoming light into a cluster of 109 photomultiplier

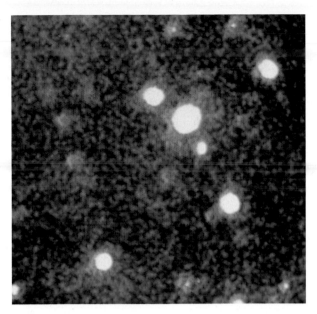

Quasars may spawn cosmic rays. The word quasar is short for quasi-stellar, which means "star-resembling," even though most quasars are probably not stars. Their brightness, which varies periodically, is generally greater than that of an average-sized galaxy. Quasars may be small, very distant galaxies. The quasar 3C 275.1, the first to be found at the center of a galactic cluster, appears as the brightest object near the center of this pseudocolor image. Its nucleus is surrounded by a rotating elliptical gas cloud. The 0.55 redshift of the quasar places it about 7 billion light-years from Earth.

tubes. Like several similar instruments around the world, the Whipple infers the presence of gamma rays at energies of 100 GeV to 10,000 GeV from a characteristic forward-directed beam of extremely faint light several hundred feet in diameter and 3.281 feet thick.

This light, called Cerenkov radiation, is comparable to shock waves. It appears when the speed of particles exceeds that of light in the medium through which the particles are traveling. The particles emit light along their direction of motion, thereby enabling scientists to trace their paths and the paths of their parent gamma rays.

By determining in nanoseconds the order of arrival of signals at the various detectors, investigators can calculate the angle at which a cosmic ray collided with the atmosphere, in addition to its point of origin. From ground-based detectors, scientists have lo-

cated several likely sources of high-energy gamma rays. The most convincing findings come from scans by Whipple Observatory of the Crab pulsar. A pulsar is a celestial body that emits regular radio impulses.

The Crab pulsar is located in the Crab nebula. Seen in the nighttime sky, nebulas are misty, cloudlike patches of stars too distant to be seen singly. The Crab nebula is in the constellation Taurus.

The Crab pulsar is a single-neutron star. Neutron stars are extremely small, dense stars composed almost entirely of neutrons that spin rapidly and produce periodic pulses of intense radio waves.

Whipple Observatory researcher Trevor Weeks and his colleagues determined that a steady gamma-ray signal from the Crab pulsar occurred at widely separated times and seemed unrelated to the pulsar's own X-ray pulsing interval of 33 milliseconds. The Crab data seems to contradict physicists' belief that high-energy gamma rays are a byproduct of extremely violent collisions between protons and other charged particles. The Crab pulsar is surrounded by empty space, which makes it difficult to understand what other charged particles might be available for collisions.

University of Maryland scientist Jordan Goodman suggests that the Crab data may not be due to violent collisions, but instead may be the result of a different phenomenon known as inverse Compton scattering. In the process known as the inverse Compton effect, some particles give up energy to long-wavelength radiation, converting it to shorter-wavelength radiation. Goodman proposes that a beam of high-energy electrons gives up almost all its energy to photons, thus transforming them into gamma rays. If Goodman's theory is correct, the number of gamma rays produced above 100,000 GeV can be expected to be limited, since Compton scattering cannot produce photons at these higher energy levels.

Contradictions Keep Controversy Simmering

In 1979 Soviet researchers at the Crimean Astrophysical Observatory in Nauchny, which is now in the Republic of Ukraine, reported finding gamma rays emerging from Cygnus X-3, an X-ray emitting binary star (a pair of stars connected by a bond of mutual gravitational attraction). This star system made up of a neutron star and a smaller companion located at about 30,000 light-years from Earth—appeared to emit 10,000-GeV gamma rays. Four years later, researchers at the University of Kiel in Germany also saw evidence of gamma rays near this system.

More recent observations failed to reveal any excess of cosmic rays from Cygnus X-3 and its companion. Physicist Eugene Loh of the University of Utah, a researcher with the Fly's Eye experiments, told *Science News:* "If you're a pessimist, you say the previous results were statistical fluctuations. If you're an optimist, you say that previously the source was on. Now the source is off."

Observations of even higher energies from Cygnus X-3 resulted in similar contradictions. Data collected over several decades by the Fly's Eye experiments and by similar work at the Akeno Cosmic Ray Observatory in Japan suggested that Cygnus X-3 may emit 1-billion-GeV gamma rays. But detectors at Havarah Park in England found no such evidence during a 1989 cosmic shower.

The most controversial observations concern Hercules X-1, another binary system containing a neutron star. Separate teams of researchers—at the CYGNUS project, at the Whipple Observatory, and at the Haleakala Gamma Ray Observatory in Maui, Hawaii—during 1986 independently reported signs of cosmic-ray bursts. The period exhibited by the bursts was slightly longer than the period of the neutron star's X-ray pulsing cycle. Evidence suggested that the pulses came from high-energy gamma rays. However, contradictory evidence came from the Los Alamos underground detector, which determined that the particle shower contained many more muons than gamma rays normally create.

Showers triggered by gamma rays point directly to their source. But the showers from Cygnus and Hercules contain a lot of muons, as do showers triggered by protons.

Scientists speculate that Cygnus X-3, as well as Hercules X-1, might consist of a superdense, spinning neutron star that is orbiting a giant companion and acquiring gas from it. Cosmic-ray protons could be hurled into space by the powerful electric field generated by the neutron star's magnetic field. Some of the protons might slam into Earth's atmosphere and set off a shower of secondary particles, including muons.

After nearly two decades of intense observations, cosmic-ray investigators have narrowed their focus to a few possible sources of energetic gamma rays. Scientists hope that more-sensitive detectors will be able to verify the reports made by the Whipple Observatory, the Haleakala Gamma Ray Observatory, and the CYGNUS experiment.

University of Maryland researcher Jordan Goodman told *Science News:* "To be very candid, nobody understands what's going on and nobody is even convinced at this stage that they've observed these things. There's enough controversy in the field now that people aren't 100% happy with anything."

Despite the controversy—or possibly because of it—ground-based cosmic-ray astronomy is thriving.

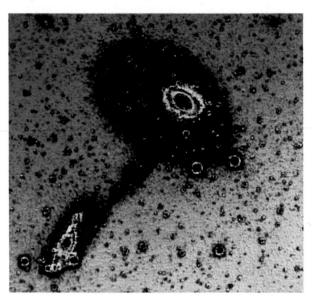

In addition to the possibility of being created by quasars, cosmic rays also may come from galaxy collisions, as in the colliding "Toadstool Galaxies," ESO B138 and IG 29/30. Located in the constellation Ara, the galaxies are connected by a bridge of hydrogen gas, made visible by bright, newly formed stars in the bridge. The false-color computer-enhanced image was taken by the 4-meter Mayall telescope at Cerro Tololo InterAmerican Observatory.

The U.S. Cerro Tololo Telescope's Long Record of Success Faces Challenges From New Competitors

Established in 1963 in north central Chile, Cerro Tololo Inter-American Observatory is America's national center for astronomy in the southern hemisphere. Named for the 2,200-meter (7,218-foot) Cerro Tololo—cerro is Spanish for mountain—on which its telescopes stand, the observatory is located about 70 kilometers (43.4 miles) inland, where the dryness of the Atacama Desert becomes a countryside like Southern California's.

The area's rare combination of cold ocean currents, onshore winds, rising land, and distance from urban centers provides an atmosphere of unique clarity and stability. Since the 1960s, Cerro Tololo has been a magnet for astronomers and a center for the construction of some of the world's best telescopes.

Cerro Tololo is operated by the National Optical Astronomy Observatories (NOAO), which runs several facilities on behalf of America's national community of astronomers. In addition to Cerro Tololo, NOAO also is responsible for Kitt Peak National Observatory in Arizona and the National Solar Observatory, which has telescopes at Kitt Peak and at Sacramento Peak, New Mexico.

In January 1976 Cerro Tololo's giant 4-meter (13.12-foot) reflector began operation. The fifth-largest optical telescope in the world and the largest optical telescope in the southern hemisphere, Cerro Tololo was built as a counterpart to NOAO's 4-meter Mayall telescope at Kitt Peak. Together they cover the northern and southern hemispheres.

Many astronomers consider Cerro Tololo to be one of the finest telescopes in the world. The critical component of Cerro Tololo's 4-meter telescope is a mirror with a fast prime focus and a unique capacity to make rapid changes in instrumentation, that is, the use of physical instruments for processing. Housed in a 38-meter-high (124.68-foot) building and dome, the telescope is 14 meters (45.93 feet) long and its movable portion weighs 223,800 kilograms (101,515 pounds). Nevertheless, it is so delicately balanced that

The Cerro Tololo Inter-American Observatory (CTIO), elevation 6,800 feet, is about 60 miles from La Serena, Chile, on the western slope of the Andes Mountains, near the Atacama Desert. The Humboldt Current, a cold stream within the Pacific Ocean, flows near the observing site. A combination of cold air moving across the current, skies that are almost free from light pollution, a dry desert climate, and high altitude provides one of the world's finest observing sites.

Astronomer John Graham prepares to take a photographic plate with the 4-meter telescope at CTIO. Known as "first light," the 1975 observation was the first taken by this telescope, which is the largest in the Southern Hemisphere.

one person can move it by hand.

Six other telescopes share the mountaintop with the 4-meter reflector: a 1.5-meter (4.92-foot); two 41-centimeter (16.14-inch) reflectors; a 61-centimeter (24-inch) Schmidt telescope on loan from the University of Michigan; and a 1-meter (3.281-foot) on loan from Yale University. An ongoing instrument-development program at the observatory has benefited the use of all the telescopes.

NOAO scientists and engineers have pioneered new techniques. For example, they developed light-detecting electronic "chips," so-called charge-coupled devices (CCDs), to enhance sensitivities to light as much as a hundred times beyond that of photographic film. Cerro Tololo researchers are working on an electronic array for observations in the near-infrared, meaning invisible rays just beyond red in the visible spectrum, with waves longer than spectrum colors but shorter than radio waves. In the near-infrared, objects under scrutiny must be pulled out of a background filled with objects emitting infrared radiation.

Another area of pioneer research at Cerro Tololo has been in the transmission of images through fiber optics, thin, flexible fibers in parallel bundles. This technique is used to transport light signals from a telescope to instruments. Its goal is to carry light captured in a telescope to a central point with little loss.

Such a system would mean that instrumentation designed for use on a large telescope could also be used to analyze signals gathered by smaller telescopes, thereby increasing the performance of the smaller telescopes. It would also mean that new spectrographs (cameras attached to a spectroscope, a measuring device) would not have to be designed to fit on a telescope. If spectrographs were free of telescopes, they could be designed to become stationary, controlled environments.

Among the many innovations developed at Cerro Tololo, one outstanding one was described in a December 1, 1991 *New York Times* article entitled "In Chile, Galaxy-Watching Robot Seeks Measure of the Universe." To understand the overall structure of the universe, it is essential to measure the distance to faraway galaxies, large-scale collections of stars, gas, and dust. This is a difficult and time-consuming task. Estimates have been made for only a few of the billions of galaxies. The Cerro Tololo innovation, a machine called Argus, simultaneously measures distances to 24 remote galaxies.

Argus does not change the principal method of measurement, which gathers light from a galaxy and

In this wide-angle view toward the center of the Milky Way galaxy, the teapot shape of the stars in the constellation Sagittarius can be seen, however the central region of the galaxy is obscured from sight by intervening gas, dust clouds, and stars between Earth and the galactic core.

breaks it up into a color spectrum, using a device called a diffraction grating, which is a plate of glass or polished metal ruled with a series of very close, equidistant, parallel lines. When light is passed through a prism, the result is a spectrum, bands of color arranged in the order of the light's respective wavelengths from red, produced by the longest visible wave, to violet, produced by the shortest.

The lines on a galaxy's spectrum shift toward the red (the longer wavelengths) in proportion to the galaxy's speed away from Earth. Because the universe is expanding, a galaxy's recession (movement away from) is a measure of its distance from Earth.

Light is very faint by the time it reaches Earth from a galaxy billions of light-years away. A light-year is the distance light travels in one year, approximately 6 trillion miles. After being broken up into a spectrum, the light is fainter still.

To adequately measure a faint galaxy's red shift requires an enormous curved telescope like the 4-meter at Cerro Tololo. However, even with a huge mirror, it takes many minutes of exposure to measure the light from one galaxy and a whole night to produce just a few distance measurements.

To cope with the problem, Argus permits the 4-meter telescope to measure as many as 24 galaxies in the time it once to took to measure one. Light from the big mirror is focused at the opposite end of the telescope, where each of an array of 24 robotically controlled arms carries a pair of optical fibers.

Dr. David Koo of the University of California at Santa Cruz and other astronomers working with Argus maneuver each of the 24 arms to place an optical fiber at the exact spot where a target galaxy's light is to be focused on the mirror. Light from each galaxy is sent from the telescope along its own fiber to a diffraction grating, where its spectrum is automatically measured. In a control room, Koo and an associate, Dr. Christopher Willmer, an astronomer from Lick Observatory at Santa Cruz, subject the measurements to computer analysis and the computer calculates the red-shift distance.

Koo and Willmer confine their search to a narrow corridor expanding into the depths of space far beyond the "Great Wall" of galaxies that have already been extensively studied. By collecting distance measurements along a thin channel between Earth and the outermost reaches of the universe, Koo and Dr. Richard Krone of the University of Chicago discovered in 1989 that, at least in that direction, clusters of galaxies seemed to be concentrated in evenly spaced layers. Astronomers don't know whether the finding is a fluke. With powerful time-saving devices like Argus speeding up the pace of discovery, they may some day find out.

Competing and Complementary Telescopes

With their abilities to cover the skies of the northern and southern hemisphere, Cerro Tololo and Kitt Peak astronomers since the 1970s have flooded scientific journals with reports of their discoveries. Some astronomers fear that the accomplishments of Cerro Tololo may soon be overshadowed by those of the newly built European telescope, the so-called New Technology Telescope. The European telescope automatically corrects for distortions due to gravity and the wind and captures images up to six times more revealing than those captured by American telescopes of conventional design.

Some American astronomers predict that if European astronomers capture a large share of major astronomical discoveries, then funding by U.S. agencies and universities will diminish. Although plans for building new American telescopes continue, a February 4, 1992 *New York Times* article entitled

These two photos of the Halley Comet were taken 76 years apart. The top photo is a computer-reconstructed image, processed at Kitt Peak, from an original black-and-white plate taken of the comet by the Lowell Observatory in Flagstaff, Arizona. The false colors indicate varying levels of brightness. The bottom photo, taken at CTIO, shows the Halley Comet as it races across a background of star trails toward its nearest approach to Earth, at 4:44 P.M., Eastern Standard Time, April 10, 1986. This was a one-hour exposure taken using the 24/36-inch Curtis Schmidt telescope.

"Europe's New Telescope Rivals U.S.'s" reported that plans for a new 8-meter (26.24 foot) telescope near Cerro Tololo remain uncertain.

NOAO believes that two new 8-meter telescopes must be built, one in northern Chile and the other at Mauna Kea on the island of Hawaii. Construction of the Hawaiian telescope has been approved, but funding for the Chilean telescope can proceed only if half the cost is borne by foreign partners.

By the end of the century, well-financed consortiums drawn from eight European nations expect to complete a telescope that will be known as the European Very Large Telescope. Many design principles developed for the New Technology Telescope will be incorporated into the Very Large Telescope.

The new instrument, to be built atop Cerro Paranal in Chile, will consist of four linked telescopes, each more than 8 meters in diameter. Together the four can combine their images to achieve the equivalent of a single mirror 16 meters (52.5 feet) in diameter.

The gloom of American astronomers is somewhat relieved by the building of two 10-meter (33-foot) telescopes in Hawaii, financed by the private Keck Foundation. They predict that the paired Hawaiian telescopes will provide broader coverage than the Very Large Telescope and have other advantages that offset size.

The idea that linking smaller telescopes offers advantages seems to be gaining ground. According to a July 6, 1992 *Georgia Tech Research News* bulletin, the National Science Foundation entered into an agreement with the Georgia Institute of Technology and Georgia State University, both in Atlanta, to design and fund an array of seven small telescopes.

The two institutions will design and oversee construction of a Y-shaped array of seven telescopes that together will have the imaging power of a single 400-meter-diameter (1,312.4-foot) telescope. Dr. Hal McAlister, Georgia State astronomer and project director, said: "With this array of telescopes, if you put a baseball stadium on the moon, you could tell who was pitching and who was at bat. Right now, if you used the best existing optical telescope under the best observing conditions, you could see detail no smaller than mile-diameter craters. We'll be able to see things we've only been able to imagine before. We can't really anticipate all of the things the array will let us do."

To improve astronomers' ability to see distant objects, the array will apply reconstructive imaging, interferometry and adaptive optics. To produce an image, reconstructive imaging will use a camera with a high-speed charge-coupled device to enhance sensitivities to light and a computer to analyze the digital data it produces. Interferometry, an optical process by which the light collected by the seven telescopes will

The Southern Ring Galaxy, in the constellation Volans, located 6.5 degrees east-southeast of the Large Magellanic Cloud, was thought to be part of the cloud. Measurements of the Ring's redshift place is well beyond the local cluster of galaxies. The galaxy is as large as the Milky Way. Theoreticians believe its structure was caused by a small, compact intruder penetrating a symmetrical disk galaxy.

be combined, will channel light beams over hundreds of meters with accuracies of 0.0001 inch. Adaptive optics will use a computer to direct a mirror that can be deformed to compensate for the way the atmosphere appears to shift incoming light, which creates twinkling.

Because light will not reach each telescope at the same time, the system will have a so-called variable-path-length delay system that will permit the light from each telescope to reach the data-collection equipment at the same time. To provide the delay, the telescope array will include a system of fixed and movable mirrors controlled by computers to precisely vary the distance traveled by light from each telescope.

The facility, to be built in a remote area of the southwestern United States, will be designed to be versatile to accommodate astronomers' future needs. The new array is expected to have 150 times the resolution (capacity to produce images) of the Hubble Space Telescope—if the Hubble were operating at optimum level—at 1% of the cost.

A different kind of linkage is contemplated by scientists at the National Optical Observatories in Tucson, Arizona. They announced plans for a network of telescopes spanning five continents to measure the

oscillation, that is, the rise and fall, of the sun's surface. For an April 17, 1991 *Phoenix Gazette* article entitled "Tucson-Based Telescope Network to Solve Sun's Mysteries," Frank Hill, a survey scientist with the federally funded Global Oscillation Network Group, reported that a network will permit scientists to more accurately predict sunspot activity and solar flares.

Sunspots appear in the extremely bright visible portion of the sun, called the photosphere, as a result of intense, coiled magnetic fields deep within the sun that erupt to the solar surface. A solar flare, an abrupt increase in radiation intensity, spews radiation and billions of tons of matter into space.

Magnetic storms set off by solar flares and other solar activities create havoc on Earth. Among other things, they disrupt navigation systems and long-distance telephone cables beneath the sea, and they can knock satellites out of orbit.

Solar scientists arrive at inferences, which are conclusions based on something known or assumed, about the structure and activities of the sun's interior in ways similar to those used by geologists, who analyze the behavior of sound waves traveling through the materials that make up the Earth's interior. Using a method called helio-seismology (helio meaning sun

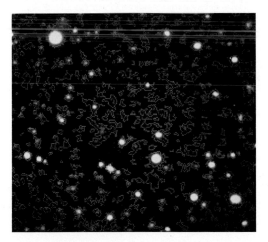

This two-hour exposure with a charge-coupled device (CCD) at the 4-meter telescope at CTIO shows abundant galaxies in an area nearly bare of objects in standard sky survey charts. It has been estimated that this image, taken in a program to count galaxies at extremely faint magnitudes, captured images nearly as faint as those expected to be detectable by the Hubble Space Telescope.

and seismology referring to the study of earthquakes), scientists have taken many measurements of the sun. They have calculated the sun's interior temperature, its inner rotation rate, and the depth of its convection zone, a region of interior instability in which radiation is carried outward.

Scientists hope that accurate measurements of vibrations within the sun that cause its surface to rise and fall may make it possible to determine whether the sun's cycle affects weather on Earth. They also seek to arrive at a clearer understanding of the sun's inner workings.

After six years spent studying 15 sites around the world as potential network participants, scientists chose six: Cerro Tololo; the California Institute of Technology's Big Bear Solar Observatory; either the University of Hawaii's Mees Solar Observatory on Haleakala or the High-Altitude Observatory on Mauna Loa; the Ionospheric Prediction Service Learmonth Solar Observatory in Australia; the Physical Research Laboratories Udaipur Solar Observatory in India; and the Instituto de Astrofisica de Canarias' El Tiede Observatory on Izana in the Canary Islands.

When observations begin in 1993, each telescope will track the sun for three years. When the sun sets at one station, the next station to the west will pick up coverage.

In short, a flood of astronomical discoveries in the 1990s seems assured, given the creativity of scientists and engineers in expanding the capabilities of older telescopes and the numerous new telescopes that will be coming on line.

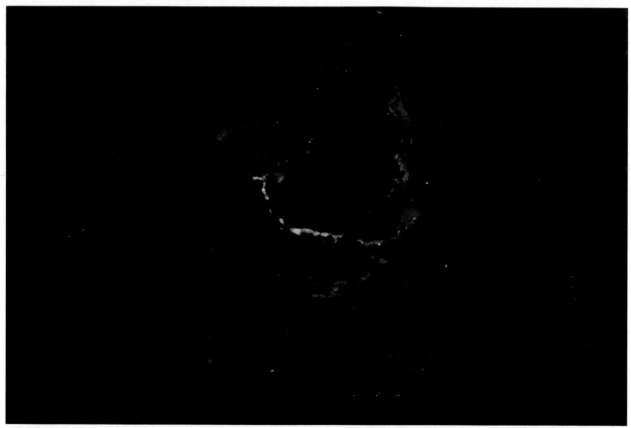

This color image was created from three images of ancient supernova shell Puppis A. They were taken by CTIO's 4-meter telescope. The three separate images were obtained through filters that isolate the emission lines of different elements. At the Harvard-Smithsonian Center for Astrophysics, the images were combined and the stars were removed from the image. The image shows the light from nitrogen as red, oxygen as blue, and sulfur as green. The fact that distinct, unmixed debris is visible is a strong clue that these elements, cooked in the nuclear oven of a massive star, are the fresh result of a recent explosion. This small swirl of emission is a possible second explosion inside the large, old Puppis A remnant.

7

EARTH IN THE PAST

Hydrothermal and Other Kinds of Vents, Riches From Inner Earth

In 1977 at a depth of 8,500 feet, too deep for the sun to penetrate, Columbia University geologist Katherine Crane discovered hydrothermal vents in the floor of the Pacific Ocean. Discoveries like Crane's, which was off the northwestern coast of South America near the Galapagos Islands, have come to be known as "black smokers" for the chemicals that color their plumes. They are openings in the ocean floor where cold seawater and molten rock from the interior of the Earth meet.

The discovery of ocean-floor openings has roots in work done during World War II. At the time, Princeton University geologist Harry Hess was assigned to the ship U.S.S. *Johnson,* which engaged in searching for submarines by using newly developed sonar equipment. Sonar stands for **so**und **na**vigation **r**anging. The equipment sent out high-pitched sounds and scientists analyzed the sound's returning echoes. With a similar device, the scientists also mapped the ocean floor.

Following the war, Maurice Ewing of Columbia University led a group of scientists in gathering rocks from the sea bottom and in using war-developed instruments to map a string of sea mounts—underwater mountains—known as the Mid-Atlantic Ridge. As the details of the maps grew, Ewing and his colleagues learned that the Mid-Atlantic Ridge is a mountain range, varying in height from 60 feet to 10,000 feet.

Over time, scientists determined that the Mid-Atlantic Ridge is part of a system of ridges 46,000 miles long that extends around the world. Running along the length of the Mid-Atlantic Ridge is a steep narrow valley discovered by oceanographer-geologist Marie Tharp in 1950. Together the ridge and the rift make up the longest mountain range and the longest valley on the planet.

Ewing's team expected that the rocks they gathered from the ocean floor would be among the oldest on Earth. Instead of being billions of years in age, the rocks turned out to be no older than 150 million years.

In pondering the age of the rocks, geologist Hess, by then back at Princeton, New Jersey, surmised that the long valley beside the Mid-Atlantic Ridge must be a rift, which is a narrow opening in rock caused by cracking and splitting. He suspected that rock from the Earth's interior continued to rise through the crust, or the layer that formed when the planet cooled from a fiery ball.

The newly formed materials, he theorized, would move away from the point of eruption at a rate of a few inches per year to make way for lava coming behind them. Half of the Atlantic could be moving west, while the other half moves east. The cycle Hess proposed was in time dubbed "sea floor spreading."

What Hess only imagined was confirmed in the 1970s in a series of dives by tiny submarines called *Cyana, Archimede,* and *Alvin.* Submarine headlights piercing the inky blackness of the ravine in the center of the Mid-Atlantic Ridge revealed a landscape of dark boulders, long, twisted tubes, and black pillows, the solidified remains of once-molten lava welling from beneath the sea.

113

This hydrothermal vent is on the floor of the Pacific Ocean. More of the Pacific's hydrothermal sites seem to support thriving communities of sea life than do hydrothermal sites of other oceans and seas. The plume spews forth from mounds of anhydrite and sulfides. These chemicals color the plumes. Dozens of vents have been found near underwater ridges between two tectonic plates.

It was during a dive to look at this deep ocean lava that Katherine Crane first encountered on the floor of the Pacific Ocean hydrothermal vents surrounded by creatures never before seen. Among the most astonishing organisms were large clusters of red-plumed tube worms, emerging from thick white tubes 6–10 feet long.

Dr. John Corliss of Oregon State University and Robert Ballard of Woods Hole Oceanographic Institution in Massachusetts were among the first scientists to examine the newly discovered Galapagos Rift hydrothermal vents. An October 1977 *National Geographic* article entitled "Oases of Life in the Cold Abyss," written by the two scientists, described their expedition.

Inside the submersible *Alvin,* they descended 2.5 kilometers (1.56 miles). In the near-freezing depths of the Pacific, their temperature probe registered 17 degrees Celsius (63 degrees Fahrenheit). Hovering near the vent, they witnessed dense communities of giant tube worms, clams as large as dinner plates, crabs, lava encrusted with limpets, and pink fish.

In their article, Corliss and Ballard described their understanding of the mechanism involved in the development of the hydrothermal vents and their strange residents. The hydrothermal vents exist along the rift separating massive plates that form the Earth's crust. When lava erupts, it cools and cracks. Cold sea-water penetrates into the fractures, grows hot, drops off some chemical elements while picking up manganese and silicon from the crystal rocks, and flows as mineral-laden hot water up through the cracks where the metal oxides separate.

The scientists confirmed their suspicion that nutrients picked up in the seawater's journeys through the oceanic crust provided nourishment for the sea creatures. When they opened clams taken on board, the familiar rotten-egg odor of the chemical hydrogen sulfide assaulted their noses.

Microbiologists provided an explanation for the vent's food chain. Certain bacteria metabolize hydrogen sulfide and multiply. They in turn serve as nourishment for larger organisms. Thus, in the absence of sunlight as an energy source, chemicals are able to trigger life in a process called chemosynthesis. The abundance of food at the vents probably contributes to the giant size of the creatures.

Deep-sea populations of animals and microorganisms typically have low rates of metabolism, growth, maturation, and slow increases in population size. Hydrothermal vent populations violate ecologists' normal expectations because they grow fast and flourish in the dark at high pressures and low temperatures, the usual environment of the deep sea. Despite high temperatures in the immediate vicinity of the vents, rapid mixing of the hot water with the surrounding water keeps most vent animals living at temperatures close to 2 degrees Celsius (35.6 degrees Fahrenheit).

The vents introduce water to the sea floor that may be as hot as 400 degrees Celsius (752 degrees Fahrenheit). As much as 10% of the heat leaving Earth escapes through these hydrothermal vents; therefore, some scientists believe that ocean vents may play a role in global climate change. As the heated water dissolves a number of chemicals in rock, complex reactions create carbon dioxide, some of which ultimately enters the atmosphere.

Changes in the motions of Earth's plates may affect sea-floor hydrothermal activity and thus the amount of carbon dioxide that enters the atmosphere. This natural source of carbon dioxide must be taken into account to model climate change on geologic time scales.

A March 24, 1992 Georgia Institute of Technology research bulletin entitled " 'Black' Smokers Under the Sea: New Theory Explains Formation of Ocean Vents Which Play a Role in Global Climate Change" described efforts to explain the circulation of fluids that forms hydrothermal vents. Because it is fundamental to understanding how the Earth works as a heat engine, scientists need to understand how hydrothermal vents transfer energy.

The plates that form the Earth's crust rest on molten lava like skim on a cooled pudding. As they pull apart by as much as 20 centimeters (7.8 inches) a year, they produce cracks into which seawater flows. At the same time, magma (molten rock) from the Earth's mantle (the layer beneath the crust that covers the core) flows upward into the zones of fractured rock. The meeting of the water and magma creates hot water that ascends buoyantly to the sea floor.

Scientists have many questions about how the water flows through the complex network of cracks. A particular interest is how the circulating flow of water that extends laterally for tens of yards becomes focused into only a few vents that measure inches in diameter.

Scientists know that when hot fluids rise through cold cracks they exert forces that tend to close vertical cracks. In the past, scientists theorized that a chemical sealing process restricted the fluid flow. Heated water passing through the rock dissolves such chemicals as silica and sulfides. As the hot water encounters cooler rock near the surface, the chemicals come out of solution and theoretically seal the cracks.

However, Dr. Leonid Germanovich of the University of Oklahoma and Dr. Robert Lowell of Georgia Tech's School of Earth and Atmospheric Sciences have a different view. They theorize that the flow itself of hot fluids coming up through cold cracks exerts forces that tend to close the vertical cracks by thermal expansion of the rock. Their research is aimed at determining the kind of thermoelastic stress needed to close enough cracks to narrow the flow to a single pathway.

Other Vents

Scientists estimate that there may be 20,000 active vents associated with centers of oceanic spreading around the world. But hydrothermal vents are not the only underwater sites where communities of strange creatures make their homes.

The petroleum industry hired James Brooks and his colleagues with the Geochemical and Environmental Research Group (GERG) at Texas A&M University, College Station, Texas, to survey for oil seeps on the continental slope. (Moving out from a continent, the underwater land is divided into the continental shelf, the continental slope, the continental rise, and the abyssal plain).

The goal of the survey was to identify targets for potential exploration. In 1984, the scientists not only found oil seeps, they discovered abundant life at those sites.

A crab walks along the basalt rubble near a vent on the Southern Juan de Fuca Ridge of the Pacific Ocean. As scientists study the vents they continue to discover new life forms. Recently, scientists from the Woods Hole Oceanographic Institution came upon swarms of an unknown, tiny amphipod. These shrimplike creatures swim in swarms of 5,000–50,000. The vents seem to be short-lived. How animals spread from one vent to another has been a mystery. However, at the annual meeting of the American Society of Limnology and Oceanography, oceanographer Craig Smith of the University of Hawaii proposed bones from dead whales that have sunk to the sea floor as a possible bridge. In 1988, Smith and other investigators from Hawaii and the University of Washington examined a whale skeleton in the Pacific's Santa Catalina Basin. The skeleton was covered with thick mats of bacteria and by clams and mussels similar to those that surround hydrothermal vents. Smith suggested that such a skeleton contains sufficient organic material to support a chemosynthetic animal community for several years. The researcher reports, "Deaths among gray whales alone could create at least 500 new deep-sea habitats a year in the North Pacific."

In addition to hydrothermal vents, there are other kinds of underwater chemical habitats—hydrocarbon seeps and brine pools. Scientists also have discovered hot, clear-water vents. Recently, an expedition backed by the National Oceanic and Atmospheric Administration (NOAA), discovered an undersea river of super-salty water feeding a 20,000-acre brine pool in the Orca Basin on the Louisiana Continental Slope.

The scientists also discovered communities of what may be new species of giant chemosynthetic tubeworms and mussels on the sea floor 200 miles east of Galveston, Texas. They are growing on fast-forming rock outcroppings near seep sites 9,000 feet down. The outcroppings are being produced from the buildup of massive volumes of calcium and magnesium carbonates as byproducts of microbes in the sediment digesting the seeping hydrocarbons.

Subsequent studies by GERG and by researchers at the University of California at Santa Barbara (UCSB) found extensive life at petroleum seeps at many locations along the U.S. coast. A December 1990 *Sea Frontiers* article entitled "Methane Eaters" reported that the U.S. Minerals Management Service, a federal regulatory agency, now requires offshore drillers to refrain from disturbing these lush oil-seep communities.

Life at the seep is made possible because the clams, mussels, and tube worms that thrive there have formed a unique type of symbiosis, a process in which two dissimilar organisms live together. For instance, bacteria actually live within the cells of their hosts.

Russel Vetter of UCSB told *Sea Frontier:* "It's analogous to the symbiosis that exists between certain plants and nitrogen-fixing bacteria, where the bacteria actually live within—not just on—the plants' root cells. This is something not seen before in animals."

In mussels, bacteria live within the animals' gill cells, or respiratory organs, and use methane as their sole energy source by extracting it from seawater flowing by the gills. By bubbling natural gas into the water of an aquarium, UCSB biologists James Childress and Chuck Fisher were able to raise methane-using mussels.

As long as there was methane in the aquarium water, the mussels grew. When the scientists turned the gas off and provided other types of energy sources, the mussels remained alive but stopped growing. Childress explained: "While these mussels can extract some energy by feeding, it's clear that they must not be able to grow without getting energy from the bacteria; otherwise, you might find them all over the ocean floor and not just at the seep sites."

The distribution of mussels on the continental slope serves as an indicator of where such seeps exist. Scientists have not been able to study the bacteria separate from the mussels to determine how they get their energy from methane. Outside of their hosts, the bacteria don't survive more than a few hours.

Still another kind of seep was found in the Gulf of Mexico in 1989. Using the Navy's nuclear-powered submersible NR-1, Brooks and his colleagues at GERG found what they called a brine pool, a spot on the sea floor that leaks a concentrated salt solution that contains dissolved methane gas.

The salty water is so dense at this seep that it does not mix with the surrounding seawater. The Texas A&M scientists found a thriving community of mussels living in a thin ring surrounding the high-salt water. Partially submerged in the brine, which is 3.5 times the salinity of most seawater, the mussels live in a transitional zone between the toxic-but-nutritious brine and the oxygen-containing, but nutritionless, seawater.

The Place of Vents in Origins-of-Life Theories

The discoveries of hitherto unknown creatures at ocean-floor vents have given rise to speculation by some scientists that life on Earth might have evolved in the deep ocean independent of the sun. A February 1991 *Scientific American* article traces the arguments about the origins of life that have been going on since 1953, when University of Chicago graduate student Stanley Miller seemed to solve the issue with a simple experiment.

Miller re-created the primeval Earth in a sealed glass apparatus he filled with a few liters of methane, ammonia, and hydrogen to represent the atmosphere and some water to represent the oceans. A sparked-discharge device zapped the gases with simulated lightning, while a heating coil kept the water bubbling.

Within a few days, the water and glass were stained with a reddish goo. When Miller analyzed the substance, he found that it was rich in amino acids, organic compounds that link up to form proteins, the basic ingredient of life.

In that same year, 1953, James Watson and Francis Crick deciphered the structure of deoxyribonucleic acid (DNA), whose double-strand helix (spiral) carries the information that cells require to build and organize proteins. Over the next few decades, experiments similar to Miller's demonstrated how the components of DNA, as well as those of proteins, could have been synthesized while accumulating in tidal pools or shallow seas.

Experiments in the early 1980s revealed that ribonucleic acid, RNA, a single-strand molecule that aids DNA in manufacturing proteins, might have the ability to make copies of itself without the assistance of enzymes (organic substances that cause change). Some investigators concluded that Earth's earliest organisms consisted of RNA, and that RNA organisms provided a bridge from simple chemistry to the complex DNA-based cells found in modern organisms.

The RNA-world hypothesis has been seriously challenged and to complicate matters further, recent findings suggest that life may have arisen in an environment far less hospitable than Miller's apparatus. The primordial world may not have contained methane and ammonia as Miller assumed.

Observations of organic compounds in meteorites and comets have led to speculations that the raw material from life fell to Earth from outer space. A German patent lawyer, who holds a doctorate in organic chemistry and speculates on genesis as a hobby, contends that life began as a gummy film on the surface of iron pyrite, better known as fool's gold.

Advocates of the idea that life began in hydrothermal vents argue that the vents could have provided the protection, steady flow of energy, and nutrients needed to make matter animate. Critical of the vent theory, Miller has done experiments that suggest superheated water inside vents would destroy rather than create complex organic compounds.

Miller points out that modern vents seem to be short-lived, lasting only a few decades before they are plugged up. His contention is supported by J. Frederick Grassle's article, "The Ecology of Deep-Sea Hydrothermal Vent Communities," which appeared in *Advances in Marine Biology*, Vol. 23 (1986). Grassle determined that the age of some previously active hydrothermal vents can be dated by the presence of shells of dead bivalves known as *Calyptogena magnifica*.

Scientists know that it takes only about 15 years for *Calyptogena* shells to dissolve. Their presence at a site indicates that a hydrothermal vent existed there within the previous 15 years.

Estimates of heat loss at vents indicate that vents may have life spans of decades or less. An average vent

Pyrite may be a viable structure upon which life can form, as shown in samples of pyrite and tubeworm fossils from the Southern Juan de Fuca Ridge.

puts out 100 megawatts of thermal power, substantially more energy than scientists estimate is provided by a single batch of magma.

None of the origin-of-life theories has gained enough support to be accepted as a new model. But none has been ruled out, which annoys Miller, a rigorous experimentalist. He calls the organic-matter-from-space concept a "loser," the pyrite theory "paper chemistry," and the vent hypothesis "garbage."

Miller grumbles that such work perpetuates the notion that the origin-of-life field is a fringe pursuit of science unworthy of serious pursuit. But other scientists welcome the new ideas.

A major proponent of the theory that vents were wombs of life is John Corliss, who with Robert Ballard explored vents in the submersible *Alvin*. Corliss argues that the vents would not only have supplied the energy and nutrients needed to create and then sustain life, they would have provided protection from all the biggest extraterrestrial impacts.

Support for the vent hypothesis comes from studies conducted by Carl Woese of the University of Illinois at Urbana-Champaign. By comparing the genetic makeup of single-cell organisms, Woese identified a class of microbes he calls archaebacteria, which seem to have undergone less evolutionary change than any other living species. All archaebacteria prefer hot environments. Some survive in temperatures ranging as high as 120 degrees Celsius (248 degrees Fahrenheit). Some species prefer an oxygenless acid environment supplied with sulfur. These are conditions that can be found at hydrothermal vents.

Indiana University biologist Norman Pace pictures the primordial Earth's crust as a "thin roiling scum" of rock pocked by myriad hydrothermal vents. Unlike Corliss, who believes that life originated at the vents, Pace speculates that the first organisms could have been spawned elsewhere—possibly at the surface of the Earth during a lull between impacts—spreading later to the security of the vents. Pace believes that even today great communities of bacteria may exist in networks of geothermal fissures and caverns beneath the mid-ocean ridges.

Much Remains Unknown

Study of former ridge crests that have been placed by plate movement on dry land leads geologists to believe that the process of hydrothermal venting has existed for a long time. Hydrothermal venting has been found beneath the world's oldest and deepest lake, Lake Baikal, north of Mongolia in the southern mountains of Russia.

During a 1990 expedition Katherine Crane, who discovered the first hydrothermal vent in 1977, was the chief scientist on a search for a source of heat in Lake Baikal when her colleagues found hydrothermal vents 1,350 feet below the lake's surface. An August 20, 1990 *Maclean's* article entitled "Discovery in the Deep," described the Lake Baikal find.

Crane used information from U.S. navigational satellites and an underwater sled equipped with cameras, heat sensors and other equipment in her search. On the sled's seventh run, Crane knew they were in the right area because the equipment registered a sharp temperature spike in the near-freezing water.

On July 17 Emory Kristof, pioneer deep-sea photographer for the National Geographic Society and organizer of the expedition, accompanied by a Soviet pilot and technician, descended in *Pisces,* a Soviet-owned, Canadian-built submersible, to look at the vent. They found a teeming community made up of colonies of bacteria, translucent shrimp, mushroom-shaped sponges, worms, snails, and fish never before seen.

Battle Lines in the
War for the West Are Being Redrawn

The lure of America's West has been a constant spur that has kept the nation's population mobile. California continues to grow at a furious pace.

The symbol of a tanned, strong-jawed man on horseback squinting west into a prairie sunset represents individualism in a free country not only to Americans, but also to many who yearn to be free in other parts of the world. Yet the prairie has been trampled into near extinction and the reality of the cow and the cowboy in the West have always been at odds with the myth.

At the height of the cowboy era in the 19th and early 20th centuries, the cowboy's social status was barely above that of the cow. Wealthy cattle barons, who spent little if any time in a saddle, seldom left their corporate headquarters in San Francisco, Chicago, New York, London, and Edinburgh.

Although American historian of the West Frederick Jackson Turner described the frontier as closed before the turn of the century, generations of Americans, including many government officials, continue to believe in the idea of an inexhaustible West. But that notion is under serious challenge.

The myth of boundless wealth lured waves of white settlers to defy the arid desert geography of the West. They shoved aside or killed Native Americans, cut down dense forests, fenced ranges, drained swamps, irrigated deserts, and diverted rivers with massive dams without ever solving the water shortage.

With a population explosion in the West's cities, a growing constituency of new Westerners has rediscovered the solitude of the wilderness and reveres the land for its natural beauty and recreational value.

A satellite image depicts the western United States

America's grasslands have shrunk considerably due to various forms of overuse and abuse. Here, Wayne Paintner of the U.S. Department of Agriculture's Forest Service inspects an old oil drill site that is being rehabilitated to a specific plant density standard.

These new Westerners have risen in opposition to the power of traditional land users, who regard the area as their own to do with as they please. No longer does political power reside in the hands of those whose major interest is grazing, mining, or timber. Power now lies in the cities, where a major anxiety is the acquisition of sufficient water.

Other myths have been added to the notions of freedom and an everlasting frontier. A September 30,

1991 *Newsweek* article entitled "The Custer Syndrome" pointed out that following the Civil War, winning the West became a symbol of restored unity. For some white Westerners who consider themselves settlers of the West, the West serves as a symbol of accomplishment.

America's myths about the old West serve a purpose. They contribute to the national credo that, given hard work and clear thinking, most problems have solutions. But much is left out of the myths such as the massacre of Indians; overgrazing of the range; elimination of the buffalo; ruin of the rivers; clear-cutting of the forest; and gutting of mountains in search of precious metals.

Urban Westerners have had help from historians in re-evaluating the myths and lifestyles of the West. A December 17, 1989 *New York Times* article entitled "Among Historians, the Old Frontier Is Turning Nastier With Each Revision" discussed a group of historians with a bleak view of the West. One goal of those with the new perspective is to demolish the enduring myth of the West as an empty land settled solely by rugged individuals. The work of women, neighbors, and minorities contributed more to settling the West than did loners with guns.

University of Colorado historian Patricia Nelson Limerick, author of *The Legacy of Conquest: The Un-*

Particularly heated are arguments over the management of Western timberland. A new type of feller can selectively cut and remove timber from a site without damage to surrounding vegetation. The equipment is being used to create a harvest unit that also will enhance forage materials for grizzly bears and other wildlife.

Frontier people were an eclectic group. The Old West was a bustling place as people of all backgrounds, including American Indians, traveled extensively. One tribe, the Kiwigapawa (He Moves About), also known as the Kickapoos, is famous for its nomadic habits. This wagon train was made up of Kickapoos heading south toward Mexico. Over the centuries, the Kickapoos migrated from Wisconsin to Illinois to Missouri, and ultimately to Kansas, Oklahoma, Texas, and Mexico.

broken Past of the American West, shatters the notion that the West set Americans free from dependence on the federal government. Western economic exploitation depended on favors from Congress and on complicity between business leaders and politicians, often one and the same people. Moreover, settlers were given free public land by the government.

A prime target of the new history is historian Frederick Turner Jackson, who, while declaring the frontier closed, characterized it as a factor that gave America its unique character by promoting individualism and a democratic culture. Extreme critics call Turner "ethnocentric, racist, and sexist." More moderate is Howard Lamar of Yale University, who told the *New York Times:* "Mr. Turner gave Americans the first theory that told them they had made their own

culture and history. He tapped so many feelings that he has to be celebrated, but that was 100 years ago, and you can't go back to 1890 to explain everything."

Conflict Over Cattle Grazing on Public Lands

The myth of the cowboy is so much a part of the culture that it is not likely to disappear, but the presence of the cow in the West is coming under increasing fire. According to a Spring 1991 *Wilderness* article entitled "Aspects of Grass," environmentalists are no longer alone in their criticism. A growing army of economists, ecologists, and federal land managers contend that the presence of cattle in the West is ecologically disastrous and economically backward, particularly because cattle grazing on public lands jeopardizes a heritage belonging to all Americans.

Many ranchers and Western communities with strong social and economic ties to the livestock industry believe that the granting of grazing rights on public lands of the West is a proper use for the land. A Spring 1991 *Wilderness* article entitled "How the West Was Eaten" explains why land in the West and the cow are incompatible. Cows need enormous amounts of water—an estimated 2,500 gallons for every pound of beef produced. Most cow breeds evolved in water-rich northern Europe, therefore they are inefficient users of water. In other words, an animal highly dependent on water is being raised in a water-poor environment.

Just how water-poor the West is can be seen on a rainfall map. An isohyet is a line on a map connecting areas of equal rainfall. Such a line begins in the vicinity of the eastern border of North Dakota, moves southwest, and veers to the west of Abilene, Texas. In the area west of this isohyet, evaporation is high and precipitation—rain, snow, ice, and hail—drops below 20 inches a year. To complicate matters further, west of this line, precipitation is erratic. Since production of forage, or food for animals, is tied to precipitation, frequent droughts require either massive reductions in livestock herds or they result in destruction of the land from overgrazing.

Recognition that the cow is not suited to the West is not new. John Wesley Powell, founder of the U.S. Geological Survey, noted in a landmark 1879 report that traditional agriculture was ill-suited to the West. In moist, humid Georgia, a cow can be raised year-

The buffalo, or bison, although generally associated with the plains states, were also found once in America's eastern woodlands. The last recorded bison killed east of the Appalachian Mountains was in 1801, near Lewisberg, Pennsylvania. And in 1825, the last buffalo known east of the Mississippi River, a cow and her calf, were killed at Valley Head, West Virginia.

The West's great herds were not decimated until some time after the Civil War. The many people traveling west had some effect on the number of buffalo extant. But the herds could still have sustained millions of people. The herds were destroyed by a relatively small group of hunters, often shooting from trains. Most of those doing the shooting did not bother either to eat the buffaloes or take their hides. Some did it just for kicks. Others were deliberately trying to eliminate the Indians' best means of sustaining themselves.

round on an acre or less. In arid Nevada, it may take 200 acres to raise the same cow. Despite its size and despite the fact that almost the entire state is devoted to livestock production, Nevada raises only as much meat as Vermont.

The majority of the nation's livestock is raised by ranchers in the East, Midwest, and South, not those in the West. However, the livestock industry is the single largest consumer of water in the West. In Montana, agriculture—primarily irrigated hay fields—use 97.5% of the state's water.

To gain water, many dams have been built on Western rivers, with catastrophic results. Dams fragment river ecosystems, and irrigation reduces the amount of water in streams and rivers, thereby concentrating pollutants. As waterways become uninhabitable, wildlife populations crash. Ripple effects

follow. Fewer airborne insects are available to feed birds, bats, and fish. The absence of fish starves otters, minks, and bald eagles.

The presence of cattle worsens the water shortage in other ways. Countless stamps by cattle hooves compact the soil and reduce water infiltration (sinkage into the soil). When not held in place by soil, water runs off rapidly, creating gullies and erosion. Spread out in gullies, water evaporates faster.

Livestock create great damage in fragile riparian zones, the thin lines of lush green vegetation adjacent to streams and springs. Although riparian zones constitute less than 1% of the land base, an estimated 80% or more of the animal species in the West are dependent on these zones. Moving the livestock out of the riparian zones into nearby areas would not solve the problem because watersheds, those regions draining into a body of water, are all connected. Cattle would compact the land in their new locations.

Livestock damage does not stop with watershed destruction. Cows trample the eggs of ground-nesting birds and eat the ground cover in which birds and small mammals live. They also eat forage that would otherwise be eaten by wildlife. The Burns, Oregon district of the federal Bureau of Land Management (BLM) annually allots 252 million pounds of forage for livestock and 8 million for wildlife.

It is clear that funding biases in federal agencies support cattle owners rather than refuge wildlife. One wildlife refuge manager told *Wilderness,* "Nearly all the refuge funding goes towards managing cattle owned by eight permittees. What little is spent on wildlife is mostly damage control. _ While I have people to build and maintain fences, stock ponds, water pipelines, and other developments for permittees and a range conservationist to oversee the grazing program, I don't have one biologist on my staff—and this is supposed to be a wildlife refuge."

Strife Over Sensitive Environments

There are few Western wilderness controversies more emotionally charged than timber disputes. The timber industry buys an estimated 35% of its Northwest harvest from national forests and claims it needs more to stay in business. Conservationists argue that the industry's problems are not due to curbs on cutting U.S. Forest Service trees on public lands, but a result of automation and competition from Canadian timber.

A September 30, 1991 *Newsweek* article entitled "The War for the West" described a bitter battle over 260,000 acres of elk sanctuary in the midst of glacial lakes in an area of northern Idaho called Mallard-Larkins. The timber industry wanted the U.S. Forest Service to open the region's cedar, hemlock, and Western spruce for logging. Environmentalists wanted Congress to designate the area a wilderness.

In northern Idaho, timber provides 45% of the economy. As a consequence of their lobbying for a wilderness, environmentalists were hung in effigy in St. Maries, a timber community of 2,794, about 80 miles from the Mallard-Larkins area.

Another locale of bitter discord is in the Great Plains, the center of the continental United States. The destruction of the tall-grass prairie that once blanketed the eastern third of the Great Plains may have been the greatest ecological tragedy of the continent's settlement. Only 2% of the original tallgrass remains, scattered in patches in a dozen states.

A July/August 1992 *Earthwatch* article entitled "Battle for the Prairie" described a clash that began between environmentalists and ranchers in 1989 in Chase County, Kansas. At the center of the dispute is environmentalists' efforts to turn the Z-Bar ranch, less than 1% the size of Yellowstone Park, into the Flint Hills Prairie National Monument.

For conservation groups, the Z-Bar proposal represents perhaps the last chance in a 40-year failed campaign to preserve some of the nation's remaining tall-grass prairie. In 1960, the National Park Service proposed that 23,000 hectares (56,833 acres) of the Flint Hills area be turned into the Tallgrass Prairie

The West has some of the most spectacular waterways in the country. But the western United States is much drier than the East and, even in good years, water is scarce. For several years the West has suffered a drought.

The desert supports a great deal of life. It has its own kind of arid beauty. At left is a desert tortoise, one of many creatures threatened by loss of habitat. At right is the barrel cactus (Ferocactus acanthodes var. canthodes) found in the Colorado and eastern Mohave deserts. Growing at first in a globular form, it eventually becomes cylindrical as it reaches a height of 5 or 6 feet. Its spines are white or rose-colored. The cactus' slimy, alkaline juice is, despite popular myth, unfit to drink except to save one's life. This species is threatened by vandalism as well as by poachers. Like the very popular saguaro cactus, the barrel cactus is stolen by horticultural collectors for private landscaping. It is also threatened by candy makers of Mexico, who use the pulp.

National Park. Broadly supported by environmentalists and by Secretary of the Interior Stewart Udall, the proposal seemed certain to pass in Congress.

The proposal died after a rancher pointed a double-barrel shotgun at Secretary Udall and ordered him off his land. Some time later, the Kansas Grassroots Association (KGA), a group strongly opposed to the idea of a tall-grass park, was formed.

In 1977 Kansas City Congressman Larry Winn proposed a 75,000-hectare (185,325-acre) national park in Flint Hills to be created out of private land acquired by eminent domain, the takeover by government by a payment to the owner. KGA, in a coalition with the American Farm Bureau and the National Cattleman's Association, put an end to Winn's idea.

By 1989, when the drastically scaled-down Z-bar proposal was made, an entire generation of political leaders and citizens had become divided on the issue. For many ranchers the park symbolically condemned their way of life. One rancher told a congressional subcommittee: "The ranching culture that has kept the Flint Hills in good condition for 150 years is the threatened species. These people are today's Indians."

KGA supporters contend that environmentalists who once wanted a prairie preserve with at least 20,000 hectares (49,420 acres) and a complete watershed are not going to settle for a 4,000-hectare (9,884-acre) ranch. They fear that in time, government will take property by eminent domain. Advocates respond that the real threat to the ranchers' way of life is not the park, but mechanization, which has forced family farms to expand or go bankrupt. When big farms swallow up smaller ones, the younger generation migrates to the cities, and a way of life comes to an end. In mid-summer 1992, these philosophical differences remained unresolved, making chances for a tall-grass park remote.

Another arena of bitter dispute is mining in the Castle Mountains of California's Mojave Desert. A gold rush in 1907 lasting three years left behind a hillside scarred by abandoned claims. Remaining gold was difficult to reach with picks and shovels.

Miners have returned to get the gold left behind—

this time with earth movers and chemicals. They drench multiton scoops of soil with cyanide to draw out gold specks. In 1979, 60,000 ounces of gold were recovered with cyanide. By 1989 the yearly yield had climbed to 3.4 million ounces. Shared concern about the practices of miners who drench the land in cyanide to extract gold has made prickly bedfellows of environmentalists and area ranchers.

Miners of gold and other hard minerals operate under an 1872 law that allows them to file a claim and mine it for little money. Claimants investing only $100 a year in their sites can buy them for as little as $2.50 an acre and resell them.

Mining is just one of many threats to dozens of vulnerable species in the Mojave Desert. The wide expanse of the 15,000-square-mile arid basin in southern California appeals to motorcyclists and off-road-vehicle drivers who destroy wildlife habitats and nests—sometimes inadvertently, often deliberately.

Mining is a source of contention in the West. Strip mining for coal and the use of dangerous chemicals to extract precious minerals from soil are practices that have come under attack all over the country. Many old mining sites are in need of rehabilitation. But mines do not always have to use the most destructive methods to obtain the substances they seek. In the spring of 1992, the Viceroy Resource Corporation of Canada made 4.4 million dollars worth of environmental concessions before ever extracting any gold from its Castle Mountain site. The company's president, Ross Fitzpatrick, agreed to: create a habitat for the endangered desert tortoise, including fencing to keep tortoises out of the mining site; restore the mining site after the company is through with it; and, perhaps most important, to become the first company to build an enclosed cyanide leaching system. The use of cyanide for gold mining is controversial. In a technique called Heap Leach Mining, a solution of cyanide and water is dripped or sprayed on a mound of finely crushed gold ore which rests on an impermeable plastic lining. The solution picks up gold particles as it percolates through the mound. The solution is diverted to giant collecting ponds. From there, to remove the gold, the solution is pumped through coconut shell charcoal filters. The gold goes through further purification and the cyanide solution is recycled. Unfortunately, the giant ponds have always been open. Many birds have been poisoned by them. Closing the system would create a more controlled system and protect wildlife.

Peace Does Not Loom on the Horizon

Battle lines in the war for the West are not as predictable as they once were. They often divide towns in which long-time residents choose up sides over whether increased tourism is desirable. Tourists attracted to the Flint Hills by the presence of a park might bring economic life back to the area. To many ranchers turning their local culture over to outsiders would be agony. However, some nonranchers who live in the towns believe that conservation and economic revitalization are compatible.

Overall, water shortages in the West's arid lands always have been and will continue to be divisive.

After the Civil War, citizenship for former black slaves was granted via a single constitutional amendment. But American Indians acquired U.S. citizenship piecemeal fashion, not receiving full citizenship until 1924. A push was made to register Indians to vote, but they still lacked clout at the ballot box and enough political savvy to easily remedy past injustices and present problems. Often, tribes that have retained some autonomy over reservation lands, have been more likely to have greater success in the federal courts than in legislatures. In 1992, Ben Nighthorse Campbell, a Cheyenne and a three-term member of the U.S. House of Representatives, became the first Native American to be elected to the U.S. Senate.

This photo was taken nearly 50 years ago. Dallas is in the background. This simple illustration of the conflicting demands on the western lands still holds true.

8

EARTH AND ITS OCEANS

Balance of Nature, A Theory Under Fire

Ecologists have long held that there is "a balance in nature," nature meaning the physical world. But this notion is being replaced with a new one in which plant and animal communities perpetually fluctuate. The work of biologist David Botkin at the University of California at Santa Barbara has contributed to this change.

Botkin conceives of the biosphere, those regions of the Earth occupied by living organisms, as "nature" in its largest sense. He believes that current knowledge about the biosphere is not in harmony with entrenched beliefs about nature. His thinking is described in his 1990 book *Discordant Harmonies*.

Botkin uses the history of climate variations during the lifetime of the human species on Earth to illustrate the difficulties involved in assuming stability. There has been no obvious pattern in the Earth's temperature from the ninth century to the present, with the exception of the 20th century, which has been warmer. Viewed from 30,000 years ago to the present there has been a gradual warming, but no constancy or regular cycles of temperatures. Viewed from 150,000 years to the present, the recent 30,000-year warming trend appears to be a fluctuation.

From the perspective of a million years ago, Earth's surface temperature has apparently wandered up and down the scale. Mostly, it has been colder than the present, yet there have been periods of great variation, and periods of little variation, times with apparent cycles and times with no cycles.

The influence of Botkin's thinking was reflected in a July 31, 1990 *New York Times* article entitled "New Eye on Nature: The Real Constant Is Eternal Turmoil." The article reported the findings of a symposium on the balance-of-nature concept held during the 1990 annual meeting of the Ecological Society of America. There, Dr. Stewart T.A. Pickett, a plant ecologist at the New York Botanical Gardens in Millbrook, told the conference: "[The] balance-of-nature concept makes nice poetry, but it's not such great science."

The balance-of-nature theory inevitably leads to the notion that nature knows best and, by definition, human intervention is bad. Ecologists have operated under the assumption that organisms compete and coexist in an ecological system that is essentially stable. The theory assumed predators and prey, for example, moose and wolves or cheetahs and gazelles, maintained an equilibrium. It also assumed that once a forest reached a stage of persistent self-perpetuation, that state became permanent.

Scientists who reject the balance-of-nature concept have determined from their research that ecological communities of plants and animals are inherently unstable due to differences among members of the community. For example, an overly aggressive wolf-pack leader could increase a pack's hunting efficiency and could reduce a pack's source of food to the point of elimination, thereby disrupting the ecosystem. On the other hand, the death of a wolf-pack leader could lead to the breakup and dispersal of the pack, which would tilt the scales of the ecosystem if the wolf's normal prey boomed and, through its increased numbers, eliminated its own prey.

One natural disaster can trigger a domino effect through the so-called equilibrium of nature. Drought that cuts crop yields in turn cuts the food supply for animals as well as people. That can lead to the early slaughter of still-young animals with lower yields of meat for the market and lower yields of leather and wool for the manufacturers—thus, lower profits. The following year may or may not see a recovery depending on how many animals are available for breeding and how depleted the topsoil is.

But even if ecological communities did have some kind of internal equilibrium, external disturbances such as disease, hurricanes, windstorms, fires, and climate change make it difficult—if not impossible—for ecological communities to settle into a steady state. Scientists have found this instability to exist on many scales of time and space, from glacial and global to seasonal and local.

From this new perspective, humans have emerged as just one of many sources of ecological disturbance. For eons, humans and their near relatives have interfered with ecological systems around the world, leaving an indelible mark.

To examine the impact of constant change, Botkin developed a computer model to reflect some of the myriad aspects that contribute to changing a forest's ecology. The variables included: latitude; temperature; amount of rainfall; amount of water in the system due to evaporation, runoff, and storage by vegetation; death rate of trees; characteristics of various tree species; diameters of tree trunks; design of leaves, which determines the amounts of available shade; and composition, depth, and amount of nitrogen in the soil.

From the beginning of recorded history until the industrial revolution that took place from about 1750 to 1850, during which Great Britain shifted from an agricultural to an industrial economy, there were essentially two theories about the character of

nature. The most prominent belief held that Earth was divinely created by God to be perfectly ordered, perfectly stable, and when disturbed to be capable of returning to its steady state.

The notion of an orderly nature was common among the Greeks and the Romans. The same idea was expressed in the 19th century by George Perkins Marsh, the father of American conservation, in his 1864 book *Man and Nature*. A world traveler, Marsh wrote that in countries untrodden by human beings, nature changed "only from geological influences so slow that their geographical condition may be regarded as constant and immutable."

Marsh's position about the constancy and stability of nature have been the predominant view held by environmentalists over the past two decades. The idea of nature undisturbed by human influence is also one generally advocated in textbooks and in popular literature on the environment. Moreover, this idea forms the basis for 20th-century theories about populations and ecosystems and undergirds most national laws and international agreements about the use of wildlife and wild lands.

Despite the predominance of the view of nature as stable, going back as far as the Roman philosopher-poet Lucretius (circa 99–55 B.C.), there has always been a minority view that nature is organic, that is, ever-changing. That notion assumes that Earth is, or is like, a living creature. The organic view perceives nature as passing through major life stages: birth, youth, maturation, maturity, reproduction, old age, senility, and death.

Uncertainty is an organic quality. Although what happened yesterday may determine what happens today, from an organic view, chance can affect the outcome of an organism. A rosebud may not open or, if it does blossom, it may be ugly instead of beautiful, or it may die prematurely. Scientists are beginning to believe that change is inherent and natural in organisms at all levels of complexity. In fact, change appears to be essential for the persistence of life.

The Development of New Metaphors

Until the 17th century, people viewed nature as divinely ordered. Nevertheless, observations of plants and animals, including people, were usually expressed in organic metaphors. The Earth was described as a fellow creature.

But Beginning in the 19th century, the work of two scientists inspired new metaphors about Earth. The research of British mathematician Isaac Newton (1642–1727) on gravitation and motion, and that of German astronomer and mathematician Johannes Kepler (1571–1630) on optics and planetary motion, helped shape the perception of the solar system as comparable to a clock.

Although the three metaphors—the divinely ordered, the organic fellow creature, and the machine operation—are seldom discussed today, they continue to dominate modern thought about nature. The divinely ordered and the mechanistic share a notion of stability, consistency, and an ability to return to a constant state if disturbed.

Today new metaphors about nature are emerging. In Botkin's opinion, they will be based on the space age and on computers. Other scientists believe that metaphors arising from chaos theory, a perspective used term used to describe the behavior of physical systems like flowing water or weather, will be dominant.

Scientists who work with chaos theory report that chaos begins in constantly changing systems when increasing speed or energy forces a system beyond a certain point. A familiar example of chaos is the turbulence that arises when a smoothly moving stream of water reaches a certain speed. Although turbulent, chaotic systems look as if they behave randomly, according to scientists, they exhibit an underlying, long-term order that is not wholly determined nor wholly random.

University of Minnesota ecologists Dr. David Tilman and Dr. David Wedin conducted a study that undermined the balance-of-nature theory by demonstrating a factor that chaos theorists call "sensitive dependence on initial conditions"—often referred to as the "Butterfly Effect." The semiserious analogy implies that a butterfly stirring the air in Peking, China can, within a month, change storm systems in New York City.

The Minnesota scientists experimentally manipulated populations of a native American wild grass, *Agrostis scabra,* known to farmers as "pant-creeper" for the tendency of its thorn-equipped seeds to cling to pant legs. The researchers sewed several *Agrostis* seeds at two initial densities on plots containing 10 different levels of nitrogen, the plant's nourishment.

A plot's expansion and contraction in biomass related to the amount of nitrogen used. Plants in low-nitrogen soils maintained a stable amount of above-ground biomass. But plots with high levels of nitro-

Catastrophic events can contribute to Mother Nature's good health. Destruction can foster growth. In the aftermath of a forest fire, biodiversity flourishes and growth is lush in the cleared area due to the nutrient flush. For some tree species, the high temperatures of a fire are necessary to propagate.

Efforts to preserve wetland habitats, and the wildlife dependent on them, can be wiped out by one major storm that can kill the wildlife and tear up the terrain.

gen expanded and contracted wildly. In 1988, they declined to near extinction. Not only have the plots with low concentration more stable, they recovered faster from a downturn.

The scientists were certain that environmental conditions were not responsible for their findings because four other species of grass growing in the experimental garden at the same time did not crash or lapse into chaotic behavior. The mechanism by which the crashes came about was evident, according to Dr. Tilman.

Increased nitrogen spurred greater plant growth. When the above-ground growth died in winter, it left in place a heavy layer of litter. In spring, the litter prevented new shoots of grass from growing, thereby leading to the crash.

In Botkin's opinion, if the Minnesota experiment had been done 15 or 20 years ago, the explanation for the crash would not have seemed obvious because the basis for interpreting the results was not available then. With a new model, scientists can look at their results from a new perspective.

The study of chaos is particularly difficult in ecological systems because such systems don't operate with the preciseness of a flow of fluid in a tube or of a chemical reaction. Dr. William Schaffer of the University of Arizona, a pioneer in the chaos of ecological systems, believes that ecologists tend to look at chaos in a system as a mathematical curiosity. This attitude unfortunately may make them inclined to assess the work of Tilman and Wedin with skepticism.

Schaffer thinks striving to achieve a mythical balance point in nature ignores the many species in which population densities fluctuate enormously. As a practical focus of study, the dynamics of a population or an ecosystem in nature take too long to unfold. The Tilman-Wedin research makes possible an experimental approach with seminatural systems that can be completed in reasonably short periods of time.

Botkin insists that efforts to manage natural resources based on the notion that nature undisturbed is constant and stable have failed catastrophically. In his book, he described a disastrous attempt to manage the elephant population in Kenya's Tsavo National Park.

Tsavo Park management avoided human intervention on the assumption that the herds would achieve an equilibrium. The sought-after equilibrium was never achieved. Instead, a park was reduced to a wasteland, stripped of vegetation, and 6,000 elephants starved to death. Similar management approaches in the United States have resulted in the extinction or near extinction of one fish species after another.

In Botkin's opinion, the notion that nature knows best alienates and separates people from nature. If the concept is abandoned, he believes: "We can arrive, with the best information available for us in our time, at a new organic view of the Earth, a view in which we are a part of a living and changing system whose change we can accept, use, and control to make the Earth a comfortable home."

An obstacle to acceptance of an organic view of nature is the fear that by accepting some change, conservation managers and environmentalists would be forced to accept any and all changes. Botkin recognizes that some changes are undesirable, but he does not accept that as a reason for clinging to an out-

Hurricane Andrew is a prime example of a disaster that can affect the life of a region for years. With more than 50,000 buildings leveled, businesses and industries were wiped out along with families' homes. Air pollution is up dramatically in the affected area because debris from destroyed buildings and rotting garbage has to be burned. Moreover, oil and other toxic contaminants from smashed boats spilled into the waters.

Although not as badly as first feared, wildlife in Florida, already suffering due to loss of habitat and excessive strain on the water supply by an increasing population, were further affected by the hurricane. Crops were destroyed. Farmers agreed to plant winter crops only after the state pledged to rebuild a needed food-processing plant in two months. The old plant, lost to the hurricane, took nearly two years to build.

moded theory.

Without the theory for support, conservation management is unnerving. In a June 10, 1991 *Boston Globe* article entitled "Perhaps Nature Doesn't Have All the Answers," historian Richard White of the University of Washington asserted that acceptance of responsibility for the condition of the future environment will remain a formidable barrier to discarding the balance-of-nature theory.

Some environmental historians share Botkin's view

that there is no discoverable pristine nature unaffected by human activity. They point out this perspective means that even if the notion of a stable environment were accurate, there would be nowhere to look for guidance in directing the environment of the future. Naturally, from an organic perspective, nature can in some cases act as a guide, since biological limitations often set terms. But nature cannot tell humans what is the best of a range of alternatives. Therefore, Botkin argues that humans must intervene as best they can: "We don't have any choice. We are already messing with nature and we have already set in motion things that will not be relieved if we stop."

Whether fluctuation is an inherent property of systems or the result of external disruptions remains a critical unanswered question. Either way, chaos theories suggest that, at least in principle, such processes can be analyzed and understood.

Viewed from a perspective of chaos theory, the position that systems should just be left alone and everything will turn out right are unreasonable. In Schaffer's view, "What we have to do is understand how these systems behave and then we as people can decide what we want, how to manage them appropriately."

Human efforts are a factor in the equation of nature's forces, constantly affecting events in the environment. Here, a soil conservation technician directs some Boy Scouts as they collect and harvest Volga giant wild rye for sand dune planting.

Scientists Who Are Women Are Gaining Recognition for Their Work

Although efforts have been made in recent decades to recruit women into science, as an occupation it continues to be dominated by men. The explanation most frequently offered is that men are drawn to science in greater numbers because they are better at it.

Many social scientists believe that a more accurate explanation is that barriers in education and industry deflect women from pursuing careers in science. Historian David Noble of York University in Toronto, Ontario, Canada believes that the social barriers reflect a long tradition of exclusion.

In an excerpt from his 1992 book *A World Without Women,* which appeared in the May/June 1992 issue of *Technology Review,* Noble wrote: "For the most part, the exclusive identification of science with men has been taken as a given. Yet such a phenomenon demands an explanation. Throughout most of its evolution, science has not simply excluded women; it has been defined in defiance of women and in their absence."

Noble traces the exclusion of women back to the Christian clerical tradition of the Middle Ages. As Western science evolved, early practitioners were monks living in monasteries, a world that excluded women. The 13th-century friar Roger Bacon, who anticipated modern technology, perceived science as a sacred means for interpreting the Bible and for converting unbelievers.

But outside the walls of the monasteries, a movement of humanists, people who emphasized human interests rather than religion, redefined Christianity and created new arenas for intellectual activity. The humanists were just as averse as the clergy to women, but since their philosophy stressed the education of each individual, learning for women was sanctioned.

The humanist movement revived ancient traditions of alchemy, a search for a universal remedy for disease and a method to transform base metals into gold. Alchemical traditions were spiritual, but they also were based on observations of the natural world.

The 16th-century alchemist Paracelsus transformed medicine by searching beyond the walls of universities. He sought knowledge from such groups as "old wives," gypsies, wandering tribes, and robbers. Much of the knowledge he derived came from so-called "cunning men," that is, village practitioners of popular magic—most of whom were women. Along with their stores of charms and amulets, which were worn around the neck to ward off evil, the village women had developed a pharmacy of remedies, including pain killers, digestive aids, and anti-inflammatory agents. Their practical remedies were far superior to those developed by university-trained physicians.

In the 16th and 17th centuries, an explosion of small religious sects separated themselves from established churches. They shared a deep-seated hostility toward the clergy. The new sects promised salvation through direct connection with God. The connection was gained through spiritual guidance, prophecy (being influenced to speak by God), and through the ancient magic known to wise women. In this way, for the first time since the Middle Ages, women were included in the development of Western philosophy and science.

Unfortunately, women's identification with these diverse social and intellectual movements provided orthodox believers an excuse to accuse particular women of heresy, that is, of being a witch. Almost all of the millions of victims accused were women, including a great number who were executed. In one day, 400 women were murdered in Toulouse.

Increasingly in the 18th century, European women were defined as creatures of passion rather than reason. They were perceived as emotional, irrational, and intuitive—terms synonymous with heresy and religious radicalism. These traits were thought to make them unfit for involvement in objective science. While scientifically trained men excluded women from participation, they had no qualms about appropriating women's knowledge, particularly in medicine.

A trend toward the exclusion of women also took place in America. In the summer of 1889 the American Chemical Society held a "Misogynist's [woman hater's] Dinner." Modern women scientists have inherited this long tradition of ill will, which Noble believes should never be underestimated, given its long history.

Barriers Continue But Some Are Being Breached

The social barriers to women's participation in science begin early and influence vocational choices. Wellesley College Sociologist Paula Rayman, director of the Center for Research on Women, was quoted in a May/June 1992 *Technology Review* article entitled "The Lost Girls" as saying: "All kindergartners are natural scientists." But a whole range of pressures from inadequate teaching, to learning styles, and family pressure removes girls permanently from consideration of science as a career.

The women who make it past the initial obstacles still face problems. The March 13, 1992 *Science* included a special section entitled "Women in Science: 1st Annual Survey." In an essay entitled "Women in Science: From Panes to Ceilings," Dr. Bernadine Healy, Director of the National Institutes of Health, commented that women scientists, like women in many other fields, eventually hit the "mommy track" or the "glass ceiling."

By the mommy track she meant that for women scientists—unlike men scientists—having children subtracts time from an ongoing career and is often viewed by superiors and colleagues as a lack of commitment, when in fact it means the woman has taken on two full-time jobs.

The glass ceiling refers to organizational norms, or customary behaviors, that exclude women from rising to positions of power. The types of organizations with glass ceilings are tremendously varied. Among others, they include colleges and universities, research companies, and professional societies. An organization's widely accepted norms are seldom stated aloud or written down. Their existence can be denied even while, like an invisible glass ceiling, they block women's promotions beyond a certain level.

A major problem for women, according to the *Science* survey, is a lack of mentors, the senior professionals who serve as friends and counselors. Individual science faculty members—mostly male—take on male students as protégés and help guide their careers.

Through a mentor, a young scientist makes contacts with meeting organizers, journal editors, and other researchers, all of which lead to career advancement. The few women who are able to find mentors are apt to be accused of having a sexual relationship with them. Mathematician Jerry Marsden, of the University of California at Berkeley, told *Science*: "I had a female graduate student who wrote a fine thesis. Around the time it was being completed, a graduate student told me that it was 'common knowledge' that I wrote her thesis in exchange for sexual favors—which of course was not true."

Many successful women scientists graduated from women's colleges, where they were counseled well by both male and female faculty mentors, with whom they formed long-lasting alliances. One innovative solution to the mentor problem emerged at a 1987 Austin, Texas computer conference. Out of 400 attendees at the conference, only about 30 were women. A couple of women began talking in the ladies' room. Every time someone new came in, they stayed to participate in the talk.

Madame Marie Sklodowska Curie obtained an education and an entre to a world generally denied to females. However, it was her genius that earned her international acclaim. With her husband, Professor Pierre Curie, she discovered the element radium.

As a consequence of the ladies'-room interaction, the women launched a computer network called Systers, a combination of sisters and systems. The network of 900 members ranging from undergraduates to senior faculty serves a variety of functions in addition to a mentor program. It is run from the terminal of computer scientist Anita Borg at Digital Equipment Corporation's Western Research Laboratory in Palo Alto, California.

Women who aspire to be scientists also face a shortage of role models, people whose presence serves as an example. In the United States, a total of 186,300 faculty members teach science at four-year colleges and universities. The breakdown is 151,400 men and 34,900 women; 68% of the men but only 36% of the women hold tenure. Some 14,171 women represent 21.5% of all medical school faculty. Only 9.8% of them are full professors, and there are no women deans.

Yet some women scientists are avoiding being sidelined by the mommy track, are cracking the glass ceiling, and are becoming role models for younger women who may choose to follow in their footsteps. Their efforts are finally receiving some media recognition.

In the course of discussing problems faced by women scientists, the March 13, 1992 issue of *Science* provided biographical sketches of 29 women. In an issue devoted to women, the December 1991 *Discover* provided longer sketches of 11 women scientists. And the October 8, 1990 issue of *Fortune* included three women among the 12 people considered to be "America's Hot Young Scientists."

The controversial views of biologist Lynn Margulis have been covered in many publications, including *Smithsonian, Time,* and *Newsweek.* Marine Scientist and deep-sea diver Sylvia Earle, former director of the National Oceanic and Atmospheric Administration (NOAA), has been written about in several publications, including the October 15, 1989 *Boston Globe Magazine* and the June 23, 1991 *New York Times Magazine.*

Some of the Women Making a Difference

Although it is not possible to do justice to the scope of their work, biographical sketches can help to provide a glimpse of the breadth of the arenas in which women are making a difference.

Lynn Margulis of the University of Massachusetts at Amherst advanced the understanding of the Kingdoms of Life.

LYNN MARGULIS, a biologist at the University of Massachusetts at Amherst, has amused, provoked, and enlightened her colleagues for more than two decades. Margulis believes that symbiosis, (physical association between different organisms who are members of different species) is a major force behind the appearance of new kinds of beings in evolution.

In her opinion, study should not be directed toward individuals but toward symbiotic systems, which are typically self-maintaining, or autopoietic. Autopoietic systems preserve their boundaries and regulate their biochemical compositions. The smallest autopoietic entity, according to Margulis, is the bacterial cell. The largest is Earth.

Margulis has always been willing to take on scientific sacred cows. Her current target is neo-Darwinism, the reigning set of ideas of evolutionary biology. These involve a synthesis of a concept of natural selection developed by Charles Darwin and Mendalian-style genetics. New living forms are claimed to evolve by change, by "random mutation" in neo-Darwinism, but Margolis does not agree.

Margulis also works with the Gaia hypothesis, first proposed in the 1960s by the unorthodox British chemist and inventor James Lovelock. He contended that Earth as a whole is alive, a position he subsequently modified. However, Lovelock continues to insist that life on Earth regulates aspects (temperature, gas, composition) of the environment. Margulis rejects the idea that Earth is a single live being. Instead she envisions it as an ecosystem with many interacting living beings that greatly modulate their surroundings.

Although the general public has shown great interest in the idea, the concept of Gaia has been described by many of Margulis' peers as fantasy. Stephen Gould, the essayist and evolutionary biologist, described the public's interest in the idea by say-

Mimi Koehl holds an artificial insect modeled to resemble ancient insects that existed about the time flight emerged. With handmade insects, under an artificial sun, Koehl and Joel Kingsolver of Brown University developed the first solid evidence on the evolution of flight. They demonstrated that the earliest insect wings were of no aerodynamic value. Instead, they may have served as miniature solar panels to warm up the insects.

ing: "Gaia is warm and fuzzy and it strikes a chord."

Not all of Margulis' peers dismiss her stance as fantasy. Many believe it is important to have scientists whose ideas counter the prevailing wisdom to keep science from bogging down in old ways of thinking.

MIMI KOEHL, a bioengineer who has gained fame in the field of comparative mechanics, received in 1990 what is commonly known as a MacArthur genius award, a large grant free of any obligations, based on past creativity. She seeks answers to such questions as: How does an organism's size and shape affect how it lives and moves? How do the laws of physics make an impact on whether an organism is predator (eats) or prey (is eaten)?

Born to an artist mother and a physicist father, Koehl's innovative ways of obtaining answers often combine serious science with great fun. When observations of organisms are impossible because they are too small or too fast or extinct, she builds models out of unlikely materials, such as carpet scraps, dental plastic, and gelatin.

She finds bioengineering more satisfying than straight biology because it adds precision to the answers she seeks. On an October day in 1987, in a search for precise answers she hurled pink plastic frogs off her redwood deck, while 17 feet below evolutionary biologist Sharon Emerson watched the frogs' trajectories (paths of movement).

Emerson, who holds a joint appointment at the University of Utah and the Field Museum of Natural History in Chicago, has been doing fieldwork on the evolutionary origins of "flight" among frogs that leap 40 feet from tree to tree to work their way from the intermingled treetops, or canopy, to the ground. The frogs need to get to the ground to breed because there are not enough large, long-lasting puddles in the canopy to sustain tadpoles.

In several ways, the frog fliers are different from their nonflying relatives. They have enlarged hands and feet, full webbed fingers and toes, and rubbery skin protruding from upper arms and thighs. Instead of stretching their legs straight out as most frogs do when they jump long distances, the fliers fling themselves into the air with arms and legs akimbo.

Textbooks suggested that the strange flight pose enabled the frogs to fly faster, but no one really knew. Koehl and Emerson set out with models to find the answer. Emerson's dentist made the frogs' arms and legs out of plastic gel normally used to fit dentures. Koehl and Emerson stuck stiff wires through the plastic so the models could be posed as flier and nonflier. To make webbing, they strung thread over five wire toes and dipped each fake foot into a gel used to make plastic flowers.

To measure the forces that largely determine a leaping frog's travel ability, they suspended each frog in front of an 8-foot-long cardboard tube with a fan blowing at one end. The critical forces are lift and drag. Lift is the upward thrust of air, and drag is air pushing back as an object moves forward. Lift is analogous to water holding up a swimmer, and drag is analogous to the resistance of the water as the swimmer tries to move forward.

To their surprise, Koehl and Emerson found that the frogs' bent-legged flying posture and special anatomy detracted from flight distances. The combination improved the frogs' capacity to parachute and the bent leg prevented them from landing upside down. They also improved the frog's ability to turn sharply, important in their fall through the trees.

SUSAN SOLOMON, a chemist with NOAA in Boulder, Colorado, was entranced as a 10-year-old by Jacques Cousteau's televised adventures. In 1985, like other scientists, she was shocked when researchers detected a hole in the ozone layer over the South Pole. The ozone layer, located between 32,000 and 74,000 feet, shields the Earth from the sun's ultraviolet radiation, which in moderate doses can cause skin cancer and, if not blocked by the ozone layer, would

Susan Solomon, one of the National Oceanic and Atmospheric Administration's well-known chemists, is recognized for her study of the Antarctic ozone hole.

destroy life on Earth.

Scientists suspected the hole was caused by chlorofluorocarbons (CFCs), gases manufactured for use in refrigerators, aerosol cans, and in the production of semiconductors (substances whose ability to conduct electricity is dependent on temperature).

Like many chemists around the world, Solomon spent months working on the problem. While watching a slide presentation on polar stratospheric (upper atmosphere) clouds, she solved the puzzle. She noted that stratospheric clouds are more extensive in Antarctica than anywhere else and wondered whether CFC derivatives reacted with the cloud surfaces.

To test her hunch, Solomon organized an expedition to Antarctica to gather data. Her theory was confirmed within a year, and industrialized nations began regulating CFC use. In 1989 she was awarded the U.S. Department of Commerce's gold medal for "impeccable science in the cause of humankind."

SALLIE BALIUNAS, an astrophysicist at the Harvard-Smithsonian Center for Astrophysics, dreamed as a child of being an astronaut. Instead, she studies sunspots, dark spots where coiled and twisted, intense magnetic fields deep within the sun erupt to the surface.

Every 11 years, on the average, the sun's activity becomes frenzied. Magnetic storms revealed by sunspots suddenly increase. Hot gases hurl themselves into space in enormous arcs, and great eruptions pitch charged particles in all directions. Baliunas and her colleagues established that other stars the same age and size behaved in the same way.

While writing her thesis on solar dynamics in 1977, Baliunas visited a group of astronomers at Mount Wilson in Pasadena, California who were looking for sunlike characteristics in nearby stars. When the astronomer who had begun the Mount Wilson study retired in 1978, no one on the team

was willing to take his place. Baliunas took the job, and began commuting back and forth between Cambridge, Massachusetts and Mount Wilson. By 1980 she was in California full time, overseeing observation of up to 50 stars.

The closest stars are mere points of light on the most powerful telescope, and sunspots, or star spots, that serve as clues to magnetic storms are invisible. Therefore, astronomers have to rely on the fact that gases glow with very specific wavelengths. The signature, or characteristic, wavelength of singly ionized calcium (calcium with one electron knocked off) can be easily identified by spectrographs, which are pictures of an array of wavelengths. When this tiny sliver of the star's spectrum is brightest, it serves as an indicator that magnetic activity is at its highest.

On several occasions, the Mount Wilson researchers found that some stars under observation, after holding steady for several star years, brightened in the calcium wavelength. They brightened in approximately the same 11-year pattern as the sun.

The peak of one of the sun's 11-year cycles, the solar maximum, came in 1980. During that year, while Baliunas and her colleagues trained their instruments on distant sunlike bodies, they kept an eye on the sun. The sun's radiance, long thought to be constant, increased by about 0.1%. At the same time, magnetic activity began to rise.

Astrophysicist Sallie Baliunas specializes in the study of the sun.

Along with other sun watchers, the Baliunas team found over the next several years that as solar maximum began to wane toward solar minimum, the sun's brightness also faded. They reasoned that the same might be true for sunlike stars as well.

Because they had collected data only on magnetism over the years but none on brightness, they linked up with a radiance observing project at the Lowell Observatory, outside Flagstaff, Arizona. The two teams found that as stars rotated and their magnetic readings rose or fell, their brightness changed in the same way. However, about one-fourth of the stars surveyed had no discernible cycle.

Baliunas reasoned that the stars that displayed no apparent cycle might be comparable to other longer cycles of the sun that last several decades, during which sunspot activity rises to higher maximums and lower minimums than they do during the shorter 11-year cycle. Nineteenth-century astronomer Walter Maunder determined from astronomical records that during such a cycle from 1645 to 1715, a period of seven decades, sunspot activity came to a virtual standstill. Those years are now known as the Little Ice Age.

Baliunas reasoned that such dramatic solar fluctuation could produce significant temperature changes on Earth. To check her hunch, she examined tree-ring data compiled by paleontologists at the Universities of Arizona and Washington and found reflections of high and low magnetic activity extending back at least as far as the 10,000-year ring records go. She found similar confirmation in records of ancient crops. Her findings are significant for computer climate models that calculate greenhouse warming.

In honor of her research into the cycles of stars that are like the sun, Baliunas was awarded the 1988 American Astronomical Society's Newton Lacey Pierce Prize, a yearly award to an outstanding young observer.

MARY-CLAIRE KING is a geneticist in the Department of Environmental Health at the University of California at Berkeley. Her primary work is a search for the genes responsible for breast cancer. She took time out to help develop methods to identify abducted children in Argentina. Following the overthrow of Isabel Peron's civilian government in 1976, a military regime seized power and embarked on a

Mary-Claire King is a professor of epidemiology at the School of Public Health, University of California at Berkeley.

seven-year program of kidnapping, torture, and murder. An estimated 12,000 people—known as the disappeareds—were picked up and never seen again. At least 210 children were either kidnapped or born in captivity.

In 1977 a group called the Grandmothers of the Plaza of May began a weekly vigil in the plaza across from the military government's offices demanding the return of their children and grandchildren. The grandmothers became a powerful intelligence-gathering organization tracking down the fate of their children.

By the time the military relinquished power in 1983, it was apparent that most of the adults had been killed. But the fate of the children remained unknown. Some of the children had been given to the military. Others had been given away or sold to collaborators. The grandmothers' goal was to find the children and return them to their natural families.

First, the grandmothers had to find a means of identifying the children that would stand up in court. They were referred to Mary-Claire King by the American Association for the Advancement of Science. King's task was to show that a given grandmother and a given grandchild shared genetic markers, variations in patterns of their deoxyribonucleic acid (DNA), so specific that a match had to be the result of biology and not chance.

King developed an approach based on genes that code (set up the arrangement of chemicals) for human leukocyte antigens (HLAs), which are proteins that stud the surface of white blood cells and distinguish "self" from "nonself." HLAs enable organ donors to be matched with organ transplant recipients. King's technique works best when more than one relative is available to make a match.

To overcome the need for more than one relative, King turned to a technique used by one of her mentors to trace the human race back to "Eve." King and Cristian Orrego, director of the DNA Laboratory at the Museum of Vertebrate Zoology at Berkeley, developed a test based on small bodies that supply a cell's energy, called mitochondrial DNA. The new approach requires only a single maternal relative.

SYLVIA EARLE, an oceanographer and marine biologist, and for a time NOAA's chief scientist, is one of the world's foremost divers. She was one of the first of three pilots to take a one-person submersible vessel to a depth of 3,000 feet, and she hopes one day to reach the deepest known point in the ocean, a very

Sylvia Earle is a marine biologist.

dark 35,800 feet. Earle is passionate about the ocean and concerned about the destruction of the Earth's environment.

Although the whole world watched when Neil Armstrong and Buzz Aldrin planted a flag on the moon in 1969, a single underwater camera recorded the moment in 1979 when Sylvia Earle planted a flag on the bottom of the ocean floor, following the deepest untethered dive in history. Strapped to the front of a submarine, dressed in a spacelike suit, Earle descended 1,250 feet.

In 1981 Earle founded a company, Deep Ocean Engineering, with her husband Graham Hawkes, who designed an easy-to-use one-person submersible he calls *Deep Flight*. Earle hopes *Deep Flight's* ease of operation will someday coax even nondivers into the sea. She said, "If a critical mass of people had an opportunity to see the ocean from the inside out there would be far more respect for what we're losing, far more concern."

For 30 years, Earle has collected and pressed plant specimens. One of her goals in life is to create a complete catalog of the Gulf of Mexico's plant life.

Earle's life reflects some of the difficulties associated with being a scientist who happens to be a woman. She has been married three times. The first two marriages ended in divorce and, although she still works closely with her husband, they no longer live together. She told the *New York Times,* "It's repeatedly been my choice to opt for a career as a scientist—if you want to call 'being a scientist' a career. A scientist is what I am, fundamentally, beyond being a woman, beyond being a wife, beyond being a mother. It's just who I am."

One factor that is clear, even from brief glimpses of women scientists at work, is their enjoyment of science and their relish in finding answers that elude them.

9

WEATHER AND CLIMATE

Solar Architecture and Technology Are Rediscovered Periodically

The evolution of solar architecture is regularly interrupted by the discovery of cheap, seemingly plentiful fuels, such as newly discovered forests, or deposits of coal, oil, natural gas, or uranium. Whenever the new sources run out or turn out to have disastrous consequences, solar technology is once again rediscovered and hailed as an exotic energy source.

In a preface to *A Golden Thread: 2,500 Years of Solar Architecture and Technology* (1980) by Ken Butti and John Perlin, energy expert Amory Lovins reported that people who have championed the merits of solar energy have always faced the same obstacles. Those hurdles include misinformation spread by competing vested interests, and a lack of accurate comparisons of the costs, rates and risks of using solar energy compared with those of using other fuel sources. Most daunting to solar advocates is widespread ignorance about what solar energy has accomplished recently and in prior ages.

Solar Architecture's Long History

Almost 2,500 years ago, fuel shortages in Greece spurred the use of the sun as an alternative energy source. By the fifth century B.C., many parts of Greece were almost denuded of trees. Advocates like Socrates urged the Greeks, who were blessed by a climate that was sunny almost all year-round, to construct their homes to take advantage of the sun's rays during moderately cool winters and to avoid the sun's rays during hot summers.

The Greeks understood that in winter the sun travels in a low arc across the southern sky and in summer it passes high overhead. Greek homes were built so that the slanted winter sun's rays entered each house through a south-facing portico similar to a covered porch. In summer, the sun's position higher in the sky cast rays at too steep an angle to enter the portico, and the roof acted as a shade.

The northern Greek city of Olynthus, where temperatures often fell below freezing in winter, revolted in the fifth century B.C. to escape the domination of Athens. Adjacent to the old city of Olynthus, the citizens erected a more defensible community, North Hill, for the city's 2,500 inhabitants.

Since they were building a completely new community, the city's designers incorporated the principles of solar architecture. They set the town atop a sweeping plateau and built the streets perpendicular to each other, running north and south and east and west. Constructed all at the same time, block-long rows of houses, each with a southern exposure, ensured equal access to the sun for all residents. The 18-inch-thick north wall of each block made of adobe brick kept out winter winds.

Solar architecture and urban planning in China evolved along lines similar to those in Greece. The streets of important cities were aligned with the points of the compass. The preferred house plan strongly resembled that of Olynthian homes. There were few window openings on the north, east, and west walls. Large, wood lattice windows on the south were covered by translucent rice paper or silk. Decorative overhangs on the south-facing courtyard protected the interior in summer.

The sunlit atrium was a common feature of Roman homes. This one was excavated at Pompeii.

China's use of solar architecture and urban planning continued and reached greater heights than it had in ancient Greece. One of the first Europeans to visit China, Gabriel Magalhaes, a 17th-century Portuguese priest, returned to Europe with praise for the way Peking and other cities were built. Homes were designed according to the cosmology, a philosophy of the universe that pervaded Chinese culture. South was equated with summer and warmth, and north was equated with winter and cold.

In ancient Rome, wood consumption was even more extravagant than in Greece. In the third century B.C., the Mount Cimino region a short distance from Rome was heavily forested. By the first century B.C., Romans were importing wood from the Caucausus mountains, which lie between the Black and the Caspian seas, more than a thousand miles away.

Unlike the Greeks, solar heating was used only by the very rich in Rome. Just how much the Romans used the sun is impossible to say, but the "solar fur-

nace room" (*heliocaminus*) was sufficiently popular that the building of objects that blocked solar access prompted those who were thrown in shadow to sue. Ulpian, a second-century jurist, ruled in their favor.

Because the Roman Empire covered a far greater area than the Greek city-states, solar architecture had to be tailored to many different environments. Vitruvius, the preeminent Roman architect of the first century B.C., recommended that buildings in extremely hot regions, such as North Africa, should be opened to the north. But in temperate parts of the empire, such as the Italian peninsula, he advised that buildings should be shut in on the north.

Although colored glass had been used for 3,000 years, it was not until the first century A.D. that an anonymous Roman used transparent materials to make windows that would not only let in light, but would also keep out rain and snow. The Romans used sun-heated air in glassed-in greenhouses to cultivate plants.

The Romans also used trapped solar heat to help heat their public baths. From the first century A.D. onward, public baths were immensely popular gathering places for people of all walks of life—the largest bathhouse, Caracalla, could hold 2,000 people. The south walls of bathhouses were glazed, that is, fitted with windows, and the hot bath (*caldarium*) faced the winter sun.

Sporadic Use of Solar Architecture

For almost a thousand years after the Fall of Rome, European architects virtually ignored the ideas of solar architecture advocated by Socrates, Aristotle, Vitruvius and others. Although a few indigenous examples of solar architecture continued to flourish in some areas of Europe, the main urban centers were not planned taking the sun into account.

During the Renaissance, a revival of Greek and Roman architectural styles in Italy prompted Italian designers to consult the essays of Vitruvius and others. But when the Classical influence reached northern Europe, architects copied only the outward forms of ancient buildings, without paying attention to the solar principles that made them functional. Ironically, northern Europe's wealthy classes bought fuel to heat northern- facing mansions at the same time that they served tea in solar-heated greenhouses,

where their prized peaches basked.

While the middle and upper classes sipped tea in the sunny winter warmth of glassed gardens or conservatories, the urban poor were packed into sunless rooms they could not afford to heat. England was the first European nation to industrialize and develop the squalid slums depicted in Charles Dickens' novels.

Crowded working-class neighborhoods became sites for lethal epidemics that took thousands of lives. Physicians coined the phrase, "Where the sun doesn't go, the doctor does." As epidemics threatened entire cities—including the wealthier districts—reformers pressed the government to deal with the housing crisis.

In response to the reformers' outrage, as early as the 1860s, working-class communities were developed to provide healthy residences for industrial laborers. Port Sunlight on the southern bank of the Mersey River, near Liverpool, was one of the earliest

Greenhouses may be the most common of solar heated architectural structures. Below is the most spectacular greenhouse ever built, the Crystal Palace at Kew Gardens in England.

A turn-of-the-century brochure advertises the merits of Climax Solar-Water Heaters. Solar hot water heaters were common well into the 20th century. More solar heaters were sold in 1920 than in any other year. But discoveries of natural gas seriously cut into the solar market. Improvements made over the years resulted in a faster heating process and increased retention of heat. One needed improvement, the manufacture of a solar system entirely made of one kind of metal to prevent corrosion, never came about. Although engineers understood the principle, apparently solar manufacturers did not. By the late 1940s solar tanks were bursting due to preventable corrosion.

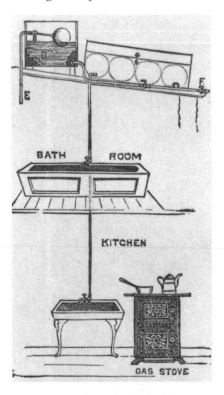

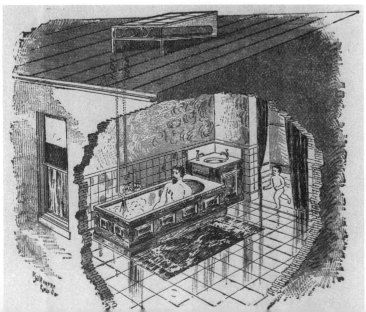

projects. The community was built by Lever Brothers for employees who worked in one of its soap factories.

Most of the spacious sunlit working-class communities of the late 19th century and early 20th century were built in the suburbs or the countryside. To investigate the feasibility of similar housing in urban areas, Augustin Rey, a French housing official, set out in 1912 to discover the minimum amount of open space needed around a structure to make sure it was not blocked from the winter sunlight by another building.

He calculated the length of shadows cast by two-, four-, and six-story buildings. Rey found that given the geographic latitude of Paris, to avoid being cast in shadow, south-facing buildings built in back of one another had to have a space between them of at least 2.5 times their height. But buildings oriented north-south and facing east or west needed to be spaced only 1.5 times their height to avoid shading.

Rey's findings raised serious questions about whether solar access would ever be feasible in urban areas. Paris, he concluded, already had a population three times the ideal size for solar housing.

Following World War I, the use of solar architecture emerged in Germany. A nation whose resources were being expropriated by the victorious Allies, Germany had to economize in any way possible. Because of an acute housing shortage, large apartment complexes were constructed instead of individual homes. Long narrow buildings several stories high were built in parallel rows.

Since, as Rey had calculated earlier, the best arrangement in terms of land economy—though not in terms of solar heating—was an east-west orientation, it became the pattern that soon dotted Germany. Rows of houses, two-rooms deep, ran north-south.

In theory, half of the main rooms received morning sun and half the evening sun. In practice, the sun's rays provided only modest amounts of heat in winter and too much heat in summer. By the 1930s, German architects perceived large-scale apartment complexes as uneconomical and moved toward building single-story solar homes in rows whose main rooms faced south. The new movement had barely ¬ when the decade's economic and political upheavals that led to World War II brought it to a halt.

Solar developments sprang up elsewhere following World War I but never gathered the momentum generated in Germany. Following World War II, growing prosperity and cheap fossil fuels dampened impetus everywhere toward further development.

Early Use of Solar Heating in America

One of the most sophisticated examples of solar architecture is the "sky city" of Acoma, built by Acoma Indians 60 miles west of Albuquerque, New Mexico, on a rock mesa 357 feet high with steep sides. Acoma has three rows of cliff-side dwelling units running east to west. Each unit has two or three tiers placed so that every residence gets full exposure to the sun. Doors and windows open to the south.

The adobe walls of Acoma homes absorb the more direct rays of the winter sun and the walls give off their heat at night. Horizontal roofs atop each tier are built of straw and adobe layered over by pine timbers and branches to block the rays of the high overhead summer sun. The community has been continuously inhabited longer than any other in North America.

Mesa Verde National Park in southwest Colorado has over 600 cliff dwellings—the greatest number ever found. The park is the largest archeological preserve in the United States and investigations have gone on there for more than a century.

A mesa is a flat-topped elevation with one or more cliff-like sides. Verde means green and refers to the area's vegetation. The highest elevation in Mesa Verde is Park Point at 8,572 feet. From there, the plateau slopes gently to the south where the elevation is about 6,000 feet. Deeply cut canyons stand out against the green forest.

Mesa Verde was the center of the northern San Juan Anasazi Culture, which existed from about the first century A.D. to the 14th century in an area known as the Four Corners, where the boundaries of Colorado, New Mexico, Arizona, and Utah come together. A Mesa Verde Museum Association publication written by Gilbert Wenger, entitled *The Story of Mesa Verde National Park,* provides a sketch of the ancient Pueblo Indians who lived in the area's harsh environment.

About the mid-sixth century, the people gradually abandoned seminomadic ways and began farming the Mesa Verde. The farmers adapted, survived, and evolved from a simple hunting-gathering culture into a complex society of thousands.

Mesa Verde is classified as having a steppe climate. Steppe climates, dry with a limited natural water supply, are suited to human habitation, but the unreliable rainfall makes the potential for economic disaster great.

To ensure sufficient rainfall, the Pueblos chose to live on the middle mesa, about 7,000 feet in eleva-

For a time, many ancient Pueblo Indians resided in cliff dwellings. Frequently, the communities were able to select sites oriented to the southern sun. The overhanging cliff gave them some protection from inclement weather. Food and water were kept in pots in the back of the cliffs in permanent shade. The Spruce Tree House in Mesa Verde National Park has 114 rooms and eight kivas and could house 125–150 people.

tion. The higher north end of the mesa frequently receives more summer rainfall and winter snow than valleys below the escarpment, a steep slope or long cliff separating two relatively level areas. During the summer, when the sun is directly overhead, the temperature is adequate for crops, while being 10 degrees cooler than the hot valleys below.

About A.D. 1200, after more than 600 years of living on the mesas, the Pueblo people began to move into cliff dwellings constructed in alcoves under canyon rims. The problems of building new houses in the cliff alcoves were enormous. Stones had to be gathered and carried up canyon slopes, along with dirt and water to make mortar, and the house arrangements had to be fitted into the contours of the alcove.

Despite the construction difficulties, the Mesa Verde homes are marvels of solar architecture. When the sun is low in the southern sky on cloudless winter afternoons, it shines deep into many of the south-southwest-facing cliff dwellings. Winter temperatures are often 10–20 degrees warmer than in Montezuma Valley 600 feet below the escarpment.

The reasons for the move into the cliff-side dwellings are not fully understood. Some archeologists suspect that they offered protection. The sites are well suited for defense. Not only would an enemy have to run uphill wearing footwear unsuitable for rough terrain, the village defenders would have time to take careful aim with their arrows. However, there is no evidence of violence on bodies found in the area, nor is there evidence that there were any other people other than Pueblos in the area.

Some archeologists suspect that the climate may have become colder, prompting the change. Doubts are cast on the climate-change theory because, despite the fact that large houses facing south-southwest were preferred, there exist a large number of small, one- to four-room cliff dwellings that provide little protection from the climate. Moreover, Balcony House, the most defendable village at Mesa Verde, faces east and has only a few hours of sunshine each day.

There were few good places to climb up from the cliff dwellings to the mesa where the fields were planted. Since arthritis was common, older people must have spent most of their time confined to their cliff-side villages rather than in working in the fields. Trash was thrown into the valley below, providing archeologists with a treasure trove of cultural information.

For centuries the farmers cultivated the mesa tops, cutting or burning away the forest to open new lands for crops. As more and more fields were abandoned from a lack of soil nutrients, the dry soils blew or washed away.

In time, the population reached numbers that required more food than marginal farmlands could offer. The development of a drought-resistant maize by the farmers could not offset the lack of soil fertility. More and more people died.

In A.D. 1273 it stopped raining and did not rain again until A.D. 1285. The people abandoned their cliff dwellings and moved on into New Mexico and northern Arizona, where some of the modern Pueblo people live. Environmental destruction, overpopulation, and climate change appear to have ended the occupation of Mesa Verde by the ancient Pueblos.

Other groups in America besides the Pueblos took the sun into consideration. Spanish colonists who settled America's Southwest often built their single-family adobe dwellings with the main rooms facing south. Shutters on the windows helped keep heat inside at night. In summer, eaves sheltered the interior.

Spanish colonial architecture did not survive the influx of settlers from the eastern United States, who often replaced the adobe structures with wood houses better suited to New England winters. Not all Easterners were ignorant of the impact of the sun. Many New England saltbox-style houses were built facing the sun, with two stories in front and one story in the rear. A long roof sloped from the high front to the lower back provided protection from winter winds.

Many saltbox houses had a lattice overhang called a pergola protruding from the south facade above the doors and windows. Covered with deciduous vines, plants that lose foliage at the end of the season, the pergola provided shade in summer but did not block the sun in winter.

More Recent Solar Developments in America

With the crush of nearly 5 million new immigrants in the last half of the 19th century, the common-sense designs of rural dwellers were lost in growing urbanization. Cities on the eastern seaboard became crowded with multistory tenements crammed with poor immigrants. Conditions became as deplorable as any of the working-class quarters in Europe the immigrants had left behind.

William Atkinson, a reform-minded architect in Boston, Massachusetts, took up the cause of solar architecture. While designing hospital buildings in 1894, Atkinson became curious about ways to maximize solar exposure. From a Harvard University observatory table, he learned the seasonal positions of the sun, and—like others before him—he concluded east- and west-facing windows were least desirable and south-facing most desirable.

To prevent Boston's population, which had tripled in the second half of the 19th century, from being deprived of the sun by tall buildings that were becoming common, Atkinson convinced the Boston city council in 1904 to restrict the height of new buildings. Optimistic about the potential of solar heat, Atkinson conducted experiments and published a book in 1912 entitled *The Orientation of Buildings, Or Planning for Sunlight.* Unfortunately, until progress in Europe during the years following World War I helped to stimulate new interest, Atkinson was forgotten.

Solar homes made enormous strides during the

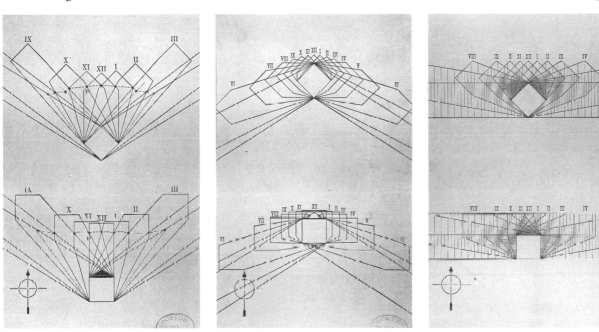

| **Figure 1** | **Figure 2** | **Figure 3** |

Architect William Atkinson plotted the shadows of two differently situated cubes, located at 42 degrees north latitude (vicinity of Boston). The four sides of the bottom cubes directly face the cardinal points (north, south, east, west). The arrow in the lower left-hand corner points north. The top cube is turned on the diagonal so that the corners face the cardinal points. The shadows are marked for every hour of the day for different times of the year.

Figure 1 depicts shadows in winter. Notice that the north face of the lower cube is in shadow for the entire day, never receiving any direct light. At 42 degrees north latitude, on the day of the winter solstice, the shortest day of the year, the sun rises about 32.5 degrees south of east, a low arc through the southern sky, reaching a height of 24–25 degrees above the horizon, then sets at about 32.5 degrees south of west.

Figure 2 depicts shadows of summer. Throughout the year, the diagonally placed cube (upper) shades less of the ground than does the other cube. At the summer solstice, the longest day of the year, the sun rises at about 32.5 degrees north of east and sets at 32.5 degrees north of west. Traveling in a higher arc, the sun reaches an altitude almost 50 degrees higher than at the winter solstice.

Figure 3 depicts shadows for the vernal (spring) and autumnal equinoxes when the sun rises due east, to an altitude of 48 degrees, and sets due west. For all times of year, the shadows of the lower cube overlap one another to a greater degree than do those of the upper.

1930s and 1940s, but interest began to fade in the late 1940s. The higher initial cost of a solar home—due to the extra expense of double-pane windows and the care needed to ensure the home's proper orientation—discouraged some buyers. Moreover, solar homes suffered from bad publicity connected with homes with lots of windows that were merely labeled solar homes with no attention being paid to their placement on their sites.

During the 1940s a number of scientists and engineers developed solar heat collectors. Often the solar collectors were piped to insulated heat-storage units to make heat available for after-dark home heating and hot water.

The earliest recorded use of a solar collector is attributed to Edward Morse, a world-famous botanist at the Essex Institute in Salem, Massachusetts in the 1880s. Morse noticed that dark curtains closed to block a sun-drenched window became hot and that warm currents were generated between the window and the curtain. He built a hot box attached to the south wall of the institute, with openings to permit the entrance of outdoor air and the exit of solar-heated air through a vent into rooms to be heated.

In 1938 Massachusetts Institute of Technology (MIT) scientists, with some of their students, began a series of on-and-off experiments that went on for many years. Hoyt Hottel, a professor of chemical engineering, assisted by graduate student Byron Woertz and others, headed the first project.

Hottel elected to study intensively the flat-plate solar collector, a type used successfully in California and Florida to heat domestic hot water. He liked the idea that water, with its high capacity for absorption and retention of heat was used to store and transfer heat.

Hottel had an experimental house fitted with 14 flat-plate collectors on the south side of the roof, at a tilt angle of 30 degrees from the horizontal. Each collector consisted of a shallow plywood box with six parallel copper tubes inside soldered to a blackened copper absorber plate. On top of the box were three glass covers separated by air spaces and on the bottom was more than five inches of rock wool (fibrous glass) insulation.

Water was pumped through the copper tubes to the roof's peak to collect the sun's heat and then down to an insulation-covered 17,400-gallon storage tank, which took up the whole basement. To heat the building, fans drew cool air from the rooms and blew it over the hot storage tank. The warmed air was then circulated back into the rooms. Unlike earlier solar homes, the system needed an external source of electrical power to activate the pumps and fans to move the heat.

Technically, the experiment was positive. The experimental house remained a steady 72 degrees throughout the winter. But the array of collectors and the heavily insulated storage tank were deemed too costly to be practical. Nevertheless, the report written by Hottel and Woertz is regarded as a classic, because it isolated the principal factors that affect solar power performance—among them, the tilt of the collectors, the amount of light transmission through the light covers, and the type of solar absorber plate.

Several other houses were built or modified in a search for the most efficient solar house. Each time the MIT scientists concluded that the availability of cheap fuel made them economically impractical. Despite the availability of cheap fuel, some scientists perceived that an energy crisis was inevitable. They founded the Association for Applied Solar Energy in 1955 and held a World Symposium on Applied Solar Energy in Phoenix, Arizona. Delegates from all over the world attended to present research papers and exhibit solar devices.

For scientists from other parts of the world, the symposium represented the beginning of a new solar age. The governments of Israel, Australia, and Japan gave direct support to their solar industries. But in the United States, despite predictions by the President's Materials Commission report in 1952 of a fossil-fuel shortage by 1973, there was little support for solar power. By 1963 the association found itself bankrupt.

Although the U.S. government admitted the possibility of an energy crisis, it chose to support nuclear power, and the rest of the world followed its lead. Even Japan opted for nuclear power, even though thousands of Japanese used solar water heaters.

About the time the first commercial nuclear power plants were being built, vastly improved photovoltaic cells were being developed at Bell Telephone Laboratories in Murray Hill, New Jersey. This work advanced the 1839 discovery by French physicist Edmund Becquerel that sunlight could produce electricity.

Silicon solar cells were briefly used as a power source for a telephone system in an isolated rural area of Georgia. But the cost was uncompetitive with conventional electricity.

Just as solar cells were about to be discarded, the National Aeronautics and Space Administration (NASA) recognized them as the perfect answer to satellites' need for compact, light, long-term, autonomous power sources. Solar cells don't need a storage system, since the sun shines 24 hours a day in space.

Despite their reliable performance in space, use of solar cells has received little support on Earth. The U.S. government and most other nations seemed hypnotized by a notion of seemingly limitless supplies of cheap fossil fuels and nuclear energy.

Time after time, fuel scarcities have stimulated a search for alternatives. Each time, solar technology has prospered until a new cheap fuel has become available.

In the late 1950s, as part of its Solar Energy Research program, Massachusetts Institute of Technology built this Solar House IV in Lexington, Massachusetts.

Underground, a Place to Live and Work and Discover Past Climates

Living underground could offer many advantages: protection from the weather and even temperatures. Whether the underground structures are residences, small businesses, or whole cities, savings in fuel costs could be substantial. However, our psychological barriers against living separated from the sun, sky, and the weather would first have to be overcome.

Finding ways to address psychological barriers to underground working and living is important for the Japanese, who suffer from a severe shortage of space. Japan's population of 123 million, slightly less than half the U.S. population of 250 million, is squeezed into a land area of 145,856 square miles, about 10,000 square miles less than the area of California.

In their quest for space, Japanese developers have built towering skyscrapers and even an artificial island in the sea. The only untapped source left is underground. A February 6, 1989 *Time* article entitled "Japan's Underground Frontier" and a July/August 1990 *Futurist* article entitled "Underground Cities" discussed the plans of some of Japan's largest construction companies. Because critics maintain that the absence of sun, sky, and weather could engender mass claustrophobia, or fear of confined places, Japanese builders have no immediate plans for underground housing projects. Their goal is to move offices and stores underground, freeing up surface land for residential buildings. Initially, workers and shoppers will commute vertically via huge elevator shafts.

Tetsuya Hanamura, the chief of the Taisei Corporation, described his company's intentions to build a network of Alice Cities, named for Lewis Carroll's heroine Alice, who went underground via a rabbit hole. He told *Time:* "An underground city is no longer a dream. We expect it to actually materialize in the early part of the next century."

Construction costs for the initial Alice City design, intended to accommodate 100,000 people, are estimated to be $4.2 billion. The first city will have two huge concrete infrastructure cylinders to house the city's basic support facilities, equipment, and installations, which will include power generation, air conditioning, and waste processing. The cylinders built 500 feet below ground will each be 197 feet tall and 262 feet in diameter. Also, passages will connect each cylinder to a variety of spheres designed to accommodate routine daily living. In addition to the infrastructure sector, each Alice City will have a "town space" sector and an "office space" sector.

The town space will be comprised of verdant underground boulevards and open-air and atrium-type plazas, free of automobile traffic. The boulevards and plazas will include shopping malls, entertainment complexes, and fitness centers. The office space will include business operations, additional shops, hotels, and parking lots. A solar dome above each complex will ease possible feelings of confinement.

Because Japan is located in an earthquake-prone area, one of the most attractive reasons for building underground is a reduction in earthquake damage. Scientists' contention that underground dwellings are preferable to those on the surface during an earthquake was reinforced by research described in an August 1989 *USA Weekend* article entitled "Underground is Safer than Surface."

University of California seismologist Ta-tiang Teng analyzed earthquake data from various parts of the world. He found that strong ground motion caused by earthquakes rapidly decreases with increasing depth. This worldwide data enabled Teng and his colleagues to explain a strange phenomenon during a 1976 earthquake in China that killed hundreds of thousands. Only 17 miners were killed among 10,000 miners working underground in the area of Tangshan. Yet one-quarter of the above-ground population of Tangshan died.

The Japanese government has set up task forces in several ministries to explore the potential of underground cities. One hurdle to be overcome is Japan's loose geological strata, which makes underground construction particularly difficult. Nevertheless, Japanese companies are confident that they have the technology to build extensive subterranean projects. For instance, the Tokyo Electric company built a power

An abandoned mining tunnel, which stayed cool on a hot summer afternoon in Arkansas, helped persuade Andy Davis of Armington, Illinois that there might be a way to escape the expense of heating a drafty house. His Davis Cave became famous and spawned Davis Caves Construction, Inc. Davis Caves builds "earth-sheltered" rather than "earth-bermed" houses. The earth-bermed home uses a conventional roof, while the top of an earth-sheltered home is covered with earth. Most of the sides of both houses are covered with earth. When built with proper insulation, waterproofing, and air circulation, the earth-sheltered house is more energy-efficient, enjoys greater safety from fire and tornadoes, and, lacking gutters and shingles, needs less maintenance than either a conventional house or an earth-bermed house. Such houses, if built with windows enjoying a south or southeast exposure, are well-lit by natural light.

station beneath a Buddhist temple. And engineers point with pride to the world's longest underwater corridor, the 33.5-mile-long Seikan Tunnel.

Reasons Vary for Building Underground

Planners have reasons besides space shortages for wanting to build underground. In a January/February 1991 *Futurist* article entitled "An Architect's Sketchbook," Malcolm Wells reported that he had been an architect for 11 years before he wondered if there was some material he could use that was less destructive above-ground than asphalt and concrete. In response to the environmental movement of the 1960s, he concluded that the surface of the Earth was made for living plants rather than dead buildings and asphalt.

So in the early 1970s, Wells made use of a tiny 60-by-90-foot lot behind his Cherry Hill, New Jersey office by building an underground office and open courtyard above. The lot had little to recommend it: on one side was a six-lane highway and on the other, a badly polluted stream. To his surprise, the open courtyard was actually quiet in spite of truck traffic only 20 feet away. The innermost rooms were silent.

Once the brick and concrete structure had been waterproofed, Wells used the subsoil that had been piled up during the excavation to cover the roof. On top of the soil, he put leaves obtained from a leaf collection at the town dump. The following spring, the site burst into life with every imaginable kind of weed and wildflower—an instant area of green without fertilizers, pesticides, or topsoil. By the end of 20 years, all signs of the building had disappeared beneath a young forest.

Housing does not have to be completely underground. Stu Campbell in his book *The Underground House Book* (1980) describes homes built into the earth with a portion of the house open to the outside. He believes an essential ingredient of any underground design must be windows that offer light and a view of the outside. The best placement of windows is facing south to take advantage of the winter sun's low slanting rays. The earth covering the north side blocks the cold winter winds.

When the Clark Kennedy School District in Georgia needed to build annexes at three elementary schools, officials elected to build earth-sheltered pods to drastically reduce additional heating costs. The pod at the Barnett Shoals Elementary (above) was designed by architect Wood C. Campbell. The concrete roof, covered with two feet of soil, was planted with wildflowers. The dirt in the foreground was eventually covered with grass.

The south-facing windows of the earth-sheltered classrooms at Barnett Shoals have an overhang just large enough to block direct sunlight in summer, while allowing the sunlight to shine through in winter. Ceiling paddle fans help to evenly distribute heated or cooled air.

Even in the absence of windows that look directly outdoors, underground living can be psychologically comfortable. High ceilings, growing plants, and see-through space dividers prevent feelings of closeness, crowding, or isolation. A proper mixture of surface colors, and varied textures on walls, ceilings, and floors can establish contrasting moods in adjacent spaces.

Both practical and aesthetic reasons guided the building of an underground library at Park College, located on the banks of the Missouri River, 10 miles upstream from Kansas City, Missouri. Founded in 1875 on 800 acres of bluff land, the scenic college campus overlooks the river.

The campus library was built in 1908, with an addition added in 1923. Designed to hold 10,000 volumes, the library's 100,000 volumes had taken over so much space by 1988 there was no longer room for people. The library could serve only as a book checkout station for students.

In December 1989, an article appeared in the *Wilson Library Bulletin* entitled "Going Under: Park College's Underground Library," written by Harold Smith, the director of the library. The article described the long process that led to Park college's underground library. With a mandate to preserve the scenic campus terrain, initial plans in the 1960s envisioned a hillside, multistory facility to blend in with the existing 19th-century "halls-of-ivy" type buildings.

About 1970 the planners turned their attention to a 30-foot-thick ledge of limestone below the surface of the campus. If excavated, the limestone could be sold to offset the costs of library construction, and the excavated underground space could be used for the library and other administrative facilities.

Excavation began in 1981. Precise planning for the library's layout had to wait almost until construction was completed. Sections of rock to serve as pillars were left in place. The channels opened by the excavation were 12–14 feet high, approximately 25 feet wide, and oriented north to south and east to west, creating essentially a grid pattern. Once blasting was completed, the floors were poured and the utilities installed. Finished walls were placed over the pillars, but most walls were simply sprayed a subdued white.

A sense of spaciousness in the underground library is enhanced by long, straight lines of unimpeded vision and a liberal use of interior windows. Around the perimeter of the library are two large seminar rooms, a 24-hour music listening room, an archives, and a special collections area. Windows in some of the rooms look out on an underground pedestrian walkway.

The entrance is a domed foyer at ground level. Visitors travel down a long hallway, past the campus switchboard, where television monitors scan the approximately one-third-mile-long hallway. The hallway skirts the library and emerges on the other side of the campus, where the dormitories are located.

Although the library staff had been initially uneasy about working underground, once the library was built they found they enjoyed it. Library Director Smith wrote: "We are not as aware of the passage of the day as when we were above ground, and consequently there is a sense of timelessness and serenity that we had not foreseen. Also it is nice to go to the car at the end of the day and not have it covered with snow or rain—at least until we drive out of the tunnel."

Historical Record of Climate

Underground temperatures respond only slowly to above-ground weather. This makes the underground not only a useful place for human activities, but also an excellent keeper of historical climate changes.

Nineteenth-century French physicist Jean Baptiste Joseph Fourier, who was interested in how heat moves, first recognized this possibility. Today, in their efforts to answer questions about global warming, dozens of geoscientists are making use of Fourier's insight. A February 9, 1991 *Science News* article entitled "Global Warming Underfoot" described their research.

By lowering thermometers into boreholes that extend more than 300 feet below the surface, scientists are able to "read" the history of the Earth's climate changes. Boreholes are made by drilling into the ground to study the stratification (layers of rock), to

extract from the Earth's crust natural resources such as oil or gas, or to release underground pressure.

The capacity to read the record of the Earth's temperature changes depends on physical events that take place in the ground during winter. As the air temperature drops, the Earth's surface cools, but the seasonal warmings and coolings creep down only short distances. On the other hand, climate coolings and warmings that persist for decades or centuries can work their way down more than 300 feet.

Because the Earth's interior is much hotter than its surface, under ordinary circumstances a descending thermometer detects progressively higher tempera-

Since colonial times Fort Sewall has guarded the entrance to Marblehead Harbor in Massachusetts. The present structure was built in the 18th century. A high ridge of land shelters from view the earth covered structure. That same ridge, along with a peninsula across the harbor opposite the fort where the lighthouse now stands, offer an unobstructed view of the harbor and surrounding waters. During most of the Revolutionary War, the Royal Navy, unaware the fort often had no gunpowder, did not try to assault what was then a major seaport. The War of 1812, under attack by a British vessel, the U.S.S. Constitution, which never lost a battle, sailed into Marblehead Harbor to seek assistance from the fort's guns. The tiny fort was a national garrison from the 1790s until the 1890s when it was returned to the town. The building is still sound and is occasionally opened to the public.

tures. A shift in the steadily increasing temperature indicates a period of climate warming or cooling. A record of more-recent events lies closer to the surface, thus the depth at which a deviation occurs indicates when it took place.

Until recently, geophysicists had scant interest in boreholes as historical records. They used them to measure the amount of heat flowing away from the planet's interior. But attitudes changed in 1989 in response to a paper by geophysicist Arthur Lachenbruch of the U.S. Geological Survey in Menlo Park, California, written after half a century of borehole study.

With colleague B. Vaughan Marshall of the Geological Survey, Lachenbruch reported in the November 7, 1986 *Science* that during this century borehold records revealed a startling warming of 2–4 degrees centigrade (from 3.6–7.2 degrees Fahrenheit) in the northern section of Alaska. The findings of Lachenbruch and Marshall stimulated other geoscientists to look for evidence of global warming in borehole temperature data from other regions of the world.

But critics question whether boreholes outside the Arctic can yield useful information. In the Arctic, the permanently frozen subsoil, called permafrost, does not permit a flow of subsurface water, which in more-temperate climates might change a borehole temperature record.

Skeptics also point out that in more-temperate climates, the location of a borehole is important. Many boreholes in the eastern United States indicate a warming trend because the holes were drilled in open treeless meadows subject to more sunlight than surrounding shady forests. In the western United States, many boreholes were drilled on the treeless south sides of hills.

Yet the critics did not have the last word. Research findings presented at the December 1990 meeting of the American Geophysical Union (AGU) indicated that scientists in North America, Africa, and the glacial ice cap of Greenland had obtained borehole temperature records that were consistent with the air and sea-surface temperature records.

A September 1992 *Discover* article in the "Breakthroughs" section reported on the work of Hugo Beltrain of the University of Quebec at Montreal and Jean Claude Mareschal of the Institute de Physique du Globe in Paris. These two geophysicists lowered temperature probes down 120 boreholes at 53 sites from the Canadian province of Manitoba to Newfoundland and found an almost unanimous record of the Earth's warming and cooling.

Among the sites with boreholes deep enough to reach sufficiently far back in time, 20 of 25 sites gave strong evidence of the Little Ice Age, which extended roughly from the 16th to the 18th century, with the coldest years being 1645–1715. During this period, the Zuider Zee, the shallow body of water that divides the Netherlands, froze over each winter, as did the canals of Venice and the Thames River in London.

Virtually all the boreholes checked by Beltrain and Mareschal indicated a steady warming since 1800, about the time carbon dioxide, a major factor in global warming, began to accumulate in the atmosphere as a consequence of the industrial revolution. The record from the Earth's interior memory suggests that global warming is a real phenomenon. If so, underground may one day become the most comfortable place to live.

In North America, the only signs of subterranean habitations ever discovered are the ceremonial kivas found in the Southwest. Here a crew stabilizes a kiva at Far View Ruin in Mesa Verde National Park. Built for religious purposes, the kivas were eventually used for habitation. A ventilation system kept them well aired. A structure resembling a well shaft allowed cool air to descend and enter a room. Once warmed by a fire the air would rise to exit via the entrance to the kiva.

PART THREE

PHYSICAL SCIENCE AND MATHEMATICS

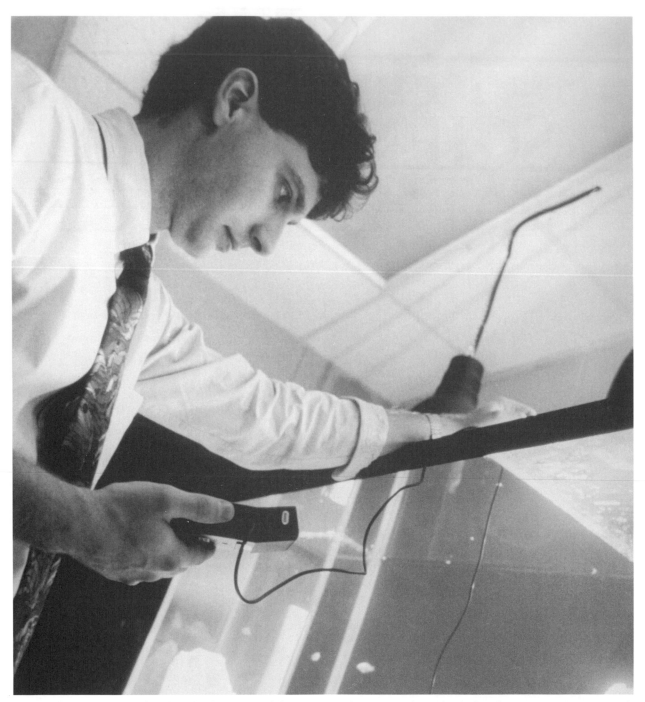

Fish tanks are sometimes found in the classrooms of elementary and even secondary schools, but they are an uncommon sight in an undergraduate chemistry class. But Dr. Ken Hughes of the Georgia Institute of Technology installed in his classroom a 300-gallon saltwater aquarium, containing 85 Damsel fish. His purpose was to teach aqueous solution chemistry and to improve the basic analytical laboratory skills of his students. The students analyze water samples daily to understand and chart complex biological and chemical processes taking place in the small ecosystem. They use traditional analytical tools such as spectrophotometry, gravimetry, titration and electrochemistry to measure the levels of nitrogen compounds, magnesium, chloride, phosphates, calcium, sulfates, and other chemicals in the tank water. The students make chemical and other adjustments needed to keep the fish healthy.

Events and Trends in
Physical Science and Mathematics

In 1992 some scientists yearned for a return to "small science." In the 1960s, experimental groups included 15 at the most. Now physicists work on projects with as many as 300 collaborators, which they refer to as factories. Nobel Prize winner Melvin Schwartz of Brookhaven National Laboratory believes that a pack mentality has stifled the emergence of new ideas in physics for a decade and a half.

Computer Science

Forensic scientists can easily detect the signs of forgery in paper documents, but detection of fake computer documents is much more difficult. Some people, known as computer hackers, are obsessed with breaking computer codes for fun or gain. The ease with which they can tamper with legal records, financial transfers, and digitized photographs troubles security experts. Personal computers provide access to a myriad of desktop publishing and image-retouching programs that make it easy to manipulate information stored as numerical digits, known as digital data.

Discover magazine's annual technology awards, featured in the October 1992 issue, declared the developers of an electronic document security system to be the computer software winners for the year. The scientists are Stuart Haber and Scott Stornetta, who both work with Bellcore, the research and engineering venture of the nation's regional telephone companies. They developed a practical, foolproof security system they call the "Digital Time-Stamp."

Haber, a cryptologist, became intrigued with document security when a prominent immunologist was accused of faking laboratory data. U.S. Secret Service forensic experts called in to examine the scientist's notebooks determined that some pages had been tampered with. In Haber's opinion, if the scientist's notes had been kept in a computer, the tampering would have been virtually impossible to detect.

Haber focused on the problem of authenticating when a digital document was created or last modified. His first solution involved using Bellcore as an electronic safe-deposit box. Computer documents would be sent to Bellcore to be stored securely with a record of the date of submission. The obstacle to that solution was the requirement of trust in a third party. Conceivably, Bellcore might have an employee who could be bribed.

The challenge was to invent a method that did not depend on trust. The mathematics he developed indicated that the task was impossible. After Stornetta joined Bellcore, he helped Haber to prove that his mathematics had been wrong. Within a month, the two researchers had laid the groundwork for a tamperproof, no-trust-necessary seal for authenticating documents. Instead of submitting an entire document, the person desiring authentication submits only a sample of the original.

A small coded representative of the larger document is generated using a process known as "one-way hashing." The technique known as hashing produces a string of numbers and letters the so-called hash value—which is unique to the document. The mathematical procedure creates a digital fingerprint of the document based on the arrangement of the letters, markers, graphics, and symbols in the original.

A change in even one character in the original changes the hash value, thus breaking the authentication seal. The one-way process makes it impossible for the stamping service or a forger to reconstruct a document from the hash value. The chance of two documents having the same hash value is remote.

In Haber and Stornetta's system, Bellcore in its capacity as time-stamper, validates the time of arrival of the document's hash value. To prevent any tampering with the data, the system links each document's time stamp to the hash value of the document processed just before it. Chaining the data together makes it impossible to later insert or delete a document.

To check the authenticity of a document's time stamp, the person doing the checking need only compute the hash value and compare the results with the chain of hash values on file with the time-stamper.

Physics

Most scientific names can best be described as quite specific, but hardly ever as memorable or provocative. But recently some scientists have injected a touch of whimsy into the naming process. According to an October 20, 1992 *New York Times* article entitled "Scientists Find Catchy Names Help Ideas Fly," "The trend may be a slap at tradition, or perhaps a shrewd sense that a popular name can win a theory more attention and more financing."

Chemists refer to carbon atoms structured in a sphere as "buckyballs." Cell biologists talk about regions of gene-regulating proteins that join up before interacting with deoxyribonucleic acid (DNA) molecules as "leucine zippers." Physicists condense the awkward phrase "weakly interactive massive particles" into "WIMPS."

Colorful names have been met with some resistance. Dr. Anne Eisenberg, a professor at Polytechnic University in Brooklyn, New York, explained to the *New York Times* that some scientists are suspicious of anything that makes science more understandable. She said, "There's tremendous snobbery against the comprehensible. The bad side is the snobbery. The good side is that it reflects the desire for scientific precision."

"Chaos" is a term that has sparked considerable controversy. Coined by Dr. James Yorke of the University of Maryland, chaos is used to describe the behavior of physical systems like flowing water or weather, which are dynamic and cannot be predicted over long time spans. The term chaos has offended a large number of scientists. Yorke defends the term on the grounds that it has attracted the attention of physicists to an unusual concept that has been known to mathematicians for years.

To attract the attention of physicists was not Yorke's only reason for coining the term. He told the *New York Times,* "Words empower us to think about other things, and we must think of the words that allow us to do that."

Not all new terms are chosen deliberately. At a 1987 news conference, Dr. Alan Dressler, who is with the observatories in Pasadena, California operated by the Carnegie Institution of Washington, D.C., was asked to clarify for journalists the discovery of a dense aggregate of matter toward which hundreds of galaxies were streaming. Groping for a graphic concept he used the words "the great attractor."

The term quickly found its way into scientific journals and the popular imagination. It also prompted great criticism of Dr. Dressler.

The modern trend toward whimsical names seems to have started with high-energy physicists. By 1960, they had used up the Greek alphabet in naming the subatomic particles they had found. So, in 1963 to designate a quite different category of particle, California Institute of Technology physicist Murray Gell-Mann named it "quark." He felt it was unnecessary to use pretentious names, particularly since after a few years most names no longer look appropriate.

To distinguish qualities associated with quarks, Dr. Gell-Mann used the words "strangeness" and "color." University of Chicago theorist Dr. Yoichiro Nambu added the word "flavor," and Harvard University physicist Dr. Sheldon Glashow described quarks as endowed with "charm."

The influence that a name can have can be seen in the work of Dr. Barbara McClintoch of Cold Stone Harbor Laboratory on Long Island, New York. A concept that she developed in the 1930s and 1940s and named "mutable loci" and later "movable elements" is a cornerstone in 20th-century genetics. But it was not until the 1970s and 1980s, when these genes that move promiscuously from chromosome to chromosome began to be referred to as "transpons," or jumping genes, that they became well known. Dr. McClintoch won a Nobel Prize in 1983 for her work.

Chemistry

A scientist who studies insects is called an entomologist. Henrich Schmuterer is a German entomologist who in 1959 became fascinated with the neem tree when he saw a horde of locusts avoid one. He brought the tree to the attention of Western scientists, but it took close to three decades before they became interested.

The neem tree is common in tropical countries. In India, farmers put neem into wheat bins to repel insects, and in nearly every community in the nation, neem trees serve as a local pharmacy. Neem tree leaves are used as a poultice, and its fruit and bark provide treatment for a wide variety of ailments, including warts, chickenpox, and malaria. A substance in neem tree twigs makes a toothpaste that prevents gum disease.

An August 10, 1992 *Boston Globe* article entitled "Scientists Shop in Living Drug Store" explained some of the reasons why it took Western scientists so long to become interested in neem. An agroforester with the U.S. Agency for International Development, Michael Benge, who brought the tree to the attention of the National Research Council of the National Academy of Sciences, believes the lack of interest has been due to the fact that neem is a natural product.

The tree's mix of active ingredients varies from one location to another and sometimes between one tree and its neighbor. Unlike synthetic molecules, neem's varied complex and complementary mixture of natural ingredients complicates regulatory testing, required by government agencies to ensure quality and standardization.

Over its 400-million-year evolution, the neem tree has developed a barrage of natural chemicals that disrupt the intricate hormonal system of leaf-chewing insects. Rather than kill insects, neem prevents them from reproducing and repulses and debilitates them.

Neem's active compounds are chemically similar to steroids and to birth-control products. One compound, azadirachtin, interrupts the metamorphosis of larvae into adults. Two other ingredients, meliantriol and salannin, make insects stop eating.

Indian researchers discovered that a neem extract is fatal to the parasite that causes malaria, a disease responsible for 2 million deaths every year. Extracts even work on malaria parasites that have become resistant to the commonly used Western drug chloroquine.

Also, German and Brazilian scientists have demonstrated neem's effectiveness against Chagas disease, a nerve and muscle affliction that affects an estimated 20 million Latin Americans. In India, which desperately needs to control its population explosion, scientists at the Defense Institute of Physiology and Allied Sciences have concluded that the neem tree could provide an ideal contraceptive.

Neem kills salmonella, the bacteria that cause intestinal disturbances ranging in effect from mild to fatal. It is effective against the fungi that cause athlete's foot, ringworm, candida (common in vaginal infections), and staph infections (pathogens that plague hospitals, often killing vulnerable patients). Moreover, neem inhibits the growth of herpes and hepatitis B viruses.

Because the neem tree's value lies in its fruits and seeds, the tree is more valuable standing than chopped down. Therefore, vast planting of neem trees could aid reforestation and slow soil erosion and desertification.

Mathematics

Understanding the motion of organisms often creates a problem for scientists. The motion of horses was not well understood until the 1880s when the American painter Thomas Eakins, who was passionate about accurate anatomy, took a series of closely timed still photographs.

To discern the movement of some bacteria presents a more difficult problem. The movement of bacteria that swim freely in liquid mediums is well understood, but until recently the movement of gliding bacteria, which resemble tiny oval rugs, has remained unclear.

The September 1992 issue of *Research/Penn State* included an article entitled "How Bacteria Glide," which described an effort to understand the locomotion of bacteria that secrete a slime which enables them to glide around on U.S. Navy ships. The bacteria are fond of ships that are in the water for extended periods of time without being occasionally drydocked. Gliding bacteria and their slime can build up to such an extent that they noticeably slow a ship's speed.

Pennsylvania State University mathematician Abdul Siddiqui collaborated with University of Maryland biologist Robert Buchard and Johns Hopkins University chemical engineer William Schwarz in what Siddiqui calls a "research triangle" to try to understand the bacteria's method of transport. Buchard collected water samples to determine the type of bacteria causing the slime. Schwarz studied the liquid's rheological properties, which show how it relates to the deformation and flow of matter. Siddiqui collected the data into a general model of hydrodynamics, which is a representation of the motion of fluids and the interaction of their boundaries. His model is intended to predict the bacteria's behavior under various circumstances.

The bacteria had nothing obvious, such as oarlike flagella, to help them move about. Examination under an electron microscope determined that they had rigid cell walls. This meant that they could not use the "bunch and stretch" motion of amoebas.

Buchard's observation of three representative types of gliders led to the hypothesis that they moved by peristalsis, contracting waves that travel the length of the bacterium's body. The movement is reminiscent of the way a snake wriggles from side to side, except that the bacteria undulate in a vertical direction rather than horizontal.

To mathematician Siddiqui, the gliding motion represented just another system governed by differential equations, which express mathematical relationships. However, complexities arose from the fact that the system was fluid and non-Newtonian.

A non-Newtonian fluid is one in which viscosity (resistance to flow) changes with the application of stress. Siddiqui offered a simple example of non-Newtonian behavior in a *Research/Penn State* article: "If you have paint in a beaker, and you place a glass rod into it and rotate the rod, the paint will climb the rod. This is a property of a non-Newtonian fluid." However, the properties of non-Newtonian fluids are dependent on conditions, therefore they complicate modeling because they begin with different viscosities. Siddiqui simplified the difficulties by approximating. His model posits that an undulating bacterial cell pushes down on its self-made bed of slime. The slime pressed against the hard surface of the ship is pushed backward. The movement of the liquid propels the bacterium forward. The speed achieved is a balance between the amount of work done in wriggling and the amount of energy dissipated by the slime's viscosity.

The peristaltic model seems to fit many of the gliding bacteria's quirks, which include sudden reversals in direction, rapid stops and starts, and lift-offs in which the glider partially detaches from the slime and does a flip. The energy requirements of the model fit with those estimated for the biology of the organism. However, the biological mechanism that operates the undulating motion is not yet understood.

Improved understanding of peristalsis has a variety of applications. Progressive waves of contraction are found everywhere in the body, including in the movement of food through the intestinal tract, the pumping of blood, and the act of swallowing. Medical researchers at Johns Hopkins would like to create an artificial esophagus, but first they have to understand how a real esophagus works. Siddiqui and Schwarz are at work on that problem.

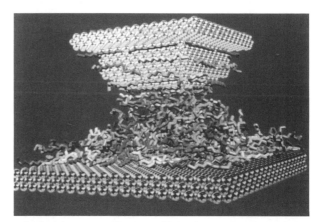

The computer, and particularly the supercomputer, has proved a great boon to the science community. Ideas can be explored, trials and experiments can be simulated, and computations can be done at great speed. This computer activity is a major supplement to other aspects of research. This computer simulation of microscopic interactions of two materials coming into contact shows molecules of hexadecane welling up toward the tip of a descending metal probe.

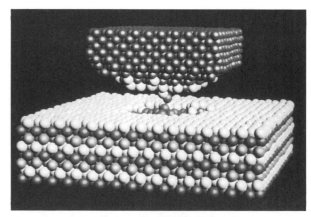

A computer simulation of a nickel/gold surface.

10

COMPUTER SCIENCE

Supercomputing in Pittsburgh and Around the Country

In 1985, the National Science Foundation (NSF) established the Supercomputing Centers Program, made up of four university-based centers. The centers were located at Cornell University in Ithaca, New York, Princeton University in Princeton, New Jersey, the University of Illinois in Urbana-Champaign, and the University of California in San Diego.

In 1986, NSF established a fifth supercomputing center, selecting as a recipient of funding a partnership between Carnegie-Mellon University in Pittsburgh, Pennsylvania and the University of Pittsburgh. The selection was made from a competition among 22 institutions. Known as the Pittsburgh Supercomputing Center (PSC), the facility is housed in the Westinghouse Energy Systems Computer Center in Monroeville, a Pittsburgh suburb.

A linkage between researchers' computers and a supercomputer center permits a researcher to do experiments that would be extremely cumbersome or even impossible on a smaller computer. Until the advent of the supercomputer centers, outside of some industries, researchers' use of supercomputers was limited almost exclusively to those in the U.S. Department of Defense and the National Weather Service. A September 24, 1989 *Philadelphia Inquirer* article entitled "Supercomputers Become Laboratories" described some of the work now possible at various supercomputing centers in the national program.

Biologist Art Winfree of the University of Arizona is linked to the National Supercomputer Center at Princeton University. He has used the supercomputer to study the swirling bioelectrical vortex (fluid rotation about an axis) thought to be responsible for the irregular contractions that precede cardiac arrest, when the heart stops beating.

Such studies are not yet possible on live hearts, and doing them on a personal computer would take centuries. One possible outcome of Winfree's study is an improvement in the electrodes used in emergencies to jolt the heart back into its normal pumping action.

Linked to the University of Illinois, David Onstad of the Illinois Natural History Survey has studied the dynamics of insect populations. He simulated the intricate life history of a tiny beetle that infests grain silos. The supercomputer circuits made it possible to understand how beetle populations are controlled by disease and predators.

In just a few hours, the supercomputer's speed and memory made it possible for Onstad to simulate the changes in a population of European corn borers (moth larvae) over the course of 25 years. The machine achieves these speeds by "vector processing" several rows of equations simultaneously.

A May 19, 1988 *Boston Globe* article entitled "Centers for Supercomputer Called Useful" covered reports from a conference on supercomputers held at Hynes Convention Center in Boston, Massachusetts. Pittsburgh Supercomputing Center physicist Ralph Roskies described a project done at PSC by Carnegie-Mellon professor of chemical engineering Gregory McRae. The research involved the complex interactions of chemical compounds in automobile exhaust emissions. McRae found that reduction in some kinds of emissions can actually increase pollution.

The Pittsburgh Supercomputer Center's CRAY Y-MP/832 computer was made available to young, budding scientists when several Pennsylvania high schools were invited to develop projects for which the Y-MP would be needed. To list just a few of those projects: Seneca Valley High School set out to determine how long it would take to fill all of Pennsylvania's landfills; Mount Lebanon wrote a program to input the velocities, positions, and masses of several objects in a "solar system" of the their own creation and computed the projected positions of the objects for a specified time; Hampton High proposed to model the dissolution of a crystal in a solvent and videotape the way individual particles crystallize and dissolve; and South Fayette High decided to model the flow of the Allegheny and Monongahela river systems. In November 1991 the center signed an agreement with Cray Research, Inc. to replace this machine with the Y-MP C90, which can run six times faster at peak speed and has eight times more memory than the Y-MP.

Insights gained from McRae's work could ultimately save an estimated $30 million of the money currently being spent by the Environmental Protection Agency (EPA).

A project well suited to supercomputers was described in a March 30, 1987 *Boston Globe* article entitled "Supercomputer Access Grows, Scientists Line up for Chance to Tackle Problems Long Considered Unsolvable." The project at the John von Neumann National Supercomputing Center in Princeton involved the study of fundamental questions about the structure of the universe. Scientists sought to determine whether there is sufficient matter in the universe to eventually cause it to collapse on itself, reversing the big bang—the theory that the universe erupted from a single dense point.

The supercomputer enabled scientists to simulate the physical behavior of a star cluster and record it on a seven-minute film. One of the film's producers, Cornell professor Saul Teukolsky, told the *Boston Globe:* "We expected the core of the cluster to collapse to form a black hole and for the remaining stars to remain unaffected. What we found was that the mass of the black hole was 10 to 100 times bigger than we expected. And by using graphics, we could watch the orbits at various stages and understand the mechanism of why our original expectation was wrong and why a much bigger mass would be captured."

Cornell professor Stuart Shapiro, who worked with Teukolsky, said about supercomputers: "We don't know the limits of their use. We do know that many, many problems that have been classic unsolved problems can now be tackled. And that usually means a revolution in the making."

Massachusetts Institute of Technology physics professor Victor Weisskopf was more cautious: "I don't think this means a revolution. The super-computer alone won't give us more insight. Analytic and creative thinking is still the most important tool of the scientists."

Supercomputers make it possible to correlate and analyze millions of pieces of data about such diverse concerns as the ocean's motion and temperatures, the arrangement of atoms in proteins, or the theoretical laws that dictate the structure of a proton, a fundamental particle of the nuclei of atoms. Because scientists believe they understand the basic physical laws in such areas, they believe they can simulate reality.

Given the speed of the supercomputers, researchers can take a model and substitute different values and conditions, experimenting in the same way a chemist experiments with different ingredients and temperatures. Even with the most powerful microscope or telescope, some phenomena in nature are not accessible. The center of the sun, for example, cannot be taken into a lab, but the laws that govern the center of the sun can be plugged into the supercomputer, making it in effect a lab.

Some supercomputer users predict that supercomputing will become a third basic research model, alongside theory and experimentation. Larry Smarr, director of the supercomputing center at the University of Illinois, believes that supercomputing is going to be like a tidal wave sweeping across various disciplines. He pointed out that scientists are not the only scholars using supercomputers. By combing through historical census data, historians are learning much about peoples' lives in the past.

NSF financially supports the five-center program with about $60 million each year, about half of the centers' combined operating budgets. The program provides access to supercomputers for more than 15,000 researchers at more than 500 institutions in the United States. By 1991, after five years in operation, work done through the centers had resulted in the publication of more than 7,000 scientific papers.

The Pittsburgh Supercomputing Center

Twenty-eight universities are affiliated with the PSC. Researchers connect to the center via a regional electronic network that feeds into NSFNET, a high-speed pathway that links NSF supercomputing centers. But universities are not the only educational facilities linked to PSC.

An August 20, 1991 *Pittsburgh Press* article entitled "Computer Center Opens to Students to Show How Super It Can Be," pointed out that one of the priorities of NSF, which provides $14 million of PSC's $18 million annual budget, is to get students interested in science. Beverly Clayton, PSC director, explained why the centers reach out to students and their teachers. She told the *Pittsburgh Press:* "The idea behind the program is that science today is inextricably intertwined with computers."

Ten Pittsburgh-area students and their science teachers won the chance to use the PSC's supercomputer by proposing projects for it. They proposed such activities as discovering the formation of a rainbow, testing water quality, and simulating a super roller coaster ride. At the end of a week each student-teacher team took back to their district a $20,000 computer station donated by the Digital Equipment Corporation. The stations provide a direct linkup with PSC.

At Gateway, one of the area high schools, physics teacher Gerald Martin told the *Pittsburgh Press* that he and his students would study "what if" questions. Such questions include: What if we kicked a football down the field and rode on it? What would we see? What would happen if gravity were stronger?

A February 9, 1992 *Pittsburgh Press* article entitled "Students Work Out Trashy Task With High-Tech Hookup" described a supercomputer project at Seneca Valley High School. From October through mid-November, students in all grades took home surveys to estimate how much garbage their households disposed of daily.

Of the more than 4,000 surveys distributed, about 1,400 were properly completed and returned. Students in physics, math, and computer classes entered the data into the computer and devised formulas to calculate how much space would be saved in landfills by community recycling.

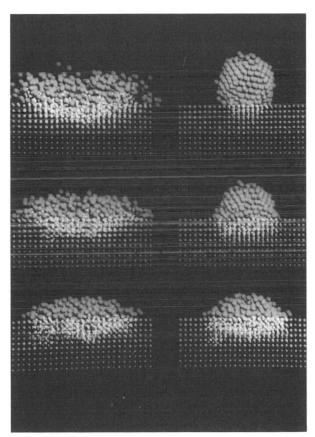

At the Georgia Institute of Technology, Dr. Uzi Landman and Dr. Charles Cleveland of the School of Physics created supercomputer simulations to study the dynamics of supersonic collisions between clusters of atoms and a solid surface. The collisions generate extreme pressure, density, and temperature pulses. Landman and Cleveland suggest that when clusters of atoms or molecules crash into a solid surface forces are generated that may produce new chemical environments that can promote new reaction processes.

Architectural student Alaa Eldin Ibrahim, then of Carnegie-Mellon University and now at Texas A&M University, designed a walkway. With the help of the Pittsburgh Supercomputing Center's Joel Welling, Ibrahim produced this video "walkthrough" of the walkway.

PSC's 1991 report, *Projects in Scientific Computing,* described some of the many research efforts that have been completed at the center or were still in progress. For example, using a novel combination of laboratory techniques and computer visualization technology, PSC scientific specialist Joel Welling and media services director Cyril Evans collaborated with Pittsburgh Shadyside Hospital pathologist Richard Siderits to construct a three-dimensional image of cancer in a human lymph node.

Siderits cut the node into thin slices and projected every 20th slice onto a projecting microscope—17 slices altogether. Evans transferred the images to graphic files on an IBM XT computer image capture board.

Welling used graphic software known as P3D, developed under his lead, to render the slices as a composite 3-D solid object. He produced a video animation that rotates and turns the node, sheds its outer wall and permits the viewer to see into the malignant interior. What looks like separate tumors on consecutive slides is revealed in three dimension as different branches of a single tumor.

Carnegie-Mellon economist Fusun Gonul did a study comparing the federal designation of "unemployed" with its designation "out of the labor force." People out of the labor force are not counted as unemployed. To be counted as unemployed, a person must be available for work, must have been searching for a job for four weeks or more, or must be on a layoff waiting to be recalled or scheduled to report to a new job within 30 days. A person who has given up searching for work is not counted.

Knowing how many people have stopped searching for work is critical in assessing how well an economy is doing. But they are seldom considered because of the difficulties involved in the tabulation.

Gonul described her work: "In social science, we tend to have more data to process than in natural science, where the research is done in controlled laboratory settings. But not only do we have more data, we have more unobservables to control for because our 'experiments' are from real lives of real people." Asked how much time she saved using the center's CRAY Y-MP, she replied, "My whole life, I'm sure."

Despite the growing availability of supercomputing, for many important research efforts—so called grand challenge problems—there is still not enough computer time available. Scientists have struggled to squeeze more computing out of supercomputers that have already reached the limits of technology. A frequent solution is to use heterogeneous computing— linkage of computers with different abilities to each do what it does best.

To gain the capacity to do heterogeneous computing, in April 1990, four years down the road from its 1986 opening, Pittsburgh Supercomputer Center obtained financial support from NSF and the Defense Advance Research Projects Agency (DARPA) to purchase a Connection Machine (CM-2), a 32,768-parallel processor.

Parallel processing uses many small processors working simultaneously, each with a small memory of its own. In tandem the small processors execute several billion instructions per second.

In 1991 PSC installed a high-speed link (HiPPI) between its supercomputer, the CRAY-Y-MP, and its parallel-processing computer, the CM-2. The value of the center's HiPPI linkage is that it not only turned a fascinating idea into a reality, it ended a seemingly endless debate of which computer works best by exploiting the best features of both.

Projects in Scientific Computing described the process that established the linkage between the two machines. Carnegie-Mellon engineering professor Gregory McRae, and graduate student Robert Clay, former lead engineer for Exxon's real-time optimization group, teamed up with PSC staff to establish the HiPPI link to solve computations for the classic "assignment problem."

The assignment problem is a problem in practical mathematics known as combinatorial optimization. It plays an essential role in many kinds of day-to-day scheduling. For example, in a modern chemical plant, such as an oil refinery, each stage of production is mathematically controlled and monitored. To optimize the production schedule and thereby reduce costs, the time must be kept to a minimum between receipt of new information from monitors and scheduling of crews in keeping with the new information.

To properly schedule operations means to solve equations describing the dynamics of the chemistry and by devising the schedule faster than the plant is running. There are many ways to deal with the assignment problem.

The method adopted by McRae and Clay is derived from a well-known solution called the "Hungarian algorithm." An algorithm is a set of rules to solve a problem in a finite number of steps. Like many efficient parallel algorithms, where several computations are carried out simultaneously, the Hungarian algorithm was developed in the days when numerical analysis was done by teams of people with desk calculators.

In McCrae and Clay's approach, the first step is given to the CM-2, which quickly establishes a large number of potentially optimum assignments. In doing so, the CM-2 reduces by as much as 80% the possible options. The data is then transferred across the HiPPI to the Y-MP, which, using an algorithm called "initial matching," sorts out the maximum number of assignments optimal at that stage.

One of NSF's goals from the outset has been to make scientific computing readily available to American industry, by not only making the hardware accessible but also by disseminating the knowledge that accompanies it. Therefore, PSC has a corporate af-

filiates program. Chevron Oil was added as an affiliate in 1991, in addition to ALCOA, USX, and Pfizer, Inc.

Chevron has had its own supercomputers for a decade. Corporation officials cited two reasons for joining the program. They wanted access to the CM-2 and they wanted to take advantage of the HiPPI program in running simulations on how to get more oil out of reservoirs. Oil wells in general yield only 30% of their oil in the ground, leaving 70% unrecovered. A 1% increase in oil recovery would yield more oil than the largest domestic oil discovery in the last decade.

Even with supercomputers, needs quickly outpace capacity. In August 1988, PSC ordered a new model Cray supercomputer from Minneapolis-based Cray Research, Inc. The center was slated to be the first academic research facility to have installed the $30-million Cray Y-MP C90 system, which the company hails as the world's most powerful general-purpose computer. Installation was made in October 1992.

The Five Centers Are Just a Beginning

A November 22, 1991 *Los Angeles Times* article entitled "Massive, High-Speed Computer Network Is Explored," reported that then-U.S. Senator Albert Gore of Tennessee proposed development of massive networks linking millions of computers at speeds many times faster than the current rate. The project would be called the National Research and Education Network and would replace Internet, a slower network of 2,000 commercial and academic networks.

Gore, now vice president, is concerned with what he calls "rotting data," information gathered—like grain in a silo—but never disseminated. He believes faster dissemination would give the United States a competitive economic edge.

According to Lawrence Lee, executive director of the North Carolina Supercomputing Center, such a high-speed dissemination could be of tremendous benefit to education because it would make possible an unprecedented sharing of resources. Students in poorly equipped schools could gain electronic access to institutions with more resources, such as textbooks and library books. It looks like supercomputing has an ever-expanding horizon.

Illinois Institute of Technology's Institute of Design

Design is the act of conceiving and planning the structure and details of a system, device, process, or work of art. The design profession grew out of the Industrial Revolution, which replaced products individually crafted with products made by machines.

Large manufacturing production runs made it impossible for tailor-made individual products to compete economically with mass-produced ones. But because the forms of early manufactured products were dictated by the capacities of the machines, the products often were shoddy. Competition from manufacturers willing to listen to consumer complaints forced manufacturers to improve quality. Those charged with making the improvements were the founders of the design profession.

Designers made production processes more effi-cient, established standard sizes, improved the functioning of products, and created more product choices. From the beginning, designers often have transformed the appearance of products into symbolic forms that have meaning for their consumers. For example, early movable type was designed to resemble hand lettering, and many products were made to resemble handcrafted goods.

Few schools of design have the distinguished history of the Institute of Design at Illinois Institute of Technology (IIT) in Chicago. The Institute of Design (ID) was a direct descendent of the renowned Bauhaus in Germany, founded by Walter Gropius in 1919 and considered to be the 20th century's most important design school.

By using industrial processes to bring art and qual-

A team of Illinois Institute of Design students took the grand prize of the Japan Design Foundation's Third International Design Competition with their "Aquatecture" project. The theme of the competition was water. The IIT team based its project on the question of what can be done on a planet that needs more land space. Their conclusion was to use the sea. The students devised plans for manufacturing, food and energy production, and transportation. To house all these activities, the students designed various modular structures that would rest on submerged pontoons.

Soundance is an award-winning design devised by IIT students. It provides an interactive home audio-visual environment. Three major levels of interaction allow users to be involved actively or passively with a sensory environment to whatever degree suits them. Each level of interaction can be engaged independently or in conjunction. On the first level, the entertainment level, this multiple disc player would allow five compact discs to be played consecutively or in parallel.

ity back to everyday products, Bauhaus strove to compensate for the loss of craftsmanship brought about by the Industrial Revolution. The Bauhaus faculty developed new theories of art and beauty based on ideas appropriate to the machine age. They devised theories aimed at making people's lives better. While under the leadership of architect Ludwig Mies van der Rohe, the Nazis deemed the Bauhaus subversive and closed it in 1933.

But in 1937, a few influential Chicagoans, members of the city's Association of Arts and Industries, rallied resources and opened the New Bauhaus in Chicago under the directorship of Laszlo Moholy-Nagy. Moholy-Nagy was a Bauhaus faculty member who had headed the school's Visual Fundamentals Program. He brought with him boundless energy and an impeccable reputation as a painter, photographer, graphic designer, and educator. More oriented to the value of experience than his former Bauhaus colleagues, Moholy-Nagy imprinted what was to become the Institute of Design with an experimental as well as a theoretical tradition.

Unfortunately, a little more than a year after it opened, New Bauhaus closed when some association members complained that the school was too experimental and withdrew their financial support. With the help of association member and chairman of the Container Corporation of America Walter Paepcke

and Paepcke's wife Elizabeth, Moholy-Nagy reopened the school in 1939 under the name Chicago School of Design. The school changed its name again in 1944 to become the Institute of Design. Then in 1949 ID merged with IIT, where Bauhaus's former director Mies van der Rohe had been directing the School of Architecture for 11 years.

Expanding on a Bauhaus major theme of unifying culture, Moholy-Nagy introduced a program of "intellectual integration" as part of students' basic foundation. One of the courses taken by all students early in their training was intended to dispel prejudices and unlock creativity.

A primary example of the continuing influence of Moholy-Nagy's tradition of experimentation is ID's continuing work in photography. Moholy-Nagy believed that experimentation was the only way to discover a medium's unique characteristics. He theorized that a new medium initially mimicked an existing medium and only through experimentation that ignored tradition could the new medium's unique language be found.

Moholy-Nagy died in 1946. He was replaced in 1947 by architect Serge Chermayeff, whose primary interest was in what he called "shelter design." He hired R. Buckminster Fuller, who, while he was at ID, designed the prototype for what eventually became his famous geodesic dome. A geodesic dome is

Tackling basic projects is as important for IIT students as elaborate schemes to save Earth's resources. Among various designs proposed for a newsstand were one that looked like a giant newspaper box, one that was triangular, and one that resembled an auto. The students eventually selected a nonsymmetrical design, proposed by Scott Skipworth, that was made of wood and glass. They found bank financing and an interested newsstand operator. After refining the design, the students built the stand of waferboard, which is not generally used for exteriors, and stained it blue-green. They also placed the windows in position to provide an abundance of light.

a structurally strong surface made up of short light-weight bars that form a grid of polygons, which are closed planes generally with more than four sides and four angles.

ID enrollment peaked in the latter half of the 1940s and dipped in the first half of the 1950s. The school lost momentum until 1955, when Jay Doblin, chief designer for the renowned New York design firm Raymond Loewy and Associates, took over as director.

Doblin believed that disciplines (branches of knowledge) go through a three-stage maturation process. In stage one, a trial-and-error process deals with a recognizable set of problems, and methods that work are remembered and applied. In stage two, insightful practitioners, based on their recognition that effective solutions have a pattern, develop underlying principles and formulate theories. In stage three, professional education develops and schools teach formal theories to new practitioners.

Doblin restructured ID's curriculum to prepare students to be practitioners. In time he launched a major effort to find methods to help designers cope with the problems they routinely faced. For example, he pioneered the use in design of "The Semantic Differential," an approach devised by psychologist Charles Osgood to measure the meaning of abstract ideas.

Osgood quantified the feelings of his patients toward ideas like life, death, love, and hate, and he used the measures to determine their attitudes toward artistic forms. He determined that if designers understood consumers' feelings about a product's style or its graphic image—as being old or new, masculine or feminine, or strong or weak, compared to other designs—they could better target their products' consumers.

Doblin perceived that design was not only getting larger, it was also moving away from single objects, like chairs or books, toward entire systems of products, like office furniture. It was also moving toward the transmission of information, such as the development of a corporate identity, or making a corporate name synonymous with the corporate product.

Following Doblin's resignation in 1969, there were few new initiatives at ID until 1979, when Dale Fahnstrom became director. One of the new initiatives was propelled by Charles Owen, an ID masters program graduate who joined the faculty in the early 1960s to develop and promote computer-supported design. In 1981, with help from Fahnstrom, Owen founded ID's first formal computer research facility called the Design Processes Laboratory. With major contributions from industry, the lab grew rapidly into a center for the invention and development of computer-supported design tools.

Learning at ID

Located on the IIT campus, ID's average enrollment of 120 students comes from around the world. Gaining admission to the school at the graduate level is extremely difficult. Out of 250 applications each year, only five students are selected. At the undergraduate level, about 25 are chosen. Many of ID's students have returned to school after having worked for several years.

Students are expected to work hard. Attending classes and working in the basement lab, most put in

On March 17, 1992, teams of two to five people each tried to transform a kit containing a pegboard, tubing, nuts, wheels, an electric motor, and a battery pack into a 40-ounce, 16" x 8" x 8" race car at the Fourth Annual IIT 100 Race. Teams competed in one of three divisions: High School, IIT Student, or IIT Alumni and Faculty. Each vehicle raced against the clock twice and pulled against a scale twice. The times and scale measurements were ranked to determine the final scores. Teams were free to build cars of any design as long as they met weight and size requirements. The more successful cars tended to have sports-car lines while long, thin cars performed poorly.

"Project Phoenix" is a series of macro proposals aimed at combating Global Warming. One proposal, "Project Phoenix: Fire Replaced," calls for the construction of a solar power generation system in outer space, reducing the need to burn fossil fuels and the amount of carbon dioxide entering the atmosphere. Sunlight converted to electrical energy would be beamed via tightly directed microwaves to Rectennas like these on Earth. The receiving surface of a Rectenna would be made up of rows of parabolic reflector/collectors. The Rectennas would be located in remote areas on land and at sea.

a minimum of 10–12 hours a day, including Sundays and holidays. The norm for students is to work, eat and, on occasion, even sleep at the lab.

The intense time spent together creates a family-like atmosphere. The school's chairman, Patrick Whitney, told the *Chicago Tribune:* "We [the faculty] know everyone. When we have a party, everyone comes."

A combination of Owen's influence, the influence of ID's current director Whitney, and the influence of the former director Jay Doblin, who has remained closely involved with ID, makes the school's curriculum a meld of arts and sciences. In Whitney's words: "We are now equally connected to the sciences, engineering, social sciences and humanities. That's why our students have a broader knowledge than students from many other design schools."

According to Whitney, of the nearly 800 graphic-design schools and 50 product-design schools in the United States, only a handful adopt ID's integrated approach. Professor Dennis Ichiyama, chairman of the Division of Art and Design in Purdue University's Department of Creative Arts, told the *Chicago Tri-*

bune: "Their students are much more information-oriented. Students from other schools are more visually oriented."

In most schools, design gets taught as commercial art. ID's program is loosely separated into three areas: product design, visual communication design, and photography. Students are taught to give physical expression to ideas, using a technique called rapid prototyping.

In the first and second years, students use basic skills like modeling to present simple product-design problems like lamps or cameras to small classes. They progress to more formal presentations using slides and audiotapes and present them to both faculty and students, who are invited to criticize.

Since design has no "right answers," students are left with a feeling that they could have done more.

Another proposal, "Project Phoenix: Fire Reversed," is aimed at extracting from the atmosphere the amount of carbon dioxide already present. Much of the thrust of the project is the regreening of barren areas. Beginning at the windward fringe of a desert, a carefully selected plant ecosystem would be sheltered under a system of tentlike, air-supported domes. This system would slowly be extended into the desert. When one section had reached sufficient maturity for probable survival without shelter, those domes would be removed to the far edge of the system to continue to extend the regreening process. The crisscrossing white air tubes in the computer-generated picture channel air to the periphery of a cluster. Returning air cools the environment and supplies fresh carbon dioxide. In addition, these large tubes, 10 meters (32.8 feet) in diameter, stiffen the structure against storms.

While demanding, the atmosphere is intended to help students regain creativity lost in normal education. But that does not mean they avoid a basic foundation. In addition to design courses, students must take the usual college core curriculum, including a substantial number of courses in physics, chemistry, and calculus. They also must complete a thesis.

IIT has a commitment to keeping the university's students and faculty involved with the residents of Chicago. *Chicago Tribune* articles on January 18, 1991 and July 26, 1992 described custom-designed newsstands built as class projects by ID students. A July 19, 1992 *Chicago Tribune* article told of a six-week ID program for 40 students ages 9–12 supported by Sony Corporation of America. Working with ID students and artists from a nonprofit organization called Urban Gateways, the children illustrated their ideas and made three-dimensional models, which were put on display at the Sony Gallery of Consumer Electronics.

The April 1, 1992 *Chicago Tribune* carried the story of IIT's fourth annual model-car competition. The competition held on campus is broken into three categories: high school students, IIT students, and IIT faculty and alumni. The designers who fared best operated on the KISS (Keep It Simple, Stupid) principle.

Revered Outside the
United States, Unknown at Home

ID's international reputation goes back many decades. As early as the 1950s, officials of Japan's Ministry of International Trade and Industry (MITI) sent students to ID to study design, an area they consider a national weakness.

For the last decade or so, ID has won in competitions involving students and professionals, nationally and internationally. The residents of Osaka, Japan are quite familiar with ID. In astonishment, two out of four times they watched students and graduates of ID win their coveted prize for the Osaka design competition held every two years. Winning the Osaka competitions made international celebrities of the Chicago competitors. Charles Owen is an honored speaker in Asia and a consultant to Taiwan. When he steps off a plane in Osaka, he is met by the press.

Interviewed for an October 29, 1989 *Chicago Tri-*

bune article entitled "They're the Best," Owen said, "It's not as if I'm a rock star, but I'm known by designers out there and by the publications out there. The reason is simple. They're attuned to design. And they know we are a hotbed of design here."

Despite its international reputation, the school remains virtually unknown to the American public, because design in the United States tends to be viewed as synonymous with styling. Robert Blaich, managing director of design for Phillips in Eindhoven, the Netherlands, told the *Chicago Tribune* that styling to Americans suggests "something you do at the end [of the production cycle], and nothing could be further from the truth."

ID director Whitney elaborated: "In this country we have the belief that engineers do all the substantial work. And then we have the designers who come in and gussy it up with ribbons and bows."

Some of ID's projects indicate that ribbons and bows are hardly what they do. To mention just a few, they have developed:

To participate in the "My First Sony" competition, students from 19 Chicago elementary schools spent six summer weeks intensively studying design. That meant direct experience in brainstorming for ideas, envisioning an idea's impact on everyday life, working out a practical design, constructing the product, and presenting it to the public. The students went through all the stages of envisioning and implementing an idea. Pictured are elementary student James Parks with two recent Institute of Design graduates Scott Ternovits and Mayur Patadia. On display is Parks' invention, The Watcher. The device is meant to alert firemen to various dangers in burning buildings, such as cave-ins.

• A seasonal landscape machine that cuts grass, blows snow, and collects leaves.

• A plastic wheelchair.

• A portable dental-care delivery system for Third World countries.

For the 1989 Osaka contest a 14-student design team attacked the problem of the greenhouse effect. The greenhouse effect is caused by so-called greenhouse gases, such as carbon dioxide, that trap some of the sun's heat in the atmosphere, the envelope of air surrounding Earth. Prevented from being dissipated in space, the heat gradually increases the temperature of the envelope. The process is called global warming and has the potential to change the Earth's overall climate.

The solution the students devised for the greenhouse effect is a two-pronged plan known as Project Phoenix. One prong, called "Fire Replaced," moves the Earth's primary sources of energy 23,000 miles into outer space. From the new locale, 1,000 solar panels, each the size of a medium-sized city, would beam down power to receiving stations on Earth. The panels, built in "lunar orbit factories," would use materials mined from the surface of Mars and catapulted to the factories.

The other prong, called "Fire Reversed," would use great quantities of plants in desert regreening centers and in floating wetlands in the oceans. With a total area of about 431,000 square miles, the floating wetlands would have thriving populations of kelp, mussels, sargasso (floating, brown seaweeds with berrylike air sacs), and huge floating islands of mangroves, which are tropical trees and shrubs in swampy ground.

The purpose of Fire Reversed's greenery would be to absorb the atmosphere's excess carbon dioxide and convert it to oxygen. The design team believes two prongs working together could restore the Earth's natural atmospheric carbon balance.

Because of the low priority American firms put on design, ID's students are not heavily recruited in the United States, but they are recruited by foreign companies. Philips, the Netherlands' industrial giant, makes a yearly recruiting trip to the campus. Gustavo Rodriguez, a Chicagoan, described as a design "prodigy," who is employed by Philips, told the *Chicago Tribune* that many U.S. design offices are "rendering factories," a factor that some of the Institute of Design's students cannot accept, so they work outside the country.

American industry's low regard for design is not new. In the early 1960s, former ID Chairman Doblin consulted with the directors of General Motors. He told them that cars did not need to be restyled each year and did not need to be so large. In fact, car designs made at ID during this period closely resemble the Japanese models so popular in the United States today. General Motors ignored his advice.

Randolph McAusland, director of the Design Arts Program for the National Endowment of the Arts, along with other designers, told the *Chicago Tribune* that concern about the American corporate attitude toward design has greater consequences than just underappreciation of a profession: "If we don't change, we could end up without a manufacturing base in this country, and that would be a mistake of unimaginable consequence. It's unfortunate because America was once a nation of inventors."

Credence is lent to that prediction by U.S. Patent and Trademark Office statistics, which indicate that the number of patents as a percentage of world patents has dropped approximately 20%. Moreover, the loss of a sizable portion of America's manufacturing base was a major campaign issue during the 1992 presidential election.

There have been some efforts to stem the tide. For instance, the Harvard University Business School has incorporated design-oriented case histories into its curriculum, and Northwestern University's J.L. Kellogg Graduate School of Management has added a course in design. Also IIT upgraded the Institute of Design from a department to a school within the university. As more people become aware of the importance of design, it will play a more critical role in our society.

11

PHYSICS

Buildings are Higher,
But Principles Have Not Changed Much

Compared with other human activities, the principles and methods employed in building, also known as architecture, are new. The discipline began about 10,000 years ago, when humans discovered agriculture and animal husbandry and gave up roaming the Earth in search of food. Until then, they had cooked over campfires and lived in tents made of animal skins, precariously protected against the weather.

Once settled, early humans supplanted tents with more substantial homes with permanent hearths. When many huts sprang up in a fertile area, it became a village. Contact between villages resulted in a network of paths, some crossing rivers and ravines, requiring the construction of footbridges made of tree trunks, or suspension bridges made of vegetable-fiber ropes.

Early communities also built larger structures to serve as central gathering places and places of worship. Throughout the history of architecture, religious needs often have inspired the building of large structures.

The span of 10,000 years, more than 300 generations of humans, has brought about enormous cultural changes—particularly since the beginning of the Industrial Revolution. However, in the opinion of Mario Salvadori, Columbia University professor emeritus of civil engineering and architecture, architectural principles have not changed much over the last 6,000 years, because the basic physiological needs served by architecture have not changed much. In his 1980 book *Why Buildings Stand Up: The Strength of Architecture,* Salvadori points out that arch bridges of the 21st century are built of better materials, but they behave according to the same principles found in Roman bridges of 2,000 years ago.

Changes in architecture over the centuries have been brought about by concentrations of people in towns and cities. The density of cities led to the construction of taller buildings. For instance, in 2000 B.C. some residents of Minoan cities on Crete lived in four-story houses, and tenements in Rome, Italy rose to heights of 10 stories.

Today, computer aided design has made the building process safer. In the past, structures were erected by the trial-and-error method: each builder dared more than his or her predecessor until failure indicated the limits of the structural system had been exceeded. One of the largest domes of antiquity, the dome of the Hagia Sophia in Constantinople (now Istanbul, Turkey), first built in A.D. 53, fell twice before it stood, where it still stands. The extraordinarily high vault of the Gothic cathedral in Beauvais, France collapsed twice before the 14th- and 16th-century masons understood the limitations of the construction.

Computers also have made possible the record-breaking high-rise structures of the modern era by carrying out millions of mathematical calculations that even two decades ago would have required calculations by hand that would have taken centuries. These tall buildings now reach heights of close to 1,500 feet, and covered stadiums span as much as 700 feet, requiring structures infinitely more complex than those of the past. But the development of struc-

The Parthenon on the Acropolis in Athens, Greece, is a classic example of the post-and-beam, or post-and-lintel, method of construction. This method is among the simplest of architectural techniques to understand. A horizontal beam, or lintel, rests on sturdy, upright posts. This was the basic Greek method of construction, and Greek architects acquired sufficient skill to enable them to erect massive structures of marble such as the Parthenon. A series of subtle curves were incorporated into the structure to correct optical illusions that might make the lines of the building appear to sag or be imprecise. Over many centuries, the temples of the Acropolis remained intact reflecting a minimum of wear until a cannonball struck a temple full of stored gunpowder. The destroyed buildings were eventually put together again from the pieces left. Today, the buildings of the Acropolis have more to fear from air pollution than from cannonballs or sheer age.

tural materials has not kept pace with computer-aided design. Except for reinforced and prestressed concrete and high-strength steel, the materials in current use are similar to those used in earlier centuries.

Wood, stone, masonry, and bricks still dominate construction and must be used in ways dictated by their properties, which have remained practically unchanged for centuries. The properties of these materials limit aspirations to build ever-higher structures. The world's tallest building, the Sears Tower in Chicago, Illinois, is only three times taller than the 5,000-year-old pyramid of Cheops. The world's largest hall, the Louisiana Superdome, spans a distance of 680 feet, which is only 4.5 times the 149-foot span of the dome of the Pantheon built in Rome 1,800 years ago.

The superiority of modern materials is in their economy. The largest modern buildings are extremely light in weight and cheaper to build. For example, the dome of St. Peter's Basilica in Rome spans 137 feet and consists of two domes of brick that weigh about 450 pounds per square foot. And the double dome of Centri National des Industries et des Techniques

exhibition hall in Paris, France is five times larger than St. Peter's but weighs only 90 pounds per square foot.

Balancing Loads

Even if architecture has not changed much, architects and engineers have a great deal to keep in mind in building modern buildings, not the least of which is loads. If gravity did not operate, the wind did not blow, the Earth's surface did not shake or sink, and the air temperature did not change, planners would not have to be concerned about structures supporting loads.

Similar to water flowing down a network of pipes, a structure's purpose is to channel the building's loads to the ground. The channels are columns, beams, cables, arches, and other structural elements.

The structure performs the task of channeling loads through two elementary actions: pulling and pushing. The structure's elements are either pulled by the loads and are stretched, or they are pushed and they shorten. In the language of structure, the loads are said to "stress" the structure, which "strains" under stress and breaks down or buckles when overstressed.

A structure will always chose to channel its loads to the ground by the easiest of many paths available, thereby requiring the minimum amount of work on the part of the materials. This behavior is called in physics "the law of least work."

But a structure of heavy elements like columns, beams, floors, arches, or domes must before anything else support its own weight, the structure's so-called dead load. The dead load is a load that is permanently present. In some structures built of masonry or concrete, it is often the heaviest load to be supported by the structure.

Dead loads also include other loads that are permanently present, such as the weights of floors, ceilings, insulation material, and partitions that divide one room from another. Even though partitions may be moved around, they will always be there.

Live loads are impermanent and may change from day to day. An apartment tenant, who normally lives alone, might invite 25 people for a party. The guests might spread out in the apartment or all congregate in one room. A subsequent tenant might fill the apartment with massive furniture rather than people. Thus the planner never knows exactly what the live load might be and how it might be distributed.

At first glance, it might seem prudent to build for the worst possible loading conditions during the entire life of the structure. But the chances are remote that each square foot of each room on each floor of a building will ever be fully loaded at the same time. Buildings designed with such a possibility in mind would be prohibitively expensive. Therefore, building codes generally allow for "live-load reductions," which may reach 60% for a high-rise building.

Estimates of live loads also depend on the building type, its geographic location, and its use. Warehouse floors must be designed to carry greater live loads than apartment houses. A Colorado roof routinely carries a much heavier load of snow than one in Mississippi. In contrast to the relatively quiet corridors and halls of private office buildings, those in public buildings often are likely to be jammed with people.

Dead loads are permanent and unchanging, and live loads are assumed to change slowly—the party guests trickle in two or three at a time. These loads are called static loads.

But other loads—referred to as dynamic loads—vary rapidly or even abruptly. A hammer laid gently on a nail head poised against a wall has little effect, but a hammer slammed into a nail head will thrust the nail into the wall. These suddenly applied, so-

In what is now the southwest United States, Pueblo Indians used the same technique for building that the Greeks used. Note the beams peeking out from under the roofs. It was a technique they stayed with, finding it as useful as the Greeks did. Post-and-beam construction is a technique common to civilizations worldwide.

Skyscrapers are a modern version of post-and-beam construction. When built with forethought, they can sit comfortably amidst older buildings. Viewed from above Boston's Copley Square are the glass-covered Hancock Tower and, in the lower right-hand corner, the shorter Copley Place, nestled among such 19th-century delights as Trinity Church, the Copley Plaza Hotel, and, across the square, the Boston Public Library. From an engineering standpoint, the Hancock Tower was not a complete success. Until structural corrections were made, many windows in the upper stories could not stand up to New England winds.

called impact loads, are briefly equivalent to many times their static loads.

Loads are never completely static or dynamic. Structural materials are never totally rigid. All buildings sway in the wind. The wind's effect depends on the structure of the building to which it is applied. Under wind pressure a tall building bends slightly and its top moves.

If wind pressure moves a building one foot to the right, the building will rebound going back through its original position and moving one foot to the left—like an upside down pendulum—swinging back and forth, or oscillating, until it stops. The time taken to make a full swing from extreme right to left and back is called the building's period. The period for the 1,350-foot steel towers of New York's World Trade Center is 10 seconds. That of a 10-story brick building might be half a second.

One of the most dangerous effects to which a structure can be subjected is resonance. Resonance is familiar in heavy church bells—often weighing a few tons—that are made to swing in response to small pulls on a bell's rope timed with the beginning of each new oscillation.

Resonant forces do not produce large effects immediately, but their effects increase steadily with time and can become catastrophic if they last long enough. An often-told resonance story is about a German infantry unit marching across a small wooden bridge in rhythm with the up-down oscillations of the bridge. Ultimately, the bridge collapsed under the resonant load and dumped the unit into the river.

The forces exerted by winds on buildings have dramatically increased with the increase in building heights. High-rise buildings built in the 1970s, which were often close to 1,500 feet tall, had to be 50 times stronger to withstand wind than the typical 200-foot building of the 1940s. In addition, the speed of wind rises with height, and wind pressure increases as the square of the wind speed.

In addition to their relationship to building height and wind speed, wind forces vary with the shape of a building. On the windward side of a rectangular building, the movement of air particles is stopped and forced to go around the building to rejoin on the leeward side. Leeward-side air particles create a suction.

During the 1960 hurricane Donna, occupants on the windward sides of New York high-rise office buildings had large glass panels blown into their offices. Occupants on the leeward sides had glass panels pulled out of their windows and dumped on pedestrians below.

Only within the last 30 or 40 years have scientists begun to understand the impact earthquakes have on buildings. Segments of the Earth's crust floating on molten rock come into contact with one another. The motion of the earth around the foundations of buildings jerks them. Since the dynamic forces due to the jerking motion are mostly horizontal, they can be resisted by the same kind of bracing used against the wind.

The last category of loads that must be taken into consideration arise from daily or seasonal changes in air temperature or uneven soil settlement. These are so-called hidden or locked-in loads. Naturally, not all locked-in loads are hidden. In many modern buildings, such as the 100-story John Hancock building in Chicago and the Columbia Broadcasting System building in New York, the structural frame is visible outside rather than hidden inside. These structures exposed to the weather are subject to extreme temperature changes.

In summer, the exterior columns may reach temperatures of up to 120 degrees Fahrenheit and become two or three inches longer than the interior columns, while in winter they may drop to 20 degrees Fahrenheit and shorten by the same amount. The variations in length do not damage the columns, but they bend the beams connecting the outer to the in-

ner columns, particularly at higher floors. Damage is prevented by allowing the beams' ends to rotate or by hinging them.

The bending of beams connecting the outer to inner columns also occurs if the soil under a building settles unevenly. For example, the rocky soil of Manhattan permitted the Woolworth Building, the first high rise, to be built in New York in 1913.

Mexico City, on the other hand, is built on a mixture of sand and water. The National Theatre in the center of Mexico City, was built with a heavy cladding, or covering, of stone. After a few years, the theater's weight squeezed the water out of the sand beneath it, and the theater sank about 10 feet. A flight of stairs had to be built down to the entrance.

The Coliseum, built of a concrete made from water, lime, small rocks, volcanic dust, and broken pieces of brick, is a series of arches, inside and out. The Romans used the arch extensively along with their very durable concrete. Salvadori explains the structural principle of the semi-circular or true arch by the example of a weighted cable. If one attached a small weight to a cable, the cable would be pulled downward and the ends of the cable would be pulled toward one another unless a force, referred to as thrust, were not applied to the ends of the cable. This force is simply the act of pulling outward on the cables. Imagine that cable as an arch so the weight is at the top, transform the cable into masonry of wedge-shaped blocks known as voussoirs, with the weight at the top becoming the keystone wedge downward, and the thrusting force at either end of the masonry "cable" pressing inward, and one has an arch.

Civilizations prior to the rise of Rome sometimes used the arch. But the Romans showed the world just how useful the arch could be by constantly incorporating it into buildings, bridges, and aquaducts. Water is still flowing through Roman aquaducts built 20 centuries ago. There are several basic arrangements of arches. When placed side by side in a series, as seen on the right-hand side, the arrangement is referred to as an arcade. A barrel or tunnel vault is a series of arches placed one in back of another as seen on the left-hand side. A dome results when arches intersect each other around a central axis.

In later years, after a large number of high-rise buildings had been built in the area, the water squeezed from beneath the other buildings raised the theater, and stairs had to be built up to the entrance.

Much More Could Be Done

Modern engineers have improved on Roman bridge engineering by using steel cable that permits spans of almost 6,000 feet. Although they did not invent the brick and stone arch, the Romans made extensive use of it to link the most distant provinces to Rome via 50,000 miles of roads. Spanning up to 100 feet, these bridges crossed innumerable rivers along the way.

Thus in Mario Salvadori's opinion, improvements in bridge building have increased 60-fold, but improvements in other types of construction have been limited. Most architectural changes have come in the use of new materials. Glass or plastic fibers are now mixed into concrete to make exceptionally strong fa-

cades only a fraction of an inch thick. Only cost has prevented the widespread use of plastics in architectural structures.

Additional improvements have come from attention to dynamic forces (rapid structural changes) through the use of feedback mechanisms to make constant adjustments. For example, in tropical and subtropical areas, the south facade of a building may reach a temperature that is sufficiently higher than the north facade to bend the building and crack its partitions and walls. A computer system that monitors the temperature differences can activate diagonal braces that pull the building back into alignment.

The Japanese created the world's first building with an active wind- and earthquake-resistant control system built on a tiny plot in a Tokyo suburb in 1989. The owners of the Kyobashi Seiwa office building, which is 12 feet wide, 100 feet long, and 11 stories high, worried that the wind would buffet their ultraslim building. So the Kajima construction company stabilized the building by suspending a 1-ton weight above a 4-ton weight. When sensors embedded in the building's base and walls become aware of motion caused by the wind or tremors in the ground, they send signals to hydraulic arms called actuators that move the weights to counteract the building's motion.

Some progress has been made in the United States in antiseismic (earthquake-resistant) design. The 1989 San Francisco earthquake revealed the value of such design. Eyewitnesses atop the TransAmerica building and other skyscrapers saw buildings around them sway like trees in a wind, and baseball fans watched the Candlestick Park upper balcony wave up and down. For an earthquake that registered 7.1 on the Richter scale, damage and the number of deaths was minimal. However, except in California, American construction companies have been slow to innovate. As a consequence, changes in building codes to provide earthquake resistance have been slow in the United States. But in Japan, where earthquakes are

By the 12th century, Gothic architects had developed a new form from the versatile arch: the flying buttress. This was one of a number of experiments with external buttressing developed to build ever-taller cathedrals. The flying buttress allowed much of the weight of a cathedral structure's soaring vaulted ceiling to be shifted to outside supporting pillars. In this rear view of the Cathedral of Notre Dame in Chartres, France, exterior buttresses can be clearly seen thrusting outward from the cathedral walls.

an ever-present threat, major construction companies compete for contracts using new technologies. The Japanese company with the best new ideas tends to win.

Interviewed for a July 2, 1991 *New York Times* article entitled "Engineers Teach Smart Buildings to Foil Quakes," Dr. Chi Liu, program manager of the Earthquake Hazard Mitigation Project at the National Science Foundation (NSF) in Washington, D.C., reported that most of the innovative ideas for passive and active controls to resist earthquakes have originated in the United States but are being developed in Japan.

Japanese construction companies invest 10% of their gross income in research and development. NSF planned to spur American involvement in earthquake-resistant buildings by awarding grants, but Dr. Liu was unsure whether American construction companies will use the research. If they do incorporate new information, American firms will improve their chances to compete in a global economy.

The interior of the Cathedral of Notre Dame has ribbed vaulted ceilings. The flying buttress reduced the need for supporting structures inside the cathedral, creating a lighter, less-cluttered interior.

Traffic Crashes, a Major Source of Death and Injury

Driving may be a familiar and straightforward activity that almost anyone can learn, but it often baffles scientists. University of Michigan researcher Michael Sivak suspects that there are global societal influences on driving that researchers have been unable to grasp.

A September 9–15, 1991 *Washington Post Weekly Edition* article entitled "Trafficking in the Unpredictable" described some of the perverse findings that researchers have been unable to predict. For example, pedestrians are twice as likely to be killed by motorists when using pedestrian cross walks than while crossing at intersections that have no special markings. The problem seems to stem from a false sense of security among pedestrians who charge across without looking. This sense of security is sufficient to offset any extra caution drivers might use when they see pedestrians in cross walks.

Technological changes that reduce crash risk often reduce safety because they make it possible for drivers to drive more often under unsafe conditions. Improved handling can encourage faster driving and cornering. Enhanced poor-weather capability can encourage faster driving under conditions of poor visibility. Drowsiness-detection devices can permit drivers to drive longer.

An example of the perverse effect of improvements was revealed in a German study that randomly assigned a group of Munich taxi drivers to cars with antilock brakes. The antilock brakes substantially increased each taxi's capacity to stop without skidding. While some kinds of accidents decreased, others increased as drivers responded to the improved braking by reducing caution.

The effect on accidents when changes, such as road signs or barrel markers, are made in traffic systems also is often unpredictable. Road users' reactions range all the way from fewer accidents to more accidents, regardless of whether the changes were introduced to improve safety or were cutbacks for economic reasons.

Safety belts definitely work, but many people don't use them. In states that have laws mandating the use of safety belts, only about 40% of the drivers comply. In states without such laws, only about 20% comply.

In industrialized countries, traffic crashes constitute one of the greatest risks to health. In his book *Traffic Safety and the Driver* (1991), Leonard Evans, a principal research scientist at General Motors Research Laboratories, points out that almost half of the 19-year-olds who die in the United States do so as a result of traffic crashes.

In his book, Dr. Evans imposes some order on an enormous unstructured body of often conflicting information. Topics range from car, roadway, and traffic engineering to driver performance and behavior. They also include impairment factors such as alcohol, drugs, and sleep deprivation, and the success and failure of countermeasures, such as lap/shoulder belts and drinking-age restrictions.

The risk of death from the same impact is closely tied to age and sex. Beyond the age of 20, fatality risk grows at a rate of about 2.3% per year for males and

Only a person who has had nothing to drink can start an automobile that is equipped with the Guardian Interlock System. The driver must exhale into the device connected to the ignition.

Objections are sometimes raised against divided highways on the grounds they divide neighborhoods, thus damaging neighborhood cohesiveness. But they do accomplish one end. By separating traffic going in opposite directions, head-on collisions are reduced. With cars all going in the same direction, an automobile must actually cross over the median dividing the highway before it can hit another oncoming auto.

about 2.0% for females. At age 70, the risk for both sexes is about three times what it was at age 20. From age 15 to 45, the same physical insult is approximately 25% more likely to kill a female than a male of the same age. The risk of being involved in a crash increases beyond the age of 40, but older drivers drive less and are involved in fewer crashes per capita than 20-year-olds, and they kill fewer pedestrians.

The recent imposition of increasing numbers of motor vehicle safety standards appears to have reduced occupant fatality risk by about 15%–20%. Vehicle mass, or size, is the one vehicle characteristic that has the largest effect on the risk of injury or death in crashes. Statistically, the increase in safety for a driver who switches to a heavier car is greater than the reduction in safety collectively for other road users the driver might hit with that heavier car.

Different types of roads also affect fatality rates. For example, the replacement of a rural two-lane roadway with a divided freeway can reduce fatalities as much as ninefold.

Driving conditions also make a difference, but not in the expected direction. Despite snow and ice and more hours of darkness, fatalities per unit of distance traveled are lower in winter months. Crash rates increase during winter, but because drivers reduce their speed, fatality risks are lower on wet and snow-covered roads than on dry roads.

Fatality rates are much higher at night, largely due to such road-user characteristics as alcohol use. Alcohol contributes more than any other factor to traffic crashes. Were it not for alcohol, 10% of the property damage, 20% of the injuries, and 47% of the fatalities due to traffic crashes would not happen.

Multidisciplinary post-crash research done in the United States and in Great Britain identified road-user characteristics as factors in 94% and 95% of crashes, respectively. The crucial factor is not driver performance, or how the driver *can* drive, but driver behavior, or how the driver *does* drive.

There is no direct relationship between safety and driving skill or knowledge. One study found skilled race drivers, who held licenses to compete issued by the Sports Car Club of America, had substantially higher crash rates than ordinary drivers.

Observations of actual drivers consistently indicate higher risk-taking among young males. Traffic crash involvement has been correlated with being unmarried, emotionally unstable, unhappy, antisocial, impulsive, aggressive, or under stress.

Many studies have determined that people drive in the same way that they live. In other words, polite, tranquil people drive in a polite, tranquil manner. Rude, angry people drive in a rude, angry manner.

Some technological devices, such as safety belts or motorcycle helmets, only affect the outcome of crashes without changing the behavior of drivers. Similarly, technological changes of which the driver is only dimly aware, such as energy-absorbing steering columns and side-guard beams in doors, are unlikely to change the behavior of drivers.

In a crash, restraints make a difference. Compared with a driver unprotected by any restraint system, the risk is reduced by 47% for a driver protected by a lap/shoulder belt and an airbag, 42% for a belt alone, and 18% for an airbag alone.

Safety Consciousness

The losses due to alcohol would be even greater were it not for such countermeasures as drunk-driving laws, which forbid driving with an amount of alcohol in the blood beyond a specified limit, typically 0.1% in the United States, but lower almost everywhere else in the world. (In Sweden, the limit is 0.02%). More important than laws in drunk-driving prevention is a broadly held national attitude that drunk driving is unacceptable.

When government economists and engineers collaborated in 1976 to predict the rise or fall of traffic deaths over the coming decades, they estimated that highway fatalities would soar from 40,000 in 1975 to 72,300 in 1985. They based their predictions on expected increases in alcohol consumption, in speeding, and in the size of the population.

Their calculations were wrong. Instead of rising by 32,000 the number of people who died in traffic accidents in 1985 went down by 700 over 1976 fatalities. While the population had increased, social factors had combined to influence the trend. Speed limits were reduced for a few years, and lobbying in the 1980s led to greater penalties for drunk driving. More important, a large segment of the population had become concerned about safety issues.

Evans points out that traffic fatalities have almost always declined over time. In 1920, there were about 175 deaths per billion kilometers (625 million miles). Since that time the number of annual deaths has fallen almost steadily to an average of about 15 for the same distance.

Evans uses the declining rate to support his contention that driver behavior is the key variable in traffic accidents. He believes the decline in fatalities has been due to a kind of "collective learning" about courtesy and safe road behavior.

In his book, Evans wrote: "I would make the analogy with health. There is an increase in collective care that people in the nation are taking. More people are interested in eating appropriate foods. There has been a dramatic decline in smoking. More reasonable behavior in driving is part of the general pattern of increased focus on taking care of oneself."

University of Michigan researcher Michael Sivak makes a similar point. He took traffic fatality data and correlated it with every conceivable factor possible—age, sex, number of cars, alcohol consumption, etc. He found that three variables accounted for nearly all the differences among the traffic fatality rates of various U.S. states.

The variables were: the percentage of a state's population under age 25; the state's death rate from accidents unrelated to traffic; and—most important—the state's homicide rate. The higher these three factors climbed, the higher the state's traffic fatality rate climbed.

Sivak explains the relationship between the three factors and the traffic fatality rate as a reflection of a population's fundamental attitudes toward life. A

Children are even more vulnerable than adults to injury. For them, adequate safety restraints are indispensable.

Since the 1960s the federal government has promoted beautification of the nation's roads with plantings, while at the same time preserving or improving visibility. Brush and trees growing too close to the edge of the roads are cut back to prevent them from blocking visibility. Other actions taken to improve highway safety include: installation of clearer signs, signals, and pavement markings designed to decrease driver confusion; removal or relocation of potentially hazardous collision objects such as boulders and telephone poles; and installation of breakaway sign supports and crash cushions aimed at reducing fatalities from collisions.

state's response to fatal accidents, recklessness among the young, and murder is mirrored by events in traffic. Sivak told the *Washington Post:* "A society's tolerance for life is reflected both in the ways we kill each other with guns and in the way we kill each other with cars."

Support for Evans and Sivak's theory of societal responsibility was reported in an October 10, 1990 *New York Times* article entitled "Fatal Accidents Are Down as U.S. Becomes Vigilant." The article discussed figures for fatal accidents from all causes released by the National Safety Council, an 87-year-old nonprofit group based in Chicago, Illinois and chartered by Congress.

According to the National Safety Council, more progress was made in accident prevention during the 1980s than in any other decade in the 20th century. Despite the growth in size of the population, the annual total of all accidents fell from 105,312 in 1979 to 94,500 in 1989.

During the decade of the 1980s, there was a 20%

decline in the rate of motor vehicle deaths, which are responsible for nearly half of all accidental deaths. The biggest decline was among drivers aged 15–24.

The national death rate from accidents in the home dropped 16%, and it would have dropped lower if home accidents due to fatal drug overdoses had not significantly increased. The death rate from accidents in public—including falls, drowning, and plane crashes—declined 22%. The death rate from accidents at work dropped 29%.

A large decline in deaths due to fire is credited mostly to widespread use of smoke detectors. But the decline in the percentage of smokers has probably contributed a great deal, since cigarettes are the leading cause of fires in the home, where four out of five fire-related deaths occur.

Most of the reduction in drunk driving came from a combination of a widespread change in social norms that made drinking and driving unacceptable, passage of greater drunk-driving penalties, and more rigorous law enforcement. Traffic safety stopped being the sole responsibility of legislators, police departments, and road and vehicle builders. The whole society took on the task of preventing a large number of people from indulging in the dangerous pastimes of high-speed driving, high-risk driving, and drunk driving, often all at the same time.

Many market researchers and academics attribute the increasing concern with safety in the United States to the increasing age of the population. The U.S. population is having fewer children and having them later in life; since the loss of a child can effectively wipe out a family, there is a greater concern for safety.

The lethal combination of drinking and driving has made it a logical target for prevention efforts. Campaigns against drunk driving have been so successful in reducing fatalities from auto accidents that similar campaigns have been undertaken to reduce boating deaths, half of which are due to alcohol.

From a practical standpoint, some changes in behavior warrant greater attention because they can have a much greater impact. For example, while reductions in the consumption of alcohol in the United States in the 1980s are estimated to have reduced traffic fatalities by 22%, shifting from a condition in which no cars are equipped with airbags to one in which all are so equipped would reduce U.S. traffic fatalities by only 5%. Probably because there are many fewer motorcycles on the road than other vehicles, if all U.S. motorcyclists wore helmets, U.S. traffic fatalities would be reduced by less than 1%.

In Evans' opinion, driver education and traffic safety education should be taught separately. The skills of driving require direct feedback. Drivers learn to execute right turns only after many errors, such as riding up over the curb or cornering too widely. But safety is not learned by feedback. Crashes are rare events making the esperience of a crash an ineffective way to learn. Safety is learned through an accumulation of knowledge about real risks.

For example, often overlooked in driver education are common events, such as being confronted with a child who has run into a roadway. Yet the National Highway Traffic Safety Administration's data bank, the Fatal Accident Reporting System (FARS), indicates that more than 100 6-year-old pedestrians are killed per year, and many more are injured.

Research observations in Great Britain of driver behavior determined that drivers behave as if avoidance of child-pedestrian crashes is the responsibility of the child. Most drivers who injure or kill child pedestrians are not held legally liable, based on their claim that "there was nothing I could do to prevent it." But good drivers give driving their full attention and anticipate problems like children or animals or other drivers who are erratic.

In his classic *How to Drive Better and Avoid Accidents* (1969), Paul Kearney quoted Professor Robert Eddy of Massachusetts Institute of Technology, who said about drivers who "could not prevent" accidents: "A small number of accidents occur through circumstances which the driver could not possibly foresee, but these are comparatively few. Beyond them the driver can, if he is willing, avoid all accidents. Bad roads, sharp curves, blind intersections, smooth tires, poor brakes, slippery pavements, etc. are all secondary factors in that they cause accidents through their effect on the driver. They are hazards only because they impose on the driver delay which he finds irk-

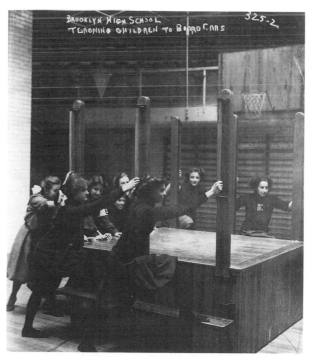

Today, schools offer driver's education. Once upon a time traffic safety instruction consisted of lessons on the proper way to clamber onto a streetcar. This particular lesson was given at a Brooklyn high school.

some, and to avoid delay he will take chances that result in accidents when luck fails."

Despite the customary lack of punishment for killing a pedestrian, a driver who kills or maims another human being cannot escape living the rest of his or her life with the knowledge. Adoption of safer driving practices, which Evans believes should be taught in traffic safety classes held after drivers have learned to drive, would encourage drivers to allow larger safety margins when in the vicinity of pedestrians, bicyclists, and motorcyclists. This is an area in which drivers could take control to halve or quarter the chances that they might kill or permanently injure others.

Slow Progress in Traffic Safety

Several factors have hindered the development of the science of traffic safety. Much has been learned in the more than 50 years of technical analysis of driving behavior and traffic safety. However, when compared to advances in traditional science, increases in knowledge about traffic safety are unimpressive.

Institutions often have agendas that influence the direction of science in general and traffic safety in particular. For example, funding sources usually want traffic safety research that addresses some current crisis.

Evans counts professional journals among the institutions that determine directions in research through their selection of what gets published. He is amazed that despite the fact that more preretirement years are lost due to traffic accidents than from the combined effects of cancer and heart disease, the *American Journal of Public Health* has consistently opposed treating traffic crashes as a public health problem. The journal has instead advocated that the only traffic safety countermeasures worthy of consideration are engineering changes to vehicles.

Another hindrance to traffic science development is a lack of specialization in narrow areas of research. Although there are hundreds of traffic safety researchers worldwide, few have devoted a substantial portion of their careers to narrowly defined areas, such as the influence of speed, or the contribution of vehicle mass or size.

In Evans' opinion, prevention of traffic crashes should not be considered analogous to the treatment of a specific disease for which a vaccine might be developed. He writes: "Improvements in traffic safety, as in public health, are produced by a rich variety of interventions, a few making large contributions, but many more making important small contributions. Any intervention which reduces U.S. traffic fatalities by 1% prevents 450 deaths per year, a total that in contexts other than traffic would be considered enormous, not small."

Mass transit systems contribute to traffic safety by reducing congestion. Sheer congestion contributes to traffic accidents. The more vehicles crowded onto a road, the more opportunities there are for accidents. Congestion reduces space needed to maneuver in an emergency. Crowding promotes more impatience, which often gives way to impulsive, sometimes dangerous actions. Weariness leads to dangerous mistakes. Subways are particularly useful because they do not take up space on the streets. As early as the latter part of the 19th century, Boston experienced gridlock downtown. It could take hours to move a wagon, auto, or trolley a mile or two. Before the turn of the 20th century, Boston opened its first subway line. That line consisted of only four stops, but on opening day 100,000 people rode the subway and by the end of one year, the line had carried 50 million passengers. Today, Boston has four long subway lines connecting with commuter rail service and numerous buses.

12

CHEMISTRY

The Rapidly Changing World of Smart Structures and Smart Materials

Smart structures—which grew out of the space program—are those with built in self-correcting devices that repair or avoid damage. Far from the care of human operators, space equipment such as antennas and booms needed programmed ability to retain required shapes, point in specific directions, and avoid jitter (small, rapid) vibrations. To automatically detect deformations and make adjustments, space scientists devised sensors that respond to temperature, pressure, etc., and convert the information into signals. To cope with damage, scientists developed actuators, which are mechanisms that activate control equipment.

The potential uses of smart structures are enormous. Structures like smart skyscrapers designed to protect themselves against swaying in high winds and from being rocked by earthquakes are already in use. Smart submarines with walls that flex to escape sonar detection are in development.

Smart materials, as distinguished from smart structures, are human-made materials that can sense and react to changes in their environment. Most smart materials, such as the substances that will make possible self-healing windshields, are still in various phases of research.

In the 1991 movie *Terminator 2*, Arnold Schwarzenegger, equipped with sensors, controllers, and actuators was the equivalent of a smart structure. His adversary, the deadly Metalloid Man, equipped with a built-in ability to change form and function and perpetually self-heal was the equivalent of a smart material.

The provision of mathematical help for scientists working with smart materials is a major thrust of North Carolina State University (NCSU) Center for Research in Scientific Computation, headed by mathematician Dr. H. Thomas Banks. In an August 12, 1992 NCSU news release, Dr. Banks said: "Smart materials, I'm convinced, are going to be one of those scientific ideas whose time has come, and they're going to be everywhere."

Banks' contribution to the growing field is mathematical modeling of the behavior of smart materials and development of better ways to control them. While at the University of Southern California (USC) Center for Applied Mathematical Science before coming to NCSU, Banks worked with a category of smart materials known as piezoceramics, which are polarized ceramics that respond to electrical current, an interest he continued to pursue at NCSU.

Arranged properly, piezoceramics can be made to expand on one side while contracting on the other, thereby producing tremendous bending forces. One use under study for such an arrangement is the control of the noise that turboprop (combination propeller and jet) engines produce in aircraft cabins.

Aircraft companies have developed a generation of turboprops that are fuel-efficient. Unfortunately, they create an uncomfortable noise level for passengers because of vibrations set up in the cabin wall by the engines.

For several years, Banks and his colleagues studied the use of voltage across piezoceramic patches in the cabin walls to alter the manner in which the walls vi-

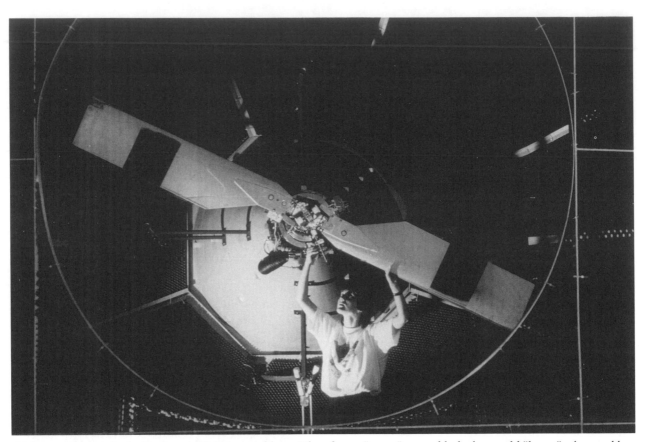

Helicopters are particularly prone to vibration problems. Therefore, a "smart" rotary blade that could "know" when and how to bend to compensate for wind changes without pilot aid would be an asset. In trying to develop such a blade, Professor Sathya Hanagud has explored possible use of shape memory alloys, polyvinyldene films, and electro-strictive actuators.

brate. They succeeded in converting sound waves caused by the vibrations from low frequencies to high frequencies less audible to the human ear.

Banks also is engaged in studying how smart materials in an aircraft wing might be used to change the airflow over the wing. A wing made of smart materials might include billions of minuscule vacuum pores that respond to the flow of air by correcting for turbulence that could decrease fuel efficiency or cause an accident.

At Georgia Institute of Technology, research engineer Kathryn Logan and aerospace engineering professor Sathya Hanagud have focused on both smart materials and smart structures. The fall 1991 issue of Georgia Tech's publication *Research Horizon* described their research.

In a study for the U.S. Army, Hanagud bonded piezoelectric sensors and actuators to slender beam models of helicopter rotor blades to "damp," or re-

duce, vibrations. By initiating their own appropriate deformations, bending as the wind flow changes, smart rotor blades could significantly improve helicopter performance.

Logan has developed a ceramic armor using a thermite combustion process. Thermite is a mix of ferric oxide and powdered aluminum. She was asked to do an Army Research Office workshop to discuss the feasibility of smart armor that could heal itself if penetrated. The workshop was an exercise to free up the thinking of scientists and engineers.

About the workshop, Logan told *Research Horizons:* "We [scientists and engineers] tend to confine ourselves to disciplined thought processes in order to solve problems. It is challenging to try to go beyond our paradigms [models] and just let our minds be free to think and imagine very extreme things."

Ultimately, Logan and her colleagues would like to create a material that would behave like skin.

When skin is cut, biological mechanisms sense the cut and begin healing. Among the categories of materials that might do the job of healing armor are:

- Dilant materials, so-called because they expand when pressure is applied but return to normal when the pressure is released.
- Micrometers to function as microvalves, micropositioners, and micromachinists.
- Energy-absorbing materials that melt under stress, flow into damaged areas, then quickly heal to repair damage.
- Miniature spheres embedded in the skin that when broken spread a repair agent, such as epoxy glue, to heal a wound.
- Solid-state (electrical, magnetic, and optical phenomena within a solid) electromigration to repair fine conductors and metal structures.

The idea of smart, self-healing armor may ultimately be deemed impossible because of the large energies transmitted by the impact of projectiles, together with the short time needed to accomplish repairs. Nevertheless, numerous spinoffs from the research are expected along the way.

The smart airplane of the future, in addition to having a multilayered composite material and built-in "nerves and muscles," will have embedded threads of fiber optics, bundles of parallel fibers that transmit images. These will monitor the skin for microcracks or dangerous stresses. Millions of tiny pressure-sensitive actuators, in response to on-the-spot information processed by the fiber-optic network, will respond by stiffening the skin or damping vibrations.

A smart bridge built with concrete endowed with its own chemical immune system could respond to corrosion of reinforcing rods or to weathering, or erosion. Fiber-filled adhesives threaded through the concrete would rupture in the advent of a crack and seal it.

Electrorheological Fluids, An Old Idea Under Revision

According to a January 28, 1992 NCSU news release, Dr. Hans Conrad, a professor of material science and engineering, is developing a metal beam that can sense a load and become stronger to bear it. The beam is made up of an electrorheological (ER) fluid poured into a hollow aluminum beam.

ER fluids are suspensions of solid particles in a liquid whose characteristics change under the influence of a strong electric field. Normally the consistency of water, upon application of a strong electric current, ER fluid changes into a rigid, solid-like material. When the current is shut off, the solid returns to a liquid state.

In his experiments, Conrad forces a beam to vibrate. When a sensory probe detects vibrations, it signals a computer to apply voltage. In response, the beam immediately stiffens and resists vibrations at a level equivalent to a material a million times stronger. When the current is turned off, the beam rapidly reverts to a liquid and once again becomes flexible.

ER fluids were discovered in the 1940s, and a major patent was issued for an ER fluid in the 1960s, but the technology to make them valuable was not developed until recently. Microcomputers are now available that can turn electrical fields on or off in millionths of a second, and the fluid can respond to the fields in a fraction of a thousandth of a second.

In the absence of an electrical field, a typical ER fluid resembles milk or cream, but when the voltage is turned on, the fluid thickens to the consistency of custard and then to butter. The degree of thickness is related to the strength of the electric field applied. When the field is shut down, the material becomes thin again.

Because most researchers did not have enough basic understanding of the mechanisms involved in the electrorheological effect to custom-design ER fluids, most of the hundreds of different particle-liquid combinations that behave as ER fluids have been found by trial and error. ER fluids have not been exotic. They have been suspensions created with a wide variety of solid particles—starch, cellulose, ceramics, glass, and even polymers (giant molecules formed by unions of simple molecules) dispersed but not dissolved in almost any kind of oil or in some other nonconducting liquid. Among the combinations that have been used are corn starch in corn oil, silica (compounds such as quartz, sand, or flint) gel in mineral oil, cellulose or wood fiber in transformer oil, and zeolite (water-absorbing silicates in rocks) in silicone oil.

The strengthening effect produced by an ER fluid

Dr. Hans Conrad of North Carolina State University experiments with a liquid-filled aluminum beam that becomes a million times stronger when exposed to electricity.

takes place when an electric field causes the particles suspended in the ER fluid to polarize and form chains that are very difficult to break. The electric current causes the strands of fiber to stretch from one electrode to another.

The alignment changes the ER fluid from a liquid to a solid. The particles behave like magnets and are hard to pull apart. Nevertheless, the force is not magnetic, but electrostatic, meaning it is electricity at rest, such as an electric charge on an object.

Although the chains may break, the particles will connect and reform another chain. Despite the fact that the chains break and reform continuously under stress, the increase in strength of the ER fluid remains intact.

With his experiments, Conrad is trying to develop mathematical equations that will explain the properties of ER fluids so that commercial applications can be more rapidly developed. Equations that apply to solid beams do not apply to beams filled with ER fluid.

ER fluids can change from liquid to solid and back to liquid at rates of perhaps 2,000 times per second. With such great sensitivity, they can be controlled directly by a computer without conventional electromagnets (magnetism due to electric charges in motion) or any other intermediate mechanical equipment or moving parts. ER fluids are, in effect, the ideal interface between computers and a wide variety of mechanical devices.

An article entitled "Smart Fluids Could Shock the Auto Industry" appeared in the 1991 *What's Happening in Chemistry?* annual publication of the American Chemical Society. It reported that major American, European, and Japanese auto makers are investigating use of ER fluids. They are particularly interested in smart suspension systems, clutches, and brakes.

Robert Ervin, head of the University of Michigan's Transportation Research Institute, explained why the auto industry will be among the first to make extensive use of ER fluid technology: "Theirs is a very high volume industry that thirsts for cheap ways of getting smart controls into the car and that's what this promises. The ER effect requires no moving parts, no precision grinding, no special fits. If you had a shock absorber using this technology, you could control it by computer over a wide range of complex interactions with the car and have nothing more inside the device than a few crude plates surrounded by the fluid."

ER fluid technology would make it possible to construct high-speed valves with no moving parts. Such valves would consist of two electrically conducting plates placed over an insulated hose or pipe that carries an ER fluid. With an electric current applied to the plates, the ER fluid would solidify, "closing" the valve and stopping the flow of fluid. With the electric current turned off, the flow would resume.

A car's clutch mechanism could be as simple as two cans, one nested inside the other, with electrorheological fluid between them. In the absence of an electric field, the fluid would be fully liquid. That would permit one of the cans, moved by the car's engine, to move without creating torque—a force that produces twisting or rotation—in the other. An electrical field set in operation by the car's computer would thicken the fluid to the desired consistency and transmit rotational power from one can to the other, and thence to the wheels. Such a device would be far cheaper than current models.

The perfect ER fluid would solidify under an extremely weak electric field, minimizing electrical equipment needs. Its particles would remain in suspension or solution for long periods of time, and it would be noncorrosive to machinery and nontoxic to humans.

Researchers are gaining insights that are permitting them to develop mathematical models that will predict how specific ER fluids will respond. The world of ER fluid research has changed rapidly in the last few years.

A May 17, 1988 *New York Times* article entitled "New Fluid Thickens in an Electric Field" reported that University of Michigan physicist Dr. Frank Filisko expected to be granted a patent for a major change he had introduced to the production of ER fluids. The major change was the substitution of liquids other than commonly used water. Water had been a formidable obstacle because it boiled away at the temperatures that prevail in machinery such as automotive mechanisms.

Just three years later, a May 28, 1991 *Detroit Free Press* article reported that Dr. Filisko had recently developed an ER fluid that is not a suspension, but a solution, a mix in which components are uniformly distributed. His development solved another of the major problems of ER fluid suspensions. When tested on real devices, dispersed solid particles in suspensions often settled out, abraded, or gummed up rubber seals, gears, and bearings.

There are indicators that overall research into smart structures and smart materials is becoming organized into a specialty. A March 9, 1992 *Boston Globe* column entitled "In a World of 'Smart Things,' Why Not Self-Sorting Socks?" by Stonehill College physicist and science writer Chey Raymo mentioned that scientists working with smart structures and smart materials now have their own publication, *The Journal of Intelligent Materials Systems and Structures*. Moreover, in Scotland in May 1992, Japan hosted the first-ever International Conference on Intelligent Materials.

Elias James Corey, Nobel Prize Winner Who Worked Backwards

Harvard University professor of chemistry Elias James Corey became an organic chemist because he wanted to become involved in solving important human problems. His field, called organic synthesis, solves human health problems by using simple, inexpensive starting materials to build complex molecules. His specific interest is "natural product" synthesis—finding ways to artificially make larger quantities of compounds which plants and animals produce in only small amounts in nature.

"It is probable that no other chemist has developed such a comprehensive and varied assortment of methods which, often showing genius, have become commonplace in the synthesizing laboratory," a Royal Swedish Academy official said when awarding Corey a Nobel Prize.

Although the Nobel Prize is awarded for scientific accomplishment rather than commercial achievement, the academy noted that the practical results of Corey's work have been as important as the scientific implications. In 1988, for example, Corey synthesized Ginkgolide B, a chemical extracted from the ginkgo tree. As a treatment for asthma and circulatory problems, Ginkgolide B quickly became a $500 million annual pharmaceutical market.

An October 29, 1990 *Time* article entitled "Playing Chess with Nature" described Corey as a "chemist's chemist." Few scientists can match the volume of Corey's significant accomplishments. His myriad contributions are based on the more than 40 years of work that he has put into developing his method, called "retrosynthesis analysis," a logical approach to synthesizing molecules.

Roald Hoffman, himself a Nobel-winning chemist, likened retrosynthetic analysis to a chess game with nature. Hoffman is not alone in comparing the process of synthesizing a complex organic (carbon compound) molecule to a game of chess.

Beginning with an idea for a molecule, the chemist works backwards by speculating how the desired molecule could be split into its constituent parts. Then he or she envisions how the parts could be split into smaller parts. The chemist continues to subdivide into smaller parts until ultimately arriving at simple molecules that can be used to build the synthesis.

At each division, the chemist is faced with a formidable number of possible choices. To add to the complexity, the chemist must look ahead at subsequent divisions to determine the best course to follow. Corey is one of chemistry's premier sleuths of the best avenues to pursue.

Organic synthesis is an extraordinarily difficult field of chemistry because of the daunting array of possible routes to a compound. Some routes are dead ends. Other routes are too long or too costly or both. Others produce only tiny amounts of the desired compound. Until Corey developed his strategy, synthetic chemists depended on intuition, educated guesswork, and plodding trial and error.

In working backwards, Corey and his colleagues trace the roots of the targeted molecule that branch out like limbs on a tree. They catalog the chains, rings, and other structural components and note the stability and reactivity of each component. Then they simplify the structure.

By removing branches and breaking chains and rings, Corey and his group visualize the likely immediate precursors (preceding substances). Each precursor is analyzed in the same manner to visualize still-earlier precursors.

During an interview for an October 1990 *Science* article entitled "Chemistry 'Grand Master' Garners a Nobel Prize," Corey described the state of synthetic organic chemistry when he acquired his doctorate in 1950: "Chemists approached each problem in an ad hoc [designed for the specific case only] way. Synthesis was taught by the series of illustrations and—generally unrelated—examples of actual syntheses."

In 1959 when Corey left the University of Illinois to join the faculty at Harvard, he decided that he would make organic chemistry more systematic by looking for underlying principles. Although the principle of working backwards had already been used by other chemists, Corey was the first to recognize the power of looking at the overall task instead of trying to solve each problem one at a time. He hoped to find the "deep logic behind it and put it in its most fundamental form."

Dr. Elias Corey of Harvard University won the 1990 Nobel Prize in chemistry.

According to the Royal Swedish Academy's analysis of Corey's contribution to science, he was so successful at his self-appointed task that chemists now have the ability to do "total synthesis, hitherto impossible, of complicated, naturally occurring active compounds according to simple, logical principles."

While other researchers tried to learn how to synthesize one large molecule at a time, Corey focused on the broad applications of reactions and reagents, which are substances used to detect, measure, or convert other substances. Harvard organic chemist George Whitesides told *Science:* "He is responsible for a change in emphasis from single molecules to big classes of problems."

Corey even opened up a whole new area of organic synthesis. He developed several synthetic techniques that used as reagents metal organometallics, which are compounds with a transition metal ion attached to a hydrocarbon. Moreover, he made it clear how the techniques could be applied. Chemists who followed his lead have made the use of transition metal organometallics a current major interest in organic chemistry.

In the same way that computers have been taught to play chess, Corey has programmed computers to do his retrosynthetic analysis method. His computer program called Logics and Heuristics Applied to Synthetic Analysis (LHASA) simplifies the process by generating trees of precursor structures.

He was the first to design a synthesis using artificial intelligence, a computer program designed to reason and learn. Although still in its infancy, computer-designed synthesis has grown large enough to employ many people.

An article entitled "Nobel in Chemistry Goes to Harvard Professor for Molecular Synthesis Research," in the American Chemical Society's 1991 *What's Happening in Chemistry?* annual publication, included an interview with Corey in which he was asked to reflect on his career. He initially wanted to be a mathematician, later an electrical engineer.

The lure of math and engineering paled once Corey took a course in organic chemistry. He recalled: "The dominant consideration was that organic chemistry could be applied directly to human health and welfare. I thought I would like to be involved in attacking and solving the very important problems concerning health by using a logical, scientific approach."

Prostaglandins and Chemzymes

One of Corey's most important contributions to human health was his synthesis in 1969 of prostaglandins and related compounds. In minute concentrations, different compounds of prostaglandins behave in different ways. Some control pain. Some contract and others relax smooth muscles. Some prevent and others encourage clumping by blood platelets, the disks that adhere to each other and clot to close a wound.

In all their different activities, these substances play key roles in many biological activities, including the development of inflammation and the regulation of blood pressure. Prostaglandins and related compounds have over time been detected in tissue throughout the body, but at the outset they were thought to originate in the prostate gland—hence their name.

Proposed medical uses of prostaglandins escalated during the 1960s; however, they remained in short supply because there was no way to synthesize large quantities in the laboratory. Researchers around the world working with the substance had to make do with minuscule quantities created by two methods.

One technique extracted prostaglandin from a coral known as the sea whip. The other used preparations of crude enzymes, which are complex proteins that induce chemical changes without being changed themselves. These preparations extracted from sheep testicles synthesized prostaglandins from unsaturated fatty acids, which are hydrocarbons. Both methods were unsatisfactory. The enzyme process cost about $1 million for a petri dish full of prostaglandins.

Countless chemists around the world struggled to arrive at an economically feasible method to produce prostaglandins. Corey and his group succeeded. Their work became the basis for the synthesis of prostaglandins used at several pharmaceutical companies.

Some of Corey's more recent work was described in a June 24, 1989 *Science News* article entitled "Building Chemicals the New-Fashioned Way." The "new-fashioned" method uses small, relatively simple molecules called chemzymes. By bringing different reactants together and forcing them to react at an accelerated rate, chemzymes accomplish feats comparable to those of huge, complex biological enzymes. They hasten and fine-tune reactions used in the synthesis of drugs and other compounds. Since virtually no byproducts are formed, many difficult chemical separation and purification steps are eliminated.

In the first step of the synthesis, a molecule—called a diene—containing two pairs of double-bonded carbon atoms reacts with another molecule called a dienophile. The dienophile readily combines with the diene to form a ring of carbon atoms.

Corey's group designed a chemzyme to catalyze the first of a series of reactions for making prostaglandins. When Corey first synthesized prostaglandins in the late 1960s, chemists had no technique for controlling how the two reactants—the diene and the dienophile—would approach each other during a step known as the Diels-Alder reaction. Chemists had to painstakingly isolate the prostaglandin precursor from the resulting brew of nearly identical products called isomers, which are substances similar in composition and molecular weight but different in structure and properties.

With Corey's new approach, the chemzyme brings together the diene and the dienophile in a very specific three-dimensional arrangement that yields only one of 16 possible products. A target chemical may have isomers based on many of its carbon atoms. For molecules of medium complexity—such as prostaglandins, which has about eight such carbon atoms—

there may be as many as 256 isomers. A method that reduces possible choices from 256 to 16 not only cuts down on the labor involved, it substantially lowers cost.

The elimination of possible reactions is paramount in the synthesis of ultra-pure drugs. For an antidepressant known as fluoxetine, Corey and graduate student Gregory Reichard designed a chemzyme for an elegant synthesis. The drug comes as a mixture of two mirror-image isomers, called enantiomers, only one of which is thought to be active and therapeutic. But scientists suspect that side effects may arise from the inactive isomer.

Using a chemzyme, the Harvard chemists designed a reaction sequence that yields either one or the other enantiomer. In this manner, chemzymes hold the potential for reducing a whole range of drug side effects.

At a meeting of the National Organic Symposium held at Cornell University in Ithaca, New York, Corey explained to those in attendance the rationale for his work on chemzymes: "Our approach has been to develop chemzymes for the most powerful synthetic construction reactions [such as the Diels-Alder reaction] because that's where they are needed and will have the greatest impact." An added bonus of the work is that chemzymes should provide insight into a whole range of basic reaction mechanisms.

Even more than Corey's influence on the development of organic chemistry strategies has been his enormous influence on the field's tactics. Unlike chess, the moves available to chemists change all the time. The discovery of new reactions or new reagents constantly provide researchers with possible new approaches to unraveling a particular synthesis.

Corey's skill at tactics was described by George Whitesides: "You can find other chemists who have developed one important technique, but Corey has developed a dozen of them that you use every day. His techniques are so widespread that some people don't even realize they are his."

Corey once described his fellow synthetic chemists as people who can get "something valuable from almost nothing" by transforming cheap materials "into new materials or substances of relatively great, or even lifesaving value."

More than anyone, Corey was describing himself.

13

MATHEMATICS

The Close Bond Between Music and Science

Those who love science are also drawn very often to music. J. Robert Oppenheimer, the famous physicist in charge of the World War II atom bomb project at Los Alamos National Laboratory in New Mexico, was especially fond of Beethoven symphonies. Edward Teller, his rival, kept his Los Alamos colleagues awake by playing Beethoven sonatas on a piano in his barracks. And Nobel Laureate Albert Einstein was a violinist.

As part of the physical plant, the Fermi National Accelerator Laboratory in Batavia, Illinois contains a small concert hall. Fermi lab director, Leon Lederman, during an interview for an August 27, 1987 *Chicago Tribune* article entitled "The Indefinable Links Between Music and Science," said: "We realized from the outset that to lure first-rate physicists back to this country from the great laboratories of Europe would mean competing at a cultural as well as a professional level."

Science students also seem attached to music. The university orchestra at Massachusetts Institute of Technology (MIT) is one of the better American university orchestras. About 80% of the orchestra members major in science and engineering. The orchestra's manager believes many to be so talented that if they had chosen to pursue music instead of science they could have studied at one of the nation's best music schools, like the Julliard School in New York.

Scientists and musicians both have found it difficult to explain what binds them together. Susumu Ohno, a geneticist at City of Hope Medical Center in Duarte, California, claims that music is present in the chemistry of life. Ohno assigned musical notes to the four fundamental chemical subunits, called bases, that make up deoxyribonucleic acid (DNA).

The carrier of genetic information, DNA is encoded in various arrangements of the bases. Ohno assigned "do" to cytosine, "re" and "mi" to adenine, "fa" and "sol" to guanine, and "la" and "ti" to thymine. When he played his "music" derived from DNA snippets, Ohno found the repetitive sequences of early-stage genes Bach-like and more-recently evolved genes suggestive of Chopin.

The common bond between musicians and scientists was evident in 1987 when they both celebrated the 100th anniversary of the death of Aleksandr Borodin (1834-1887), a Russian chemist and composer. Borodin discovered a technique for uniting fluorine atoms with carbon atoms, thereby founding a new family of compounds. His discoveries led to such familiar items as Teflon®-type plastics and Freon®, the liquid fluorocarbons used mainly in refrigerators, air conditioners, and as aerosol propellants. Away from the laboratory, Borodin was a self-described "Sunday composer." He found time to write the opera "Prince Igor," as well as memorable symphonies and chamber music.

The mentors of young scientists often are made anxious by their students' passion for music. Borodin's teacher, Nicolai Zinin, scolded him about the time he wasted on music, fearing that it would interfere with his career in chemistry.

The link between music and science goes back at least to Pythagoras of Samos, the fifth-century Greek

Self-replicating can be seen in both pictures. In the photograph of the leaf, the five sections of the leaf are repeated on a smaller scale in the five points of each section. In the bottom photo, branching and more branching, with each tributary getting smaller and smaller, can be seen coming off the Chesapeake Bay and, in the lower left, the Potomac River.

mathematician, who discovered that the hypotenuse of a right triangle equals the sum of the squares of the other two sides. By dividing a vibrating string into proportional lengths, he is also believed to have discovered the major intervals, or differences in pitch between two tones, in the musical scale.

In the 1930s theorist and composer Joseph Schillinger, who taught at New York University and Columbia University, worked out a complex system of formulas that he contended enabled users to make use of underlying principles developed by great composers. Schillinger's private students included George Gershwin, Benny Goodman, and Glenn Miller, who wrote his famous "Moonlight Serenade" as an exercise for Schillinger.

Music and Mathematics

A recent effort to bring music and science together was reported in an April 16, 1991 *New York Times* article entitled "J.S. Bach + Fractals = New Music." From the music of Johann Sebastian Bach (1685-1750), Dr. Kenneth Hsu, a geology professor at the Swiss Federal Institute of Technology in Zurich, and his musician son Andrew extracted matrices, which are arrays of numerical or algebraic quantities, each treated as an entity.

In an April 1991 paper entitled "Self-Similarity of the '1/f Noise' Called Music," published in *The Proceedings of the National Academy of Science,* the Hsus anticipated that their matrices might serve as a framework on which to build new Bach-like music "comparable in quality" to those created by the composer himself.

The Hsus' system is based on fractal geometry, a concept developed by IBM mathematician Benoit Mandelbrot. Fractals are patterns in space or time that are repeated at all scales of size. The self-similarity of fractal geometry is said to describe a wide variety of forms in nature; for example, the branching of a pine tree exhibits the same general appearance when viewed as a whole or in segments. A familiar example of self-similarity is the experience of standing between two mirrors with their endless reflections. Fractal relationships underlie the semiperiodic flickering of candle flames and some kinds of noise.

The Hsus' system is based on the fractal concept that any small section is an image of the structure as a whole. Dr. Hsu reduces a composition by expressing the notes as acoustic frequencies, the numbers of times a phenomenon occurs during an interval of time. The notes are plotted on a graph in terms of each note's relationship to its neighbors.

The resulting jagged fractal graph looks like a

Dr. Kenneth J. Hsu points to Invention No. 5 by Johann Sebastian Bach to demonstrate his mathematical "reduction" of musical compositions to basic fractal forms. The first system, marked No. 1, is the opening of the invention as written. The second system, marked No. 2, shows the same musical phrase stripped down to its essentials. This phrase or figure, particularly the melodic line seen in the G clef (upper staff) of Figures 1 and 2, is repeated constantly throughout the piece, starting on various pitches. In 3 is another example of that same figure, beginning on B flat (a pitch a fifth away from E flat, on which the invention begins) with the melodic line in the bass clef (lower staff). No. 4 shows that figure stripped down.

coastline. Coastlines created a turning point in the thinking of Benoit Mandelbrot during his development of the concept of fractals. He published a paper entitled "How Long Is the Coast of Britain?" In the paper he pictured a surveyor measuring a coast using a set of dividers open to one yard.

The surveyor would skip over turns in the coast measuring less than a yard and arrive at an approximation of the coast's length. If the surveyor set the dividers at one foot instead of one yard and repeated the measurements, more detail would be included and the approximate length of the coast would be longer.

Mandelbrot found that as the scale of measurement decreases, the length of measurement increases. Bays and peninsulas reveal ever-smaller bays and peninsulas, down to at least an atomic level, and perhaps beyond.

In common with coastlines and snowflakes, the Hsus found that much of the fine detail could be removed from Bach's acoustic patterns without changing the overall musical line. According to Dr. Hsu: "We found that basic patterns persisted in the fractal reductions of the music, even if all that remains contains only 1/64th of the original notes. To a novice, the half or quarter Bach reductions sound like Bach, although the listener gains the impression that the composition has an economy of frills and ornamentations."

The Hsus are developing a new kind of electronic instrument they call a fractal music box. The box filters music from a compact disc (CD) and reduces the composition to its underlying form. The result is an abstract comparable to the abstract of a scientific paper.

Dr. Hsu is the latest of many scientists who have searched for fractals in music. IBM physicist Richard Voss noticed that music is meaningless and disagreeable when the notes are completely random, and it is predictable and dull when they are too closely correlated. The kind of semirandom fluctuations expressed by fractals, when used to define the relationships between successive notes, results in a pleasing balance between predictability and surprise.

Several composers have introduced the self-similarity of fractal patterns into new forms of music. Among them is the Hungarian-born composer Gyorgy Ligeti, who lives in Hamburg, Germany. He has collaborated on performances with composer Charles Wuorinen of New York City, a friend of Dr. Mandelbrot.

For some of his work, Ligeti drew inspiration from studying the beautiful abstract designs generated by computers using "Mandelbrot sets," which are fractal relationships transformed by computers into graphic forms that repeat themselves infinitely on successively smaller scales.

Ligeti trained as a physicist for many years. Both he and Wuorinen contend that composers conceive music in large forms and only later fill in the details with smaller reductions of the larger forms. Although some influential music theorists have analyzed compositions in terms of their underlying forms, many musicians dispute the idea.

Music and Other Mathematical Forms

The transformation of sound waves in the air to notes on paper is mathematically complicated. Turning sound waves into digital signals, and analyzing and manipulating them, is necessary for a wide range of tasks, from building better stereo equipment to making video transmission easier. An April 11, 1992 *Economist* article entitled "Catch a Wave" described a mathematical technique called wavelets that may ease the burden.

A paper record of the minute changes in air pressure created by the sounds of a symphony results in an outline that resembles the Himalayan Mountains. The classic approach is to take the meandering, bumpy curve and pluck out its components. This technique breaks down a moment of the symphony into the characteristic frequencies of one or two instruments. Developed in the 19th century, the tool that does the breakdown is called the Fourier transform.

The Fourier transform is based on the mathematical understanding that any curve, no matter how it scrawls, can be constructed by combining a collection of regular waves, each with a precise frequency and wavelength. To build a squiggly line requires taking a collection of regular curves of differing wavelengths and enlarging or shrinking them each by a number that reflects how much the wavelength contributes to the final, composite curve. A big number reflects a large contribution and a small number a small contribution.

The Fourier transform makes it possible not only to build complex, squiggly curves from regular ones, but also to divide complex, squiggly curves into their constituents—in other words, to search through a recording of a symphony for the characteristic frequencies of a cello. A version of the process called the "fast Fourier transform" (FFT) works particularly well with computers, and can be found as an integral part of a range of devices from CD players to sophisticated telecommunications-transmission equipment.

Some scientists—particularly Ingrid Daubechies of AT&T Bell Laboratories, Jean Morlet of Elf-Aquitane, and Stephane Mallat of New York University—believe that wavelets can do a better job than the Fourier transform. Wavelets can be quicker and they deal well with short-lived signals.

An analysis of an opera with the FFT will reveal that a singer hit C two octaves above middle C, but only with great difficulty will it reveal when. The record of how a signal varies over time is converted by the FFT all at once, thus information about when a particular note occurred is lost. Wavelets retain such information by breaking signals down by frequency and time.

Typically, wavelet analysis examines a signal's record over time by halves. Initially, the method examines the waves that are so long that they take the whole length of the signal to go from crest to trough to crest again. Next, it cuts the signal in half and studies each half. Then it halves the halves and studies them, progressing to smaller and smaller segments. However, the process does not require halving every half. Attention can be narrowed to sections of the signal with the most information.

Other scientists are interested in building better concert halls and in understanding the behavior of ancient instruments. A May 17, 1992 *New York Times* article entitled "Listening to Music Scientifically: Concert Halls and Even Babies May Benefit" reported the findings of a week-long meeting of the Acoustical Society of America in Salt Lake City, Utah.

A high point of the meeting was a combined orchestral concert and physics lecture. Led by physicist Jurgen Meyer from Germany's National Institute of Standards, a student orchestra from Weber State University in Ogden, Utah performed on a stage with a projection screen above them displaying graphs and equations related to the music.

To demonstrate the importance of seating arrangements, Dr. Meyer had the first and second string sections change places. Few listeners could discern the difference, but they could see it on the view graph.

During the conference, physicist Thomas Rossing of Northern Illinois University at De Kalb described a series of experiments he and his colleagues had performed. They used a technique called holographic interferometry, in which a laser beam reflected from the surface of a vibrating instrument is combined with another laser beam to produce an interference pattern that reveals the minute and rapid changes in the shape of the instrument. Dr. Rossing visually presented a slow-motion moving picture of the vibrations of a ringing bell measured by a laser and analyzed by a computer.

Dr. Rossing and his colleagues also conducted experiments on Caribbean steel pans, musical instruments made from the ends of 55-gallon oil drums that are hammered into shape. Separate hammer indentations produce different notes when struck, allowing the performer to play complex music.

The laser technique determined that a light tap on one spot of the steel drum produced a note slightly polluted by notes coming from nearby indentations. A harder tap caused the entire lid to vibrate, with each indentation contributing to the overall, characteristic calypso-band sound.

A common interest in science and music may represent a genetic relationship, or it might simply represent a statistical variation that on closer analysis could be found to link other professionals with music. But the long history of scientists' involvement with music, coupled with their curiosity about how things work, is likely to keep music as a regular target of scientific attention for years to come.

Factoring Very Large Numbers and Spot-Checking Long Proofs

In grade school, children learn how to factor small numbers, breaking them down evenly into a set of prime numbers. They learn that "prime numbers" can be divided only by one and by themselves. Other numbers, such as 105, can be factored into longer equations, such as 3 times 5 times 7.

Computer scientists take factoring large numbers very seriously. So much so, they have a "most-wanted" list. Numbers on the most-wanted list have not been factored, but are not known to be primes.

In principle, factoring is a straightforward process of dividing the number to be factored by smaller numbers, looking for those that leave no remainders. In practice, factoring large numbers takes tremendous amounts of computer time. Using a straightforward approach to factoring a "hard" 100-digit number, one with no small factors could take billions of years.

For large numbers, the task has to be dealt with indirectly. One popular approach, known as the "quadratic sieve," was invented by Carl Pomerance of the University of Georgia in Athens in 1981.

The quadratic sieve has researchers concentrate on the simpler task of factoring a large collection of selected numbers, each considerably smaller than the number to be factored. The information gleaned from the smaller problems is then pieced together to factor the original number.

A January 23, 1988 *Science News* article entitled "Toward a New Factoring Record" reported that Pomerance and his colleagues were engaged in constructing a machine that they hoped would be able to factor a 100-digit number. Pomerance favors an approach that depends on low-cost custom built computers. With colleagues, he built the "Georgia Cracker," an inexpensive machine that worked reasonably well with numbers up to 70 digits long.

In 1984 the best anyone could do, using a general-purpose factoring scheme, was to break a hard 71-digit number into its prime-number components. But in October 1988, to factor a particularly difficult 100-digit number taken from the most wanted list, Arjen Lenstra of Bellcore and Mark Manasse of the Digital Equipment Corporation (DEC) Systems Research Center in Palo Alto, California used a form of the quadratic sieve that enabled different computers to work independently on small pieces of the problem.

The scientists developed a program capable of running on a variety of computers, from super-computers to multiprocessor workstations. They enlisted the aid of 200 collaborators using 1,000 computers scattered across three countries—the United States, Australia, and the Netherlands—on three continents. The program was designed to run whenever local computers were idle, filling in computer time that would have otherwise been wasted. Electronic mail funneled the results to DEC for the final computation.

A different accomplishment by a group of University of Georgia researchers was reported in a November 12, 1988 *Science News* article entitled "Major-League Factoring on a Low Budget." Although William Alford did not set a new factoring record, he accomplished an organizational feat. He persuaded researchers to use 100 personal computers—the most humble members in the hierarchy of computer sophistication—to assemble the data he needed to factor a 95-digit number from the most-wanted list.

To take advantage of the help of his colleagues, Alford used a sophisticated computer program to push each small computer to its limit. Not having a network connecting the machines, he hand-carried data-packed floppy disks to each collaborator. Collecting the data for the final step took about four months.

To do the final step on a larger computer, Alford used a newly developed algorithm, which is a guide of step-by-step computations. He used it for dealing with large matrices, a rectangular array of quantities treated as a single entity. His approach enabled him to complete the last step in half the time the international group took to factor its 100-digit number.

Pomerance predicted in 1988 that a million personal computers could factor a 145-digit number in a reasonable time. He felt that even a 200-digit number would be accessible if someone were willing to spend the money and could build enough factoring machines.

Although they didn't arrive at the result by following Pomerance's speculation, Arjen Lenstra and Mark Manasse found the factors for a 155-digit number. According to the June 28, 1990 issue of *Science*, they accomplished the feat in about two months with the assistance of hundreds of mathematicians and computer scientists around the world. The number was one that had spent several years at the top of the most-wanted list.

The 155-digit number factored by Lenstra and Manasse is known as a Fermat number. Some time about 1640, French mathematician Pierre de Fermat conjectured that numbers of the form 2n + 1 were prime whenever n was a power of 2. A "power" is the product of multiplication of a quantity by itself. Fermat was the founder of number theory, the study of integers and their relationship.

The first four numbers that fit Fermat's formula are primes. These are 5 (or $2^2 + 1$), 17 (or $2^4 + 1$), 257 (or $2^8 + 1$), and 65,537 (or $2^{16} + 1$). The next four ($2^{32} + 1$, $2^{64} + 1$, $2^{128} + 1$, and $2^{256} + 1$) are composites (not primes) and have been factored. The ninth Fermat number, which can be written 2^{512}, is the 155-digit number factored by Lenstra and Manasse.

Fermat 9 is the product of a previously known seven-digit prime and two new primes having 49 and 99 digits respectively. Fermat 9 makes the fifth Fermat number to have been factored and determined to be composite.

The ninth Fermat number eluded capture until Manasse and Lenstra used an algorithm called the number field sieve. The number field sieve is the brainchild of British mathematician John Pollard, who was responsible for creating two other factoring algorithms during the 1970s.

The new method is closely related to the quadratic sieve used by Manasse and Lenstra in previous factoring problems. Both sieves break down the task of factoring a large number into a huge set of smaller factoring problems and parcel them out to other scientists.

When a sufficient number of smaller factoring problems had been collected, Manasse and Lenstra used a mainframe computer to link them together. If

the first try had failed, the computer would have tried another combination.

Stitching together the separate results, a major computational task, took three hours on Florida State University's supercomputing Connection Machine. The Connection Machine is a parallel processor, a computer that uses many small processors working simultaneously, each with a small memory of its own.

Fermat 10 is the next most-wanted number on the list. Manasse estimated in 1990 that using existing methods to factor Fermat 10 would require a half-million times the resources that went into Fermat 9. But when he was interviewed for a January 1991 *Discover* article entitled "Most-Wanted Number" Lenstra was more optimistic. He said: "The tenth Fermat is still out of reach. But a year ago I would have said the same about the ninth."

The key feature of the number field sieve is that the smaller factoring problems are done using an algebraic expression that makes the smaller factoring problems still smaller, which speeds up the process. The number field sieve won't work on just any number, it was designed for Fermat numbers only. Lenstra and Manasse hope to generalize their method for use on a broader class of numbers.

Cryptographers, scientists who write or decipher code, have a stake in improvements in large-number factoring. They use large numbers to protect the privacy of such activities as transfers between Swiss bank accounts. A generalized efficient factoring algorithm could give thieves a considerable advantage.

Thus far, cryptographers have been able to stay ahead of scientists engaged in large-number factoring. The advances that have made it possible to factor 100-digit numbers also have made it possible to use codes based on 200-digit numbers.

Burt Kaliski, a cryptographic systems specialist at RSA Data Security, told *Science* that the factoring of Fermat 9 "doesn't threaten our business. It only confirms that our estimates of the difficulty of factoring large numbers are accurate."

Kaliski's serenity may be misplaced. Developments in techniques to factor large numbers have been moving at a rate much faster than experts thought possible. Gustavus Simmons of the Sandia National Laboratories in Albuquerque, New Mexico told *Science News* that government experts in 1978 believed factoring large numbers to be so difficult they were willing to base the security of an extremely sensitive nuclear facility on a 103-digit number.

A Proof Shortcut

Large-number factoring was not the only mathematical arena where major breakthroughs were being made. A group of graduate students and young researchers overturned centuries of mathematical tradition in the spring of 1992 by establishing that even the longest and most complex proof can be accurately checked by examining it in only a few locations.

A proof is the validation of a proposition by application of specified rules to assumptions, axioms (assumptions upon which a mathematical theory is based), and sequentially derived conclusions. In other words it is a deductive demonstration of a mathematical statement, or a process for testing the correctness or accuracy of a computation. A proof may be as long as 15,000 pages—the longest ever published—or it may be a single sentence that can be immediately understood.

University of California at Berkeley graduate students Sanjeev Arora and Madhu Sudan, AT&T Bell Laboratories' computer scientists Dr. Carsten Lund and Dr. Mario Szegedy, and Stanford University assistant professor Dr. Rajeeve Motwani spent $2^1/_2$ years on the effort. At age 30, Dr. Motwani was the oldest member of the group.

An April 7, 1992 *New York Times* article entitled "New Short Cut Found For Long Math Proofs" reported that the finding was so new that it had not yet been published in a journal. However it had been reviewed by leaders in the field and at least a dozen were convinced and amazed by it.

The investigators use a variety of tricks to transform a proof so that its errors, if any, show up everywhere. The new method makes it no more difficult to check a long proof than to check a short one.

An error that would negate a whole mathematical statement might be located deep in the proof. Using a conventional approach, the search for an error that might be on the first page, the last page, or any other page, requires checking each page line by line.

Dr. Lazlo Babai, a University of Chicago theoretical computer scientist, whose work helped lay the groundwork for the new discovery, explained the old method to the *New York Times*. He said: "We know by theorem 31 that a=b and by theorem 72 that b=c. Therefore, we conclude that a=c. We have to go back to theorem 31 and similarly we have to look up theorem 72 and see that it has been copied correctly."

Relying on the traditional method of data checking, the researchers compared lists of data, but in a new way. They arranged them in a grid (a setup of rows and columns) and then extended each row and each column in an arithmetic progression.

For example, a data list consisting of the numbers 1, 3, -1, 4 might be compared with a second data list copied from the first that reads 1, 5, -1, 4. A single digit is miscopied in the second list. The lists to be compared would be arranged in two-by-two arrays (each with two rows and two columns).

By extending in arithmetic progression the top row of each, the data from the first list would become 1, 3, 5, 7, 9, 11. The data from the second list would become 1, 5, 7, 9, 11, 13. In the second list, the error is magnified. The digit that should be a 3 is now a 5, the 5 is now a 7, the 7 is a 9, the 9 an 11, and the 11 a 14. With the progression, the error in one digit has become errors in five digits.

The new technique brought with it a second benefit. It revealed that it is impossible to compute even approximate solutions for a large group of practical problems that have long thwarted researchers. This group of problems involves finding the best methods for a variety of tasks, such as designing telephone networks or setting up sequences of jobs in factories.

After centuries of struggle with this group of problems, scientists concluded that finding an exact solution is impossible. Without a hope of an exact solution, they have been engaged in a search for an approximate solution.

In 1971 investigators determined that a wide range of these very hard problems were mathematically equivalent. Therefore, if one solution could be found, it would solve them all.

The research on proof checking revealed that approximate solutions are as hard to find as exact solutions, a monumental achievement.

APPENDIX

1992 Science Award Winners

NOBEL PRIZE IN PHYSICS

Georges Charpak, France

Charpak has been a world leader in development of particle accelerators—so-called atom smashers—to track and measure the results of collisions between particles. These huge detectors surround the site in an accelerator where subatomic collisions take place. They pick up signals from the spray of particle debris that occurs. Although Charpak did almost all of his work at CERN, the European Center for Nuclear Research near Geneva, his ideas and inventions have had a powerful impact on the design of detectors worldwide.

NOBEL PRIZE IN CHEMISTRY

Rudolph Marcus, United States

Marcus helped clarify what happens when atoms join to form new molecules. His work explained why chemical reactions differ in the speed at which they proceed. He mathematically analyzed the way that electrons change their behavior during reactions, sometimes switching from one atom to another or from one energy state to another within a single atom. He determined how the energy of a molecular system is affected by structural changes in reacting molecules and their nearest neighbors.

NOBEL PRIZE IN PHYSIOLOGY OR MEDICINE

Edwin Krebs, United States
Edmond Fischer, United States

Krebs and Fischer discovered a mechanism that cells use to regulate a wide variety of metabolic processes. The mechanism is now known to be a prominent player in most, if not all, normal cellular phenomena, and probably in all diseases. While trying to understand how muscle cells get a burst of energy due to an adrenaline rush when the body undergoes stress, they found that two molecules were actually the same enzyme in two different forms. The adrenaline started a chain of events that caused the inactive form to be converted into an active form. This was the first discovery that proteins could be regulated by having their structures modified in a reversible way.

NOBEL PRIZE IN ECONOMICS

Gary Becker, United States

Becker extended economic analyses to aspects of human behavior that had been dealt with—if at all—by other social science disciplines. His Ph.D. dissertation on the economics of discrimination, now widely accepted, shocked economists of the 1950s. Becker offered a practical way of predicting discrimination as well as ending it. His best-known work, *Human Capital,* laid out a case for thinking about education as an economic decision. By organizing ideas into theories that could be tested with evidence, Becker encouraged economists to collect data in new areas with the goal of measuring cause and effect.

ALBERT LASKER MEDICAL RESEARCH AWARDS

None awarded in 1992. Format may be changed to every other year.

ALAN T. WATERMAN AWARD

Shrinivas Kulkarni, Astronomy
California Institute of Technology
This award was established by Congress in 1975 to mark the 25th anniversary of the National Science Foundation (NSF) and to honor its first director. NSF is an independent federal agency, established to promote and advance science and engineering. The agency awards grants and contracts to research institutions and facilities across the nation. The annual Waterman Award, conferred by NSF, recognizes an outstanding young researcher in any field of science or engineering supported by NSF funding.

NATIONAL MEDALS OF SCIENCE
AND NATIONAL MEDALS OF TECHNOLOGY

The nation's highest honors in science and technology, conferred by the president in a White House ceremony.

MEDALS OF SCIENCE

Winner	Field	Affiliation
Eleanor Gibson	Behavior	Cornell University
Allen Newell	Computer Science	Carnegie-Mellon University
Calvin Quate	Engineering	Stanford University
Eugene Shoemaker	Geology	U.S. Geological Survey Flagstaff, Arizona
Howard Simmons, Jr.	Chemistry	E.I. du Pont de Nemours
Maxine Singer	Biology	Carnegie Institution of Washington
Howard Temin	Biology	University of Wisconsin, Madison
John Whinnery	Engineering	University of California, Berkeley

MEDALS OF TECHNOLOGY

William Gates	Computer Science	Microsoft Corporation
Joseph Juran	Quality Control	Juran Institute
W. Lincoln Hawkins	Invention	AT&T Bell Laboratories
Charles Kelman	Innovations	Charles Kelman, M.D.,P.C.
Merck & Co. Inc.	Innovations	Merck & Co. Inc.
Delbert Meyer	Chemistry	Amoco Chemical Company
Paul Weisz	Technology	Mobile Corporation

MEDAL OF MANAGEMENT

N. Joseph Woodland	Invention	I.B.M.

GLOSSARY

Abraded. Scraped off, worn out, wasted by friction, or erased.

Ad hoc. Designed for the specific case only.

Adaptive optics. An astronomical technique in which an artificial "guide star" is projected high above the ground and positioned close to an object of interest. The guide star consists of light scattered or emitted by atoms in the upper atmosphere when they are struck by lasers. Sensors connected to a telescope compare the image of the projected laser light with its image when it returns distorted by the atmosphere. Based on the distortions, computers command changes in a deformable mirror to correct for distortions in the image of the real star.

Advanced life support technologies. Equipment carried by ambulances designed to deliver a high level of care to victims at great risk of dying. In addition to high-tech communications systems, the equipment includes heart monitors, defibrillators to restart stopped hearts, intravenous fluids, and, where state law permits, paramedics qualified to administer drugs.

Airborne particulates. Tiny solid particles of matter carried by the wind.

Alchemy. The doctrine, study, and practice of chemistry in the Middle Ages. It was mainly concerned with finding a universal remedy for illness and a method for transforming metals into gold.

Alloy A mixture of two or more metals or a mixture of a metal with some other material.

Ampullae of Lorenzini An array of pores found in the center of a shark's mouth, which serve a variety of functions, including the location of prey.

Amulet. A charm worn around the neck to ward off evil.

Antilock brakes. Brakes that substantially increase a vehicle's ability to stop without skidding.

Antiseismic. Earthquake-resistant.

Autopoietic. Self-maintaining. Autopoietic systems preserve their own boundaries, and regulate their own biochemical compositions.

Axiom. (1) Any of the assumptions on which a mathematical theory is based. (2) An undemonstrated proposition concerning an undefined set of elements, properties, functions or relationships. Also known as a **Postulate**.

Axon. Fiberlike projection from a nerve cell that helps transmit chemical messages from the brain to the body.

Binary star. A pair of stars located sufficiently near each other to be connected by mutual gravitational attraction that compels them to describe an orbit around their common center of gravity; also known as a **Binary system**.

Bite-and-spit attack. One method a shark uses to capture prey. Some scientists speculate that after sharks inflict a massive wound on a victim, they back off to wait for the victim to die before returning to consume it.

Blowout specialists. Experts who bring oil-well fires under control by detonating explosives above the well.

Boom. (1) A movable mechanical support. (2) A beam that projects from the mast of a derrick to lift and to guide anything that is lifted.

Boreholes. Holes drilled into the ground, used for studying stratification; for extraction of natural resources like oil or gas; or to release underground pressure.

Brain edema. An excessive accumulation of water and other fluids within the brain.

Brain injuries, diffuse. Injuries to several areas of the brain, the result of billions of brain cells being twisted, stretched, and compressed.

Canopy. Intermingled tops of forest trees, particularly in a rain forest.

Cartilaginous. Relating to tough, elastic tissue, as in skeletons.

Catalyze. Action by which some substances increase a reaction rate between or among chemicals without being changed themselves.

Cell nucleus. A small mass of protoplasm surrounded by a membrane that contains chromosomes and functions in metabolism, growth, and reproduction. The fixed number of chromosomes in a cell nucleus is characteristic for each species.

Cerenkov radiation. A light comparable to shock waves that appears when the speed of particles exceeds that of light in the medium through which it is traveling. The particles emit light along their direction of motion, thereby enabling scientists to trace their path and that of their parent gamma rays.

Chagas disease. A nerve and muscle affliction that often has a fatal outcome, which afflicts an estimated 20 million Latin Americans.

Charge-coupled device. Mechanism arrayed with other CCDs so that the electric charge at the output of one provides the input stimulus to the next. CCDs are used in telescopes to enhance light, in some cases as much as 100 times greater than is possible using photographic film.

Chemzymes. Simple molecules that respond in an accelerated manner to hasten and fine-tune reactions used in the synthesis of drugs and other compounds.

Cladding. (1) Process of covering one material with another and bonding them under high pressure and temperature. (2) Metal coating bonded onto another metal. Sometimes used to simply mean *cover*.

Clairvoyance. Acquisition of information about an event, object, or place without use of ordinary senses.

Claustrophobia. Extreme fear of confined places, such as telephone booths, elevators, and small rooms.

Clitoridectomy. Surgical removal of the clitoris, a highly sensitive part of the female genitals.

Code. (1) System of writing to hide information by assigning numbers or letters to data and giving them an arbitrary meaning. (2) Sequence of chemicals dictated by a gene to make a substance.

Codices. Plural of codex, which is a code of laws, an ancient manuscript of the Scriptures (or parts of them), or an old manuscript of a classic text.

Composite numbers. Large numbers that have been factored and are known not to be prime numbers.

Continental slope. the sea floor beyond the continental shelf and before the abyssal plain.

Crude enzyme. Complex protein that induce chemical changes without being changed themselves.

Cryptographer. Person who writes and deciphers code. While many continue to work in the military, an increasing number are engaged in maintaining the privacy of business transactions, such as the transfer of large sums of money between financial institutions.

Damp. (1) To check or reduce energy or action, etc. (2) To gradually diminish the amplitude (the extreme range of a fluctuating quantity) of a vibration or oscillation.

Decay events. When carbon 14 decays to become nitrogen.

Decays. Gradual reduction of factors such as current, magnetic fluctuation, charge, or phosphorescence (giving off light without heat or combustion).

Design. The act of conceiving and planning the structure and details of a system, device, process, or work of art.

Diagnosis-related group. Payment classification for the medical care of patients based on the notion that treatments of similar diagnoses should generate equivalent costs.

Diene-dienophile reaction. Initial step in a chemzyme synthesis in which a diene reacts with a dienophile to form a ring of carbon atoms.

Differential equation. Equation expressing a relationship between functions and their derivatives.

Differentiation. Development of characteristics that distinguish one species from another.

Diffraction grating. An optical device that consists of a plate of glass or polished metal with a series of very close, equidistant parallel lines used to produce a spectrum by the diffraction of reflected or transmitted light.

Dilant. A material with the ability to increase in volume when its shape is changed.

Drift-netters. Boats that use large gill nets constructed of 5- to 6-inch nylon mesh openings that trap the gills of fish and other sea life that attempt to swim through. The nets hang 60 feet below the surface and extend outward for up to 100 miles.

Dynamic. Constantly changing.

Earth's crust. The outermost solid layer of the planet Earth, extending down no more than a few miles and made up mostly of crystalline rock.

Electromagnetic. Exhibiting a combination of electrictity and magnetism.

Electrorheological fluid. Liquid containing solid particles which thickens to a solid when subjected to an electrical field and returns to a liquid when the current is turned off.

Electroscope. A gas-filled, electrically insulated container in which gold leaves are suspended from a common point. An initial charge stored on the surface of the leaves cause them to repel each other and move apart. As incoming radiation ionizes the gas inside the container, the charge on the leaves dissipates and they come back together.

Electrostatic. Pertaining to electricity at rest, such as a charge on an object.

Eminent domain. Government takeover of property, generally on behalf of a project deemed to be in the public's interest, with the payment of a fee.

Enantiomer. One of an isomeric pair of crystalline forms or compounds whose molecules are nonsuperimposable mirror images; also known as an optical isomer. (An isomer is one of two or more chemical substances having the same elementary composition and molecular weight but differing in molecular weight and therefore differing in properties.)

Epigraph. Inscription on a building, monument, or tomb.

Escarpment. A steep slope or long cliff due to erosion or a fault that separates two relatively level areas.

Extracerebral. Located between the brain and the skull.

Fatal Accident Reporting System. A U.S. National Highway Traffic Safety Administration data bank that includes information on the nation's fatal accidents.

Fatty acid. a hydrocarbon in which one of the hydrogen atoms has been replaced by a carboxyl group (carboxylic acid). Saturated fatty acids have single bonds in their carbon chains, unsaturated fatty acids have one or more double or triple bonds.

Fermat numbers. French mathematician Pierre de Fermat conjectured that numbers fitting the form 2n + 1 were prime whenever n was a power of two. The first four numbers that fit the formula, Fermat numbers 1 through 4, were primes. The next four, Fermat numbers 5 through 8, were not. Fermat 9 was a prime.

Fiber optics. (1) Technique of transmitting light through long, thin, flexible fibers of glass, plastic, or other transparent materials. (2) Bundles of parallel fibers used to transmit complete images.

File-drawer problems. Research projects never published because they failed to find the sought-after effect. Their nonpublication deprives other scientists of information to be gleaned from them.

Finning. Practice of cutting off a shark's fins and throwing the dead or dying animal back into the sea. The fins are used in Asia to make an aphrodisiac and a very popular and expensive soup.

Forage. Food for animals, or the act of hunting for food.

Fourier transform. Method based on the mathematical understanding that any curve, no matter how it scrawls, can be constructed by adding together a collection of regular waves, each with a precise frequency and wavelength.

Galaxy. A large-scale collection of stars, gas, and dust.

Geophysics. Research into the physics of Earth and its environment, including the earth, air, and space.

Germination. The beginning, or the process, of development.

Glass ceiling. Conceptual name for the customary behavior that results in the exclusion of women from positions of power within an organization.

Gliding bacteria. Bacteria that secret a slime which enables them to move around by sliding. They are particularly prevalent on ships that remain in the water for extended periods.

Golden hour. That period of time immediately following a trauma, before shock sets in, when lifesaving treatment is most likely to succeed.

Great Plains. The continental slope of central North America, 400 miles wide, extending east from the Rocky Mountains to the margin of the Great Central Plain in the United States and to the margin of the Laurentian Highlands in Canada, and extending 2,500 miles south from the delta of the Mackenzie River in northern Canada to New Mexico and southern Texas.

Green Police. Conceptual name given to authoritarian governments that would enforce measures designed strictly to save the environment, even at the expense of many economic and other considerations, after previous enforcement measures and efforts failed to halt environmental degradation.

Gross National Product. The market value of all goods and services produced by a country.

Hashing. A mathematical technique that creates a string of numbers and letters to produce a *hash value,* which is a digital fingerprint based on the arrangement of letters, markers, graphics, and symbols in an original document. A change in even one character of the original document changes the hash value and indicates that the document has been altered since it was originally authenticated.

Hematoma. A swelling or mass of blood, usually clotted, which is confined to an organ, tissue, or space and caused by a break in a blood vessel.

Holographic interferometry. The reflection of a laser beam from the surface of a vibrating instrument when combined with another laser beam to produce an interference pattern that demonstrates the minute, rapid changes in the shape of an instrument.

Hydraulic. Moved or operated under pressure by a fluid, especially water.

Hydrodynamics. Study of the interaction of a fluid's boundaries with its environment and of the forces acting on it, especially in the case of the incompressible inviscid fluid. (Inviscid fluid is known as the perfect fluid, one in which there is no dissipation of energy during its flow.)

Ideograph. An idea or object conveyed by a sign with little or no pictorial reference.

Incidental bycatch. Unintended catch, such as sharks, brought aboard during routine fishing hauls. Bycatch is generally thrown back dead or dying into the ocean.

Infiltration. Sinking of water into the surface of the soil.

Infrastructure. The basic facilities, equipment, and installations needed for the functioning of a system or an organization, such as heat and air conditioning for a building, or roads and bridges for a transportation system.

Inquisition. The general tribunal set up by the Roman Catholic Church during the 13th century to discover and suppress heresy, and the punishment of those deemed to be heretic.

Insessorial. (1) Perching, as in perching birds. (2)Adapted for perching.

Instrumentation. Physical instruments used for processing.

Intertidal zone. Land at the water's edge between high and low tide. Also known as the **Littoral zone**.

Ion. An atom, group of atoms, or a molecule that is changed from an initial electrically neutral state through the acquisition of a net electrical charge by gaining or losing electrons. A loss of electrons results in a positively charged ion; a gain of electrons results in a negatively charged ion.

Isohyet. A line on a map that connects areas of equal rainfall.

Isomer. Substance similar in composition and molecular weight but different in structure and properties.

Jitter vibrations. Small, rapid, variations in a waveform due to mechanical vibrations, fluctuations in the supply of voltage, control-system instability, and other causes. (A wave is a disturbance that moves from one point to another without resulting in the whole occurring any permanent displacement. A waveform is a plotted pictorial representation of displacement.)

Keel. The principal timber extending from stem to stern at a boat's bottom and supporting its frame.

Kibbutz. Israeli collective settlement, particularly a collective farm.

KISS principle. Acronym for the principle known as "Keep it simple, stupid," which is intended to convey the idea that keeping a theory, principle, or design as simple as possible is likely to be the most productive approach in the long run.

Law of least work. Principle that a structure will always channel its loads to the ground by the easiest of many paths available.

Life history strategy. The process by which descendants come to differ from their ancestors over time.

Longliners. Fishing boats that put out long fishing lines to which huge numbers of hooks are attached.

Lumpectomy. Surgery for breast cancer during which only the lump, surrounding tissue, and some lymph nodes under the arm are removed, but the whole breast is not removed.

Mastectomy. Surgical removal of an entire breast with the goal of eliminating an individual's breast cancer.

Matrix. Rectangular array of numerical or algebraic quantities treated as a single entity.

Mature climax stage. Description used to indicate a forest that it is thought to have reached a level of persistent self- perpetuation.

Medical gridlock. A very busy period when ambulances cannot unload because an emergency trauma center is full and its hospital has reached a level of 100 percent occupancy or more.

Meta-analysis. Statistical procedure used together with rules for combining studies with a goal of determining whether a collection of experiments demonstrates a real effect.

Missiles. (1) Objects designed to strike targets. (2) Large tubes filled with exotic alloys, toxic chemicals, and explosive fuels.

Morphology. the form and structure of animals and plants without regard to function.

Natural history. Study of the origin, evolution, interrelationship, and description of natural objects and organisms.

Near-infrared. Invisible rays just beyond red in the visible spectrum of light, with waves longer than the spectrum colors but shorter than radio waves.

Nebula. (1) Interstellar clouds of gas or small particles. (2)Any of several light, misty, cloudlike patches seen in the night sky.

Neem tree. Tree, commonly found in tropical countries, whose leaves, bark, and fruit are used to treat a wide range of ailments, as well as being effective insect repellants.

Neural pruning. Concept of diminishing use of glucose as a person ages. Research has determined that in children up to age 5 the brain uses twice as much glucose as that used by an adult. Past the age of 5, the amount of glucose used and the number of neural (nervous system) circuits is reduced sharply, a phenomenon scientists refer to as pruning.

Neuropsychological skills-testing. Tests to look for deficits in functioning in persons who have suffered head trauma.

Neutron star. An extremely small, dense star composed almost entirely of neutrons that spin rapidly and produce periodic pulses of intense radio waves.

Noise. A disturbance, especially a random or persistent disturbance, that obscures or reduces a signal.

Non-Newtonian fluid. Fluid whose flow differs from that of a Newtonian fluid because the rate of force causing two layers in contact to slide upon each other in opposite directions parallel to the plane of their contract (known as shear) is not proportional to the corresponding stress. Non-Newtonian applies to problems such as flow in tubes, coating operations, rolling operations, and the mixing of fluids. (A Newtonian fluid is one in which the state of stress at any point is proportional to the time strain present at that point.)

Number field sieve. Method designed solely for Fermat numbers that breaks down large numbers to be factored into smaller problems and then, using an algebraic expression, breaks them down into even smaller problems, an approach that significantly hastens the process.

Organic. (1) Ever-changing, characterized by uncertainty. (2)Passing through major life stages, that is, birth, youth, maturation, maturity, reproduction, old age, senility, and death.

Organism. An individual so constituted that it is able to carry out all of life's functions.

Organometallic. Compound with a transition metal ion attached to a hydrocarbon

Oscillate. To vary between maximum and minimum values, such as an electric current.

Parallel algorithm. An algorithm in which several computations are carried out at the same time. (An algorithm is a set of rules to solve a problem in a finite number of steps.)

Peristalsis. Contracting waves that travel the length of an organ or a body, such as the movement that keeps food moving through an intestinal tract or the locomotion of gliding bacteria.

Piezoceramics. Ceramics that are polarized, that is, separated into positive and negative charges, and which respond to electric current.

Pika. Animal that resembles a rabbit but has a vestigial tail and short, rounded ears.

Platelets. Round or oval disks found in the blood of mammals that contain no hemoglobin. They play an important part in coagulation (clotting), hemostasis (stagnation of blood), and formation of thrombosis (clots within the vascular system). When a small vessel is injured, platelets adhere to each other and to the edge of the injury to form a covering plug.

Polarization. Partial or complete polar separation of positive and negative charges in a system.

Population crash. The decline and sometimes total collapse of a species population.

Precipitation. Rain, snow, ice, or hail.

Precognition. The acquisition of information about an event, object, or place without use of ordinary senses.

Precursor. A substance or event that precedes another.

Primary care. Routine medical care, such as that given by a family physician, internist, or, in the case of women, increasingly by gynecologists.

Proof, mathematical. Validation of a proposition by application of specified rules to assumptions, axioms, and sequentially derived conclusions. May be as long as 15,000 pages or as short as a single sentence.

Psychokinesis. Direct influence of consciousness over physical systems.

Pulsar. Short-period, variable, galactic radio sources generally believed to be from neutron stars.

Quadratic sieve. A mathematical technique that takes a large number to be factored and breaks it down into a large collection of smaller numbers to be factored, and then pieces the smaller problems together in order to factor the original large number.

Radioactive. Giving off radiant energy in the form of particles or rays by the disintegration of atomic nuclei until the substance ultimately reaches a stable state.

Radiocarbon dating method. Procedure that depends on the fact that carbon exists in three forms called isotopes, the most abundant of which is carbon 12. For every 1012 atoms of carbon, there is one of radioactive carbon 14. The isotopes differ in the weight of their atoms but not in their chemical makeup. All living things absorb carbon and the proportions they absorb remain the same as long as they are alive. Once an organism dies, the proportion of carbon 14 drops at a steady rate. Thus the concentration of carbon 14 makes it possible to date when the organism was alive.

Reagent. Substance employed to detect or measure another substance or to convert one substance into another by means of the reaction it causes.

Resonance. Phenomenon that is greatly enhanced at frequencies or energies that are at or close to a given characteristic value.

Rheology. Study of the changes in form and in the flow of matter, involving elasticity, viscosity, and plasticity (ability to change shape without breaking apart).

Riparian zone. Line of lush green vegetation adjacent to a stream or spring.

Rock wool. A fibrous glass made from slag, rock, glass, or a combination of those ingredients by fabrication into fine fibers. It is used for insulation, fireproofing, and as a filter.

Role model. A person whose presence and behavior serve as an example for another person to follow.

Runoff. The drainage into lakes, rivers, and oceans of water produced by storms, melting, seepage, evaporation, transpiration (moisture given off through the skin or through plant surfaces), and percolation (flow of groundwater through pore spaces in rocks and soil).

Salinity. Quantity of dissolved salts in sea water.

Sargasso. Floating brown seaweed that has berrylike air sacs. Also known as **Sargassum.** The Sargasso Sea, a region of calm in the North Atlantic, is noted for its abundance of sargasso.

Scintillator. Material that emits optical photons (electromagnetic energy with momentum but no charge or mass) in response to ionizing radiation.

Secondary care. Routine medical care given at a local community hospital.

Semiconductor. A substance whose ability to conduct electricity is dependent on temperature.

Sensory deprivation. Cutting off of the senses from stimulation.

Sepsis. Pathological state resulting from the presence of microorganisms or their products in the blood stream. It is often fatal if not treated properly. Also known as **Septicemia.**

Sidereal. Indicates measurement of a quantity, such as time, in relation to the apparent motion or position of the stars.

Sightline. Straight line of unimpeded vision.

Solid state. Describes a circuit, device, or system that depends on some combination of electrical, magnetic, or optical phenomena within a solid that is usually a crystalline semiconductor material.

Solution. A homogeneous liquid, solid, or gas that is a mixture in which components (liquid, solid, gas, or combination) are uniformly distributed throughout.

Sonar. Acronym for **so**und **na**vigation **r**anging equipment, which uses underwater sound at sonic (at the speed of sound) or ultrasonic frequencies to detect or locate objects within the sea.

Square brackets. Device used in international negotiations to designate areas in which agreement has not been reached.

Stasis. State of equilibrium, balance, or stagnancy.

Stealth aircraft. Aircraft designed to be difficult to detect on radar.

Stele. An upright stone slab or pillar engraved with an inscription or design and used as a monument or grave marker. (Plural is stelae.)

Steppe climate. Climate in which precipitation, although slight, is sufficient to grow a short, sparse grass; typical for any of the great plains of southeast Europe and Asia having few trees, and similar to but more arid than the prairie of the United States.

Subdural. Beneath the brain's covering, the dura mater.

Sustainable development. A concept that describes a way of life that can adequately support the human population without depleting the earth of resources needed by future generations.

Symbiosis. The act of two dissimilar organisms living together, especially if the relationship is mutually beneficial.

Synthesis. (1) Any process or reaction for building up complex compounds by the union of simpler compounds or elements. (2) Method of making large quantities of compounds usually produced naturally in small amounts by plants and animals.

Taxonomy. A system of arranging animals and plants into natural, related groups based on some factor common to each, such as structure, method of giving birth, or biochemistry; the word is derived from the Greek *taxon,* meaning to order or arrange.

Telemetry. Transmission of instrument readings to remote locations via radio waves.

Telepathy. Mind-to-mind contact, during which one mind receives communication from another without going through ordinary communication channels.

Tertiary care. Specialty medical care, such as that given at burn units, cancer hospitals, or trauma centers.

Thermite. A fire-hazardous mixture of ferric oxide and powdered aluminum. When ignited, it reaches temperatures sufficient to soften steel.

Toxemia. Distribution throughout the body of poisonous products produced by bacteria in a local site. It is common in pregnancies where hypertension is present. If left untreated, it can lead to convulsion and death.

Trajectory. The curved path of something hurtling through space.

Transpons. Genes that move without any apparent discrimination from chromosome to chromosome. Also known as *jumping genes, mutable foci,* or *moveable elements.*

Trusses. A structural framework, generally of steel, timber, concrete, or a light alloy, built so the members in concert exert tension and compression.

Turboprop. A turbojet engine in which turbine shaft drives a propellor that develops most of a craft's thrust, with some additional thrust provided by a jet of turbine exhaust gases.

Turbulence. violent, irregular motion or swirling agitation of water, air, or gas.

Vector. A mathematical expression denoting a combination of magnitude (measurable quantity) and direction, such as velocity; an ordered set of real numbers, each noting distance on a coordinate (numbers that locate the position of a point) axis.

Vector processing. The computation by computer of several rows of equations simultaneously.

Ventral. Abdominal side of the body. In humans it is the front, but in most animals it is the lower side.

Verdant. Covered with green vegetation.

Viscosity. (1) Resistance that a gas or liquid offers when subjected to stress. (2) Internal friction of a fluid that makes it resist flowing past a solid surface or other layers of the fluid.

Whiplash shaken-baby syndrome. The physical symptoms that arise following an incident when a baby is shaken. The shaking causes the soft brain tissue to bounce against the rough protrusions of the skull's hard bone. The symptoms include bulging fontanel, head enlargement, and eye hemorrhages.

Zeolite. Any of a number of hydrous (water-containing) silicates (hard, glassy minerals) of aluminum, sodium, or calcium found in the cavities of igneous rocks, which are formed by volcanoes or great heat.

INDEX

Abu Simbel, move of, 2
Abuse, lifetime estimates, 93
Adan-Bayewitz, David, 17
Adaptive optics, 111
Afro-centrist focus on Egypt, 2
Ahau, 7,8,17
Alcohol, contribution to crashes, 180
Aldrin, Buzz, 138
Alford, William, 198, 201
Alice Cities, 148
Allison, E. Jackson, Jr., 83
Alvarez, Luis, 99
Alverson, William, 23
Amaranth, a new perfect food, 65
Antiseismic building design, 177
Arch: principles of, 175;
    arrangements of, 176
Argus, machine that measures
    galaxies, 108
Armstrong, Neil, 138
Arora, Sanjeen, 200
Array of seven telescopes, 110
Aspirin study, 56, 87
Asteroid tracking, 99
Astronomers and particle physics,
relationship, 103
Aswan High Dam, 3
Atkinson, William, 145, 146
Atoms, structure of 101–102
Auto-da-fe, 8

Babai, Lazlo, 200
Bacon, Roger, 132
Baker, Nancy, 86
Balance of nature, management
    failures, 130
Balfour, A.J., 49
Baliunas, Sallie, 136
Ballard, Robert, 114, 118
Banks, Thomas, 185
Barrett, William, 49
Battlefield medicines' contribution to
    survival, 77
Battle of Migdal, 18
Bauhaus faculty, evolution of
    theories, 165
Beebe, Spencer, 68
Bellotti, Anthony, 64,
Beltrain, Hugo, 152,
Benge, Michael, 157
Benson, Elizabeth, 11
Bergstron, Jan, 98
Binzel, Richard, 99
Biological classification system:
    evolution of, 19; two-part namming,
    19-21; fossil record gaps, 21;
    Bisby, Frank, 23

Blaich, Robert, 169
Boots and Coots, oil fire fighters, 69
Borehole climate readings, 150–151
Borg, Anita, 134
Borodin, Aleksandr, 193
Botkin, David, 127
Bourland, Michael, 82
Brain cells, capacity for repair, 42
Brain drain, 65-66
Brain injuries: causes, 35-36; centripetal
    pattern, 37; diagnostic
    techniques; 35–40; statistics; 33–34,
    types, 34–35
Brain mapping, 40–42
Braun, Ann, 64
Breast cancer risk factors, 88
Breast implant controversy, 89
Brine pool seeps 116
Brooks, James, 115
Broughton, Richard, 45, 56
Brummitt, Dick, 23, 24
Buchard, Robert, 157
Buckingham, Michael, 98
Bush, George, 36, 76
Butterfly Effect, 129
Butti, Ken, 139

Campbell, Stu, 149
Campbell, Wood, C., 149
Caputi, Jane, 91
Caracalla, Rome's largest bath house, 140
Carbon-dating method, 17
Cattle, conflict over, 121–122
Ceramic armor, development of, 186
Cerenkov radiation, 105
Chadwick, James, 101
Chalmers, Neil, 24
Chaos theory, 129
Charge-coupled devices (CCDs), 108
Chemaymes, 192
Chermayeff, Serge, 165
Childhood friendship, 3–4;
Childress, James, 116
Chumship, importance of 4
Churchill, Winston, 49
Clairvoyance, 44
Clark, Eugenie, 27 Clay, Robert, 163
Clayton, Beverly, 161
Cleveland, Charles, 161
Coe, Michael, 10
Cohen, Orna, 16, 17
Compton, Arthur, 102
Computer-aided design, 171–172
Conrad, Haus, 187, 188
Copeland, Herbert, 22
Corey, Elias James, 190, 191, 192
Corliss, John, 114, 118

Cosmic rays, 101–103
Crane-drivers conundrum, 156
Crane, Katherine, 114, 118
Craters on Earth, existence of, 99
Crick, Francis, 117
Cunning men, 132
Curie, Marie Sklodowska, 133
CYGNUS, 104

Damarest, Arthur, 11
Darwin, Charles, 21, 23, 134
Daubechies, Ingrid, 197
Davis, Andy, 149
Daylight sound, 97
Death from impact, tied to age
    and sex, 179–180
De Broglie, Louis, 51
Defense Advanced Research Project
    Agency (DARPA), 74–75
Design: approach to teaching, 164-165,
    168; concept of, 164; principles,
    168-169
Design Processes Laboratory, computer
    design facility, 167
Diamond, Jared, 25
Dickens, Charles, 141
Diels-Alder reaction, 192
Diffraction grating, 109
Digital Time Stamp, 155
Dive, deepest untethered in history, 138
Doblin, Jay, 166, 1168
Dodge, Kenneth, 4
Dream lab experiments, 53
Dressler, Alan, 156
Driver education, distinct from safety
    education, 183
Driver responsibility for accident
    prevention, 183
Drunk driving, reduction due to social
    factors, 181–183
Dunne, Brenda, 50, 52

Eakins, Thomas, 157
Earle, Sylvia, 70, 134
Earth increments, environmental
    protection grants, 65
Earthquake Hazard Mitigation
    Project, 178
Earth Summit, 57–68; obstacles to
    proposal implementation, 68;
    statement of principles, 59
Ecological instability due to individual
    differences, 127
Eddy, Robert, 183
Egypt as a black society, concept, 2
Eisenberg, Anne, 156
Einstein, Albert, 45, 193

Eldredge, Niles, 24
Electrorheological fluids, 187–189; solutions to old problems, 189; use in automotive mechanisms, 189;
Emanuel, Kerry, 97
Embryo-transfer technology, 64
Emergency rooms, waiting time, 80–81
Emerson, Sharon, 135
Engleberger, Joseph 157
Environmental controls, cost effective, 63
Epigraphs, 7–12
ESP cards, 47–48
ESP-ganzfeld experiments, 53–54
Ericksson, Lief, 85
Ervin, Robert, 189
European Southern Observatory's New Technology Telescope (NTT), 75
European Very Large Telescope, 110
Evans, Leonard, 179, 184
Evolutionary concept of language, overturn of, 9
Ewing, Maurice, 113
Extrasensory perception, 44

Factoring a 100-digit number, 198
Fahnstrom, Dale, 167
Farr, Heather, 88
Fatal Accident Reporting System (FARS), 183
Feldstein, Sol, 53
Fermat, Pierre, 199
Filisko, Frank, 189
Fisher, Chuck, 116
Fitzpatrick, Ross, 125
Food hoarding, 2–3; protection strategies, 3
Forest species, underfoot, 5; arthropod contribution, 5; nutrient cycle, 5
Formulas for music, 193, 194
Fourier, Jean Baptiste Joseph, 151
Fourier transform, analysis of music, 196-197; fast fourier transform (FFT), 197; fractal framework for music, 194
Fractal music box, 196
Freidel, David, 12
Frog flight, 135
Fuller, R. Buckminster, 165
Gaia hypothesis, 134
Galilee Boat: dating techniques, 16–17; drying out, 15–16; fragility, 15; possible history, 17–18; publicity, 14; removal techniques, 15–16; rising lake, 14
Garay, Adriel, 64
Gates, Robert, 76
Gamma ray, 102
Gamma Ray Observatory, 103
Garbage survey, 161-162
Garrison, Herbert, 83

Gehrels, Tom, 99
Gell-Mann, Murray, 156
Genetic matching of children to relatives, 137–138
Geochemical and Environmental Research Group (GERG), 115, 116
Geodesic dome, 165–166
Gilbert, Gene, 33
Glass ceiling, 133
Global Oscillation Network, 111
Global Plant Species Information System, 23
Golden hour following trauma, 78
Gonul, Fusun, 162
Goodman, Jordan, 105, 106
Goodman, Lisa, 93
Gore, Albert, 76, 163
Gould, Stephen, 134
Graham, John, 108
Grandmothers of the Plaza of May, 137
Grassle, Frederick, 117
"Great Wall" of galaxies, 109
Griffin, Gillett, 10
Gropius, Walter, 164
Gruber, Samuel, 31
Guardian Interlock System, 179
Guyot, Anne, 35

Haber, Stuart, 155
Halzen, Francis, 103
Hanagud, Sathya, 186
Hanamura, Tetsuya, 148
Hansen, Richard, 12
Haughton, James, 83
Hawkes, Graham, 138
Health care for the poor, 79–81; fixed payments limit care, 82
Healy, Bernadine, 133
Heisenberg, W.K., 51
Heitmann, John, 59
Helio-seismology, 111
Henderson, I. Craig, 89
Hertz, H.R., 51
Hess, Harry, 113
Hess, Victor, 102
Hidden cities in former Soviet Union, 75
Hill, Anita, 85
HIPPI, supercomputing linkage, 162
Hoffman, Roald, 190
Holographic interferometry, 197
Honorton, Charles, 53, 54, 55
Hottel, Hoyt, 146
Hsu, Andrew, 194
Hsu, Kenneth, 194, 195, 196
Hughes, Ken, 154
Humanisms, impact on woman's participation in science, 132
Hurricane Andrew, 97
Hurricanes, relationship with climatic change, 97
Huygens, Christiann, 51

Hydrothermal vents: dating age of, 117; organisms' food chain, 114; source, 114; transfer of energy, 115; water flow through cracks, 115

Ibrahim, Alaa Eldin, 162
Ichiyama, Dennis, 168
Intellectual integration, concept of, 165
Intensive-care units: labor intensive, 82; overcrowding, 80
Interferometry, 110
Inverse Compton effect, 10

Jacobs, Lucia, 3
Jacobson, Jodi, 89
Jahn, Robert, 46, 50, 52
James, Henry, 49
James, William, 49
Japan: design contest, 165–170; geological strata, a challenge to underground construction, 148–149; space shortage, 14
Johnson, Clifford, 84
Johnson, John, 84
Joralemon, David, 10
Josephus, Flavius, 18

Kaliski, Burt, 199
Kansas Grassroots Association (KGA), opponents of tall-grass park, 125
Kaufman, Lloyd, 39
Kearney, Paul, 183
Kelley, David, 9
Kendall, Timothy, 2
Kepler, Johannes, 129
Kibbutz Ginnosar, Galilee Boat adoption, 15
Kingdoms, division of living world, 21–23
King, Mary-Claire, 137
Kitt Peak National Observatory, 107
Kleitman, Nathaniel, 53
Knorosov, Yuri Valentinovich, 8-9
Koehl, Mimi, 135
Koo, David, 109
Krippner, Stanley, 53
Kristof, Emory, 118
Krone, Richard, 109
Kuwaiti Oil Fires, 69

Lachenbruch, Arthur, 152
Lake, Celinda, 85
Lamar, Howard, 121
Landa, Diego de, 8
Landman, Uzi, 161
Lanyon, Scott, 25
Laplace, Pierre-Simon, 52
Latitude calculation, 92
Lauro, Albert, 80
Law of least work, 173
Lee, Lawrence, 163

Lefkowitz, Mary, 2
Lenstra, Arjen, 198, 199
Leon, Chris, 24
Levin, Harvey, 36, 37
Liebowitz, Michael, 57
Ligeti, Gyorgy, 196
Linnaeus, Carolus, 19, 20
Little Ice Age, 152
Liu, Chi, 178
Logan Kathryn, 186
Logics and Heuristics Applied to
    Synthetic Analysis, computer
    program 191
Loh, Eugene, 106
Lufan, Moshe, 13, 14
Lufan, Yuval, 13, 14
lumpectomy, 88
Lund, Carsten, 200

Mallat, Stephane, 197
Manasse, Mark, 198, 199
Mandelbrot, Benoit, 194, 196
Mareschal, Jean Claude, 152
Margulis, Lynn, 22, 134
Marsden, Jerry, 133 Marsh, George
Perkins, 128
Marshall, B. Vaughan, 152
Martin, Gerald, 161
Massachusetts Institute of Technology
    (MIT), solar home experiments, 146
Mastectomies, 87
Mathematical modeling, 185
Mathematical proofs, shortcut, 200
Mathews, Peter, 10
Maunder, Walter, 137
Maxwell, James, Clerk, 51
Maya: classic period, 7; Dumbarton Oaks
    conference, 11; glyphs, 12; most
    important historical documents, 7–8;
    violent past, 11–12
McAlister, Hal, 110
McAusland, Randolph, 170
McClenon, James, 45
McClintoch, Barbara, 156
McRae, Gregory, 163
Mead, Margaret, 45
Melman, Seymour, 76
Mentors, lack for women, 133
Merriam, C. Hart, 21
Mesa Verde cliff-side dwellings, 143–144
Metaphors of nature, 129
Meyer, Jurgen, 197
Micro-PK, 48
Mies Van de Rohe, Ludwig, 165
Miller, Mary Ellen, 11
Miller, Stanley, 117, 118
Miller's origin of life experiment, 117
Millikan, R.A., 102
Moholy-Nagy, Laszlo, 165
Mojave Desert mining, 124–125
Moldenke, Andrew, 5

Mommy track, 133
Morales, Moises, 10
Morin, Nancy, 23
Morlet, Jean, 197
Morse, Edward, 146
Mortise-and-tenon boat construction, 13
Motwani, Rajeeve, 200
Moyer, Peter, 83
Murder rates by sex, 91
Music derived from DNA snippets, 193
Mussel distribution, clue to location of
    seeps, 116
Mussels raised on methane, 116

Nambu, Yoichiro, 156
National Center for Astronomy in the
    Southern Hemisphere, 107
National Center of Shark Research, 27
National Oceanic and Atmospheric
    Administration investigation of the
    Persian Gulf oil spill, 70
National Organization for Women
    (NOW), 87
National Optical Astronomy
    Observatories, 107
National Research and Education
    Network, 163
National Theatre in Mexico's rise and
    sink, 175
Natural product synthesis, 190
Neem tree, multiple uses, 156–157
Neff, Thomas, 75
Nelson, Patricia, 120
Nelson, R.D. 52
Neo-Darwinism, 134
Nesbitt, Harry, 71
New Technology, 109
Newton, Isaac, 51, 129
New York City, municipal hospital
    system's dilemmas, 81
Noble, David, 132
Non-Newtonian fluids, 158
Northern Europe's misuse of solar
    design, 140
NSFNET, high-speed pathway linking
    supercomputers, 161
Nubian studies, 2
Nuclear force, 101
Number field sieve, formula for
    factoring Fermat Numbers, 199
Nun, Mendel, 13, 14
Nurse shortage, 82

Ohno, Susumu, 193
Oil seeps, 1156
One-way hashing, 155
Onstad, David, 159
Open space calculations to prevent
    blocking the sun, 142
Oppenheimer, J. Robert, 193
Organic view of nature, fear about, 130

Organometallics, 191
Orrego, Cristian, 138
Osteoporosis, 87
Owen, Charles, 167, 169
Ozone hole, conection to
    chlorofluorocarbons, 136

Pace, Norman, 118
Paepcke, Elizabeth, 165,
Paepcke, Walter, 165
Paintner, Wayne, 120
Palenque: Mayan city of, 9; dynastic
    family history, 10
Paracelsus, Philippus aureolus, 132
Park College underground library, 150
Parapsychological research
    methods, 46-54
Pascal's tomb, 10
Peristaltic motion, 158
Perlin, John, 139
Peterson, Patti, 35 Piazzi, Guiseppi, 99
Pickett, Stewart T.A., 127
Photovoltaic cells, 147
Piezoceramics, use to produce
    bending forces, 185–186
Plank, Max, 51
Polymerase chain reaction process, 22
Pomerance, Carl, 198, 201
Powell, John WEsley, 121
Precision fluency shaping, 4
Pre-cognition tester, 50
Primera Mesa Redonda de
    Palenque, 10–11
Prince, David, 76
Princeton Engineering Anomalies
    Research Laboratory, 46
Prostaglandins, synthesis of, 191–192
Psychokinesis, 44, 45
Psychophysical Research Laboratories, 54
Pulsar hunters, 104
Puthoff, Hal, 52
Pythagoras, 193

Quadratic sieve, formula for factoring
    large numbers, 198
Quantum mechanics, 50-52

Random-number generators, 48-52
Rape statistics, 91
Rapid-response care, 77
Raske, Kenneth, 81
Raynau, Paula, 133
Real-time optimization using a
    supercomputer, 163
Reconstructive imaging, 110
Reichard, Gregory, 192
Reilly, William, 66
Remote viewing, 52, 53
Reproductive tract infection, 91
Research Institute of Parapsychology, 45
Resnick, Judith, 85

Resonance, 174
Retrosynthesis analysis, 190
Rey, Augustin, 142
Rhine, J.B., 43, 45, 47, 56
Rhine, Louisa, 45, 46
Road users' reactions, unpredictable, 179
Rodriguez, Gustavo, 170
Rofer, Cheryl, 73
Rosenfeld, Allan, 90
Roskies, Ralph, 159
Rossing, Thomas, 197
Ruckelshaus, William, 60
Russel, Diana, 91 Rutherford, Ernest, 101

Salvadori, Mario, 171, 176
Savory, Theodore, 19, 21
Schaffer, William, 130
Schele, Linda, 9, 10, 11, 12
Schellhas, Paul, 7
Schillinger, Joseph, 194
Schmidheiny, Stephan, 61
Schmidt, Helmut, 48, 49, 50
Schmuterer, Henrich, 156
Schrondinger Cat Experiment, 51
Schrondinger, Edwin, 51
Schultz, Lynn Hickey, 3
Schwartz, Karlene, 22
Schwarz, William, 157, 158
Scharzenegger, Arnold, 185
Sea floor spreading, 13
Segal, Sheldon, 89
Self-healing armor, 186-187
Selman, Robert, 3, 4
Sexual harassment, characteristic
    behaviors, 85
Sexual slavery, 93
Shah, Aashit, 36
Shames, George, 4
Shanahan, John, 60
Shapiro, Stuart, 160
Sharks: adaptablity, 29-31; attacks, 26;
    decline, 26, 31–32; ecological
    niche, 28; fossil record, 28; life
    history 28–29; management plan, 32
Shure, Myrna, 4
Siddiqui, Abdul, 157, 158
Siderits, Richard, 162
Simmons, Gustavus, 199
Sinclair, Mary, 49
Sinclair, Upton, 49
Sivak, Michael, 179, 181, 182
Skipworth, Scott, 166
Sky city of Acoma, 143
Slime movement, 157
Smarr, Larry, 160
Smart materials distinguished from
    smart structues, 185

Smith, Craig, 115
Smith, Harold, 150
Society for Psychical Research, 46
Solar collectors, 146
Solheim, Steven, 23
Solomon, Susan, 135
Sony design, program for children, 169
Species Plantarum Project, 23; specimen
    preservation or release controversy,
    24-25
Spy satellite data, 76
SRI International, 46
Star cycles, 137
Star spot activity, 136
Steffy, Richard, 14, 17
Stevens, John, 32
Stewart, Balfour, 49
Stirling, Eric, 83
Stornetta, Scott, 155
Strong, Maurice, 57, 61, 62
Structural dead load, 173
Stuttering, treatment of, 4–5
Sudan, Madhu, 200
Sullivan, Harry Stack, 4
Supercomputing: a third basic research
    model, 160; in social science, 162
Sutcliffe, William, 75
Swann, Ingo, 52
Swedenborg, Emmanuel, 44
Systers, computer network, 134
Szegedy, Mario, 200

Tall-grass prairie, destruction of, 123–
    124; Z-Bar ranch proposal, 123
Teeter, Emily, 2
Telepathy, 44
Teller, Edard, 193
Teng, Ta-tiang, 148
Thin-section microscopy, 5
Third World women, death, 89–90
Thomas, Clarence, 85
Thompson, J. Eric, 7
Three-dimensional image of cancer, 162
Tilman, David, 129, 130
Timber disputes in the West, 123
Tokarev, Sergei, 8
Tracking dispersed war weapons, 72
Traffic fatality correlation with
    homicide rate, 181
Turner, Frederick Jackson, 119, 121
Twinkling, defense device to
    eliminate, 75–76

Udall, Stewart, 124
Ulpian, 140
Underground living, psychogical
    factors, 148, 150

Vander Wall, Stephan, 2
Vanek, Joan, 94
Vetter, Russell, 116
Violence among the Maya,
    theories of, 11–12
Violence-caused injuries, 35-36
Vocal Feedback Device, 4
Voss, Richard, 196

Wachsmann, Shelley, 13, 14, 15, 17, 18
Water shortage in West, 121–122
Watkins, David, 72
Watson, James, 36, 117
Wavelet analysis of music, 197
Weapon destruction, 71–73
Wedin, David, 129
Weeks, Trevor, 105
Weidenbaum, Murray, 60
Weisskopf, Victor, 160
Welling, Joel, 162
Wenger, Gilbert, 143
West, historians of, 119-121; myths
    about, 119–121; new constituency,
    119; symbols of, 120
Whiplash shaken-baby syndrome, 33
White, Richard, 131
Whitesides, George, 191
Whitney, Patrick, 168
Whittaker, R.H., 22
Williams, Bruce, 2
Willmer, Christopher, 109
Wind- and earthquake-resistant control
    system, 176
Winfree, Art, 159
Winn, Larry, 124
Woertz, Byron, 146
Woese, Carl, 118
Woo, Elaine, 36
Wood, William, 88
Women: exclusion from NIH research,
    86; exclusion from science, 132–133;
    unaccounted for in population
    statistics, 94
Wulf, Theodore, 102
Wuorinen, Charles, 196

Yeats, W.B., 49
Yorke, James, 156

Zasler, Nathan, 36
Zinin, Nicolai, 193